NAHKOM:

THE WOMAN OF WAUPACA

by

Malcolm Rosholt

NAHKOM: THE WOMAN OF WAUPACA

Library of Congress Catalog Card Number:

74-79083

Printed in the United States of America

Published by
ROSHOLT HOUSE
1 River Drive
Rosholt, Wi. 54473

1

Alvin walked slowly beside the oxen, goading them from time to time, while his own thoughts raced ahead. A Norwegian newcomer at the McHenry county seat in Woodstock, Illinois had offered to buy his two forties of land for $500. If he were to sell now he would more than double his money, since he had paid $125 for the farm in 1845, less than two years ago. But how was he going to convince Lucia? It was not that he did not like his place, or the people of McHenry county, but with this kind of money he could pay off the mortgage and buy twice as much land in Wisconsin Territory which was opening up to settlement all the way into the Pineries of the north.

But Lucia too liked her new home in McHenry county. Her brother Asahel Thompson and his family lived nearby, and the neighbors were, like themselves, nearly all young people who had migrated west from

Ohio, Kentucky and Virginia to escape the pinched attitudes and limited opportunities of older generations living on older farms.

As he drove into the barn yard, Alvin yelled, "Lucia, come here! I've got something to tell you." Lucia had heard the squeaky wagon wheels and had opened the door of the log cabin just as he called. She was carrying Caspar, their six-month old son, over her shoulder. Loretta, their first born, nearly two years old now, ran ahead to greet her father with arms outstretched, and Sport, the mongrel pup, danced and barked, happy to see the family reunited.

Alvin picked up Loretta and turned to Lucia. "Listen dear, I just got an offer of $500 for our place and I think we should take it before this Norsky changes his mind. We can move to Wisconsin Territory where I can buy a whole quarter-section for $200. That will leave us with twice as much land and a profit to boot after we pay off the mortgage here. We can build a new place and have enough money to get a few things for the house, and maybe a brand new hat for you," he laughed, begging for her approval.

Lucia did not smile. She had not been anxious to leave Ohio, but he had talked her into that, and now he was asking her to move again. This time she was determined not to let him influence her.

"What about the Indians?" she asked,

eyeing him squarely.

"Nothing to worry about. I met a feller in Woodstock just down from there. Pickett was his name. And he said the Indians were friendly. The general government has bought a big hunk of their land and moved the Indians to the west bank of the Wolf river, wherever that is. Some of the best land he's ever seen, this Pickett said. Grass up to your elbows. Mixed timber and rolling prairie lying to the north of a ferry point on the Fox river. Knagg's ferry he called it. And there's a village growing there which people are calling Os-kos or Ash-koss or some name like that."

Lucia moved Caspar to the other shoulder and again asked, "But aren't there Indians around?"

"Around maybe, but they've moved I tell you, to the west bank of the Wolf river."

"How far is that?"

"I don't know but far enough I imagine. Anyhow, there's nothing to worry about. This man Pickett said they were friendly and he even gave me a piece of maple sugar he bought from one of the chiefs when he was up there landlooking. He said if we go now we'd have our pick of the best land in Winnebago county, and we'd get there before the speculators got there and jacked up the price."

"Indian chiefs? You mean like Black Hawk?"

"Of course not, my dear," he laughed as he kissed Loretta and put her down to unyoke the oxen. Lucia sighed. Caspar was digging at her blouse. As she turned back to the cabin to feed the baby, she already knew there was no way of stopping her husband.

A week later the deal for the sale of the land was closed and Alvin at once made preparations for the journey north into Wisconsin Territory. If he left now, in mid-September, he estimated he could reach Knagg's ferry before the geese began to fly. That would give him time to make a pre-emption claim on a good quarter-section, build a log house and stable and cut some wild hay for the cattle before winter set in.

He began to hum to himself, happy in the thought that he might one day own a farm bigger than his father-in-law in Ohio.

"Lucia," he called from outside the cabin, "where's that old piece of canvas we had comin' from Ohio?"

"It's in the loft," she called from the kitchen door. He went up the short stairway on the outside of the building and found the canvas, brought it down and swept off the dust. The rest of the day he spent making new braces to hold the canvas in place, tent-like, over the wagon box.

The following day household goods and farm tools and implements were packed carefully into the wagon or tied to the sides.

He also made a box with slats on one side for ten chickens and a rooster. By the morning of the third day everything was in readiness and after shaking hands with the new owners who had arrived by prearrangement, Alvin touched the goad stick to the big oxen, Buck and Bright. It was fifteen miles north to the state line. While Lucia and the two children rode, Alvin walked at the side of the oxen with Sport keeping him company. And that evening, Flossy, the milk cow, tethered to the rear of the wagon, followed the Partridge family into Wisconsin Territory.

2

In the decade before the first census was taken in the new state of Wisconsin in 1850, there was a population explosion of New Englanders, up-state New Yorkers and Ohioans moving into the fertile farm lands lying between the Fox and Wolf rivers of Winnebago and Outagamie counties, once the planting grounds of the Menomini Indians.

Like many of the first arrivals, Alvin Partridge was anxious to share this bonanza with his relatives while there was still government land for sale at $1.25 an acre. He wrote to his father, Wakeman Partridge, and to two younger brothers, Fred and George, and in 1848-49 they came and took farms in the south of Vinland township of Winnebago county not far from one another, and two of his sisters, Maria and Sara also came and later found husbands.

In addition to his farm on Ball Prairie, Wakeman Partridge made a jack-knife claim to a forty of land lying to the north in Clayton township which the family referred to as the "timber lot". Here there was wood for the kitchen stoves and timber sufficient for building purposes, not to mention a fine grove of sugar maples which, from the wounds in the bark, had once been tapped by the Indians. Since Alvin lived two miles closer to the timber lot than the other members of the family, it was left to him to build a sugar camp, and in the middle of March in 1850 he harnessed his newly-purchased team of horses and drove through the melting snow to the timber lot, bringing materials and tools to build a simple lean-to shanty, one side open to the south. The shanty was meant not only as a shelter to sleep in overnight when he was busy cooking down the sap and could not leave camp, but as a wind-break for the fire.

Within a few days he had completed the lean-to and also made cuts with an ax in more than a hundred maple trees. Fixing a chip at the bottom of each cut, Indian style, the sap was funneled into a birchbark bucket at the foot of the tree.

During the last part of March and into mid-April, Alvin came and went, bringing home more maple syrup on every trip. At home Lucia continued the process of cooking some of the syrup into sugar for eating and baking.

The snow was nearly gone now and the

season about over. On Thursday evening, April 18, Alvin said to Lucia, "How about tomorrow? Wouldn't you like to take the children and come along? The trees are drying up and this may be the last chance for you to see what I've been doing up there."

"Alvin," she contradicted him, "you know I've been anxious to see, and the children too, but I can't go tomorrow. Tomorrow's Friday and the day after that those new people from Pleasant Valley are coming here to get married in the school house and I'm supposed to bring a roast chicken."

"But we'll be home in plenty of time, I vow. We'll cook the last batch of sap and be home by sundown. Course, we'll have to get an early start."

"Oh dear oh dear! I don't know what to do. But maybe, if it's a nice day, perhaps we *should* go."

Alvin went out to do the chores for the horses and oxen, and Lucia went along to milk Flossy. In the back of her mind she began to make plans for the family excursion. With Loretta now five and a half years old, Caspar four, and Amelia Lucinda, born in Winnebago county, two years ago, she would have to consider carefully how much food to take along without wasting anything, and of course there was Sport to think of. He had grown into a big dog now.

Everyone went to bed early that evening,

and in the morning, when the sun broke over the horizon and Lucia felt assured the weather was going to be pleasant, she began packing two baskets with food and milk. Alvin had coffee at the sugar camp.

After driving for an hour, the family arrived at the camp located in the middle of a small clearing surrounded by heavy timber. Lucia felt the depth of the forest and it made her slightly uneasy. Alvin turned to her and said, pointing to the lean-to shanty, "Now take a hard look at my great efforts as a house carpenter, will you."

She laughed lightly and said, "Why yes, sir, I think it's just too cozy for words. When do we move in?" She turned to the back of the wagon box where the children and Sport were jumping up and down, all demanding to be let out. "Quiet back there!" she called.

Alvin climbed down from the wagon and said, "Isn't this ideal, Lucia? Some day I'll buy this forty from the old man 'cuz there's enough maple trees around here to make syrup and sugar for a hundred years, and I'm tired of buying from the Indians. They say they strain the syrup through their pony blankets."

"Yeeuck!" Lucia grunted. "But I'm sure father made a wise choice and I'm all for buying as long as we don't have to pay for it right away." She laughed and reached under the seat for two multi-colored Indian baskets made of split reed which had been purchased at George Cowen's trading post near Winneconne Settlement. Handing the baskets to her husband, she climbed down from the wagon and went around to remove the end gate. Sport jumped out first and Loretta followed, but Caspar and Amelia Lucinda had to be helped.

Alvin carried the food baskets to a big pine windfall that lay near the shanty and went back to the team, humming to himself. He unhitched the horses and turned them loose to munch on the dead grass in the clearing. His heart swelled with pride as he watched them trot off, two matched chestnut geldings, probably the finest Morgan drivers in Winnebago county.

But I can afford them, he thought to himself. Got me the best damned quarter-section on Ball Prairie, and since we come up from McHenry county, I've raised more Indian corn and wheat to the acre than any of my neighbors, and what's more, I'll be living in a frame house before the ducks fly. They can say all they want to about those so-called cozy log cabins—popple, pine or piss-elm—they're all cold in winter and I ought to know after nearly four years in Wisconsin.

He returned to the big pine log where Lucia had laid a table cloth over the top. She gave the children each a cup of milk and a sandwich. Alvin grabbed one and ate hurriedly. "We got lots to do, Lucia. I'll get the sap from the trees to the north of the clearing first and you do what you can with the trees nearest the east side there, and as soon as I finish to the north I'll be over east. And don't take full buckets now. I don't want you straining yourself." He patted her slightly swollen stomach and smiled.

Lucia returned the smile and watched her husband as he started a fire under the cooking kettle which contained sap left over from the day before. She looked around and said, "Isn't it lovely to be in the woods this time of year? I can just smell the new buds coming out." She took a deep breath and exhaled.

Alvin went to the shanty for his shoulder yoke and also an old one which he rigged up for Lucia. He put his own on and hung two wooden buckets to a coarse wire hook at either end of the frame. Without another word he stalked off across the clearing and disappeared into the woods.

Lucia watched him leave and then turned her attention to the children. Caspar was feeding bits of his sandwich to Sport. "Now stop feeding that dog!" Lucia ordered. She reached down to brush Sport aside. Caspar made believe he did not hear his mother and when the dog circled the log from the back, he tossed part of his sandwich over his shoulder.

"Stop that now, will you!" Lucia shouted, "and eat your bread."

"Don wan any," he said with a stubborn shake of his head.

"All right," Lucia said, "I won't give you any then," and she bent down to kiss him, but he spurned her and wiggled away. She let him go and began to pick up the breakfast things. After she finished, she lifted the yoke to her shoulders and attached the wooden buckets. "Now children, stay near the shanty and away from the fire. Hear? Mamma and Papa are going to be gone just a few minutes. Don't come after me now, Loretta. Your dolls are in the basket there."

After she left, Caspar played with Sport and the two chased each other around the clearing. Loretta and Lucinda stood by the big log and talked to their dolls. When Caspar finally tired of the chase, he returned to his sisters and took Lucinda's doll and threw it to the ground. Lucinda began to cry and Loretta said, "I'm going to tell mamma. Naughty boy Capsar," whereupon Caspar grabbed Loretta by the hair and hit her. Loretta fell and began to scream, and Caspar, fearing trouble, ran behind the shanty, Sport after him. A few minutes later the dog returned to where the girls were playing. "Stop pulling at me Sport," said Loretta.

Presently, Alvin returned to the sugar camp carrying two buckets of sap and shortly after

Lucia emerged from the east. As she approached, Alvin called ahead to her, "Where's Caspar?"

"Isn't he there?"

"Why no. I don't see him."

"That's strange. I told the children to stay by the shanty, but he can't be far." She turned to Loretta, "Where did Caspar go, dear?"

"Capsar bad boy. He hit me."

"Never mind that. Where did he go I asked you?"

"Capsar run dat vay," she said pointing to a deer trail leading into the woods. Then she looked in another direction and said, "No, Capsar run dat vay."

"Loretta darling. Which is it? You must know."

"Don't know," she began to sob, running up to her father.

"Now, now, don't be a baby Loretta," said Lucia. "Alvin, he must have gone down that way," pointing to the deer trail.

"I'll have a look," he said, and started to walk across the clearing to the north. By the time he reached the woods, he was running. He followed the deer trail for some distance northwest, calling and calling to his son, and then returned to the clearing and made a complete circle of it. Finally he cut back deeper into the woods and made another circle, his voice becoming more strained every minute now. An hour later he returned to the fire.

"Lucia, he must be lost," he said, almost apologetically, wiping his face and neck with a handkerchief. "I can't find a trace of him. No tracks, nothin! Whatever came over that boy?"

"Now you set a while, Alvin. You're clean tuckered out," said Lucia. "And I'll look. Perhaps he will recognize my voice better." She called to the dog and went down among the trees, but she dared not penetrate the woods beyond sight of the clearing. After fifteen minutes she returned to the edge of the clearing and watched as the dog came out, howling like a creature possessed.

"Come here, Sport!" Alvin shouted, his mind suddenly distracted by the plight of the dog. Sport crawled up to his master whimpering and Alvin grabbed him by the collar and choked the strap while he withdrew several porcupine quills from its nose. "There now! Stay here, you mut!" As he released the dog, Loretta ran over to assure Sport he was still loved and he licked her nose.

By this time Lucia was approaching the camp, her eyes filled with fear. "Oh Alvin, I'm afraid," she said, and sat down on the pine log. "Come here Lucy. Loretta where are you? Alvin, what *are* we going to do?"

"We must get help, my dear. This woods is too big for a person. I think you better stay here with the children and keep calling. He might come wandering back, but we got to get help. I'll take one of the geldings and ride over to Tom Rankin's and see if we can round up some of the neighbors."

"All right," she said, clutching Lucinda. Alvin hurried to unharness one of the geldings, adjusted the bridle for short reins, folded a blanket for a saddle and jumped on. To reach Rankin's place by the existing road was a round-about route to the southeast, and instead he took a short-cut due east that ran along the section line blazed by government surveyors a few years earlier. After a quarter of a mile, he struck a trail once used by the Indians which now led south to Rankin's clearing. When he got there, he was greeted by two noisy dogs. Rankin was in the yard sawing wood for the kitchen stove when he heard the dogs and looked up. "Get down, you sonsabitches!" he shouted, raising a stick of wood at them. The dogs retreated and Alvin jumped down from the horse and approached.

"Tom, can you give me a hand?" he asked. "Our son Caspar wandered off from the sugar camp this morning and we can't seem to find him. He can't be far but we've been lookin and lookin. We drove up from the home place this morning and started to collect sap and when we got back to the shanty, Caspar was missin."

"You don't say!" exclaimed Rankin. "Hey ma!" he called over his shoulder. A heavy-set woman of about forty-five appeared in the doorway of the Rankin log cabin, her hair uncombed, a soiled apron clinging tightly to the front of a checked wool skirt.

"Mornin, Mr. Pa'tridge. How's Lucia?"

"Just fine, Mrs. Rankin," Alvin said, tipping his hat.

"Caspar's lost," Rankin said. "That's Lucia's boy. Remember him?"

"Why, rightly not sartin, but if he be lost, we better find him."

"I'll hitch up my bulls, Alvin, and drive around to the east and south here, and you go west and sound the alarm out that way. New people moving in every day, seems."

"Can I help, Mr. Pa'tridge?" asked Mrs. Rankin.

"Perhaps you could make some sandwiches for Tom. I'm not certain how much we got to eat over there. We weren't planning to stay. Have to get back to Ball Prairie for a weddin tomorrow night."

"I'll bake some biscuits. About all we got here is flour and dried venison this time of year. Times be hard, Mr. Pa'tridge. Tax man acoming around soon and we even got to pay tax on them rotten dogs, a dollar on the dog and two on the bitch, but Tom he always takes the bitch back in the swamp fer enough so the tax man kaint hear. I keep atelling him he'll be churched one of these days, but he don't pay no mind, course," and she laughed.

"That will be just fine, I mean the biscuits and stuff, Mrs. Rankin," said Alvin, impatient to be away and unconsciously wondering what Caspar might find to eat in the woods this time of year. Nothing but wintergreen leaves. But how was he to know about them? Jesus, holy Jesus, please help me find my boy, he prayed silently to himself. He mounted the gelding, waved goodbye and drove to the west. Everywhere he came people dropped their work and prepared to leave. A crisis had arisen on the wilderness frontier. A child was lost. He was a member of the community. He must be found.

Word of the missing boy sped from farm to farm and by one o'clock that afternoon there were fifty men and boys with teams and wagons in the clearing. Alvin tried to explain where he had looked, and the searchers went off at once, in pairs, in threes and fours, all anxious to be the first to find the lost child.

Lucia, carrying Lucinda in her arms and holding Loretta by the hand, walked around the edge of the clearing, calling into every opening in the woods. Alvin went to the east to make a more thorough search of the woods where Lucia had been earlier. He returned to the fire after an hour and found her seated on the log, clutching her youngest daughter.

"Alvin, what *are* we going to do? It is

getting late and we can't leave our little boy out in the woods over night. There might even be wolves around."

"Lucia, please," said Alvin. "Don't think about it that way. We'll find him. With all these men out there lookin, surely one of them will bring him back."

"But what if no one does?"

"If they can't find him, we'll just have to get more help."

"When?"

"Well, tomorrow. It's almost candle lighting now."

"But what about tonight? He's only got one shoe on. Loretta found the other one this morning after you left for Rankin's."

"You didn't tell me," said Alvin. "Now if we only had some bloodhounds."

"What *are* we going to do, Alvin?" she pleaded, her eyes filling with tears. She put down the baby and covered her face. Alvin moved over to her. "Get away from me!" she shrugged. "I'm not the one that needs help. You haven't even tried hard to find him. If you hadn't gone galloping off to Rankin's maybe you would have found him by now."

"But Lucia, we have been. . ."

"Have been nothing! Oh, if we only hadn't come to this awful country. We had a nice place in McHenry county. But no! You had to move again. Just like the Pa'tridges. Never satisfied." He coaxed her into the shanty and she sat down while he went to get a cup of coffee for her. When he returned he said, "It's getting late Lucia, and the men are beginning to drift back."

Alvin went out to meet the first group to return, and he knew without asking that they had found no clue to the whereabouts of his son. They stood around the fire now, talking about where they had been, all trying to hide the fear in their guts for the missing boy.

"Sam, I see you walked up from your place," said Alvin. "I'm wondering if you would take the geldings and drive my wife and children home." He was talking to Sam Alcott, a pint-sized frontiersman from Maine who seldom shaved, lived alone and dressed in buckskins.

"Be glad to," said Alcott.

Lucia heard this exchange and came outside. "But how can I leave, Alvin?" He walked over to her and said in an undertone. "Lucia, I'm staying. I have to keep the fire burning good all night, and it's just possible that our boy will see the flames and come back. You're worn out and if you aren't careful, we'll lose our next baby. Please, dear, go home with Alcott and get some rest."

"But the wolves. . ."

"No Lucia. No wolf has ever eaten anybody."

"But Caspar hasn't had anything to eat."

Loretta grasped her mother's hand and

tugged at it. "I wanna go home."

"That's right, Loretta," said Alvin, patting her. "You go home with mother. And when you get home, tell Uncle Fred and Uncle George and William to come here in the morning, and to brings lots of food and more coffee and tell all the neighbors to come too if they can."

Loretta looked into her father's eyes and nodded gravely. Lucia picked up Lucinda and walked to the log and sat down, a look of sullen resignation on her face.

Isaiah Pickett, a neighbor of Rankin's said, "Alvin, we got to skaddle now, but don't you worry none. We'll find him tomorrow if it takes all day."

"I'm sure he's not far off either," Alvin agreed, "and I want to thank all you men for coming. My brothers will be up first thing in the morning with more people and we'll find him, I'm sure'"

"Right you are," said Pickett, and the others nodded and began to move across the clearing to their wagons and ox carts. Rankin and Alcott remained behind.

"I'll help you hitch up," Rankin said to Alcott. Alvin sat down on the log and picked up Loretta. "You be a good girl now, won't you, and help mother."

"Capsar runned avay?"

"No Caspar. . ."

"Never mind Loretta," Lucia cut in, "your

father will find him and bring him home to you."

"When Capsar coming?"

"Real soon dear," said Lucia. "Now we must leave." She started for the wagon where Alcott was waiting in the high seat. Alvin whistled for Sport to jump into the back of the box, lifted the children in and then helped Lucia. She sat down on the marsh hay and hugged the children to her side. Alcott touched the reins lightly to the team, and the wagon started.

"You fixin to stay, Tom?" Alvin asked, rather surprised that Rankin had not left.

"Why not? You kaint stay here all by yourself. I told the missuz when I left not to wait up for me," he chuckled, "and she says what's to wait up for?"

Alvin smiled and sat down on the log and Rankin joined him. Rankin wanted to tell the story he had once heard as a youth in Vermont about a white boy stolen by the Indians in lower Canada but decided this would not be suitable, and turned his attention to Wisconsin and the end of capital punishment decreed by the new state constitution. "If I'd been here when they voted on this, I would have voted against. If a man's guilty, goddamnit, he ought to hang." He looked at Alvin and realized he had not heard a word he said and he got up to throw more wood on the fire.

Alvin got up too and went into the shanty for a frying pan and bread and butter. "Did you say you had some meat Tom?"

"Be right with you," said Rankin, and he went to his wagon and lifted an Indian basket out of the box.

The two men ate in silence, both bone tired. After Rankin finished he said, "Tell you what Al, I'll take the first watch and you get some sleep and when you wake up, I'll crawl in."

"No, you first Tom."

"No, you've had a hard day, Alvin. You go first."

After the dishes were put away, Alvin went into the shanty and lay down on a bed of evergreens and covered himself with his coat and a horse blanket. He fell asleep almost at once, but a minute later woke up. "What's that?" he shouted, rushing outside. "I thought I heard something." Rankin understood. "Just me Al. Must'a been talkin to myself."

Alvin bit his lip and returned to the shanty and lay down. His eyes would not close and he felt a strange pressure on his chest. But he had to make believe he was sleeping. Suddenly he heard a noise from somewhere deep in the forest and again jumped up, but did not go outside when he heard it again and realized it was an owl hooting. He lay down, waiting for time to pass. His thoughts raced back to Ohio where he was born and to McHenry county where he had moved with his wife and first-born child and where Caspar was born. Yes, why had he not stayed in Illinois? Lucia was right for once.

"Tom, I can't sleep any longer," said Alvin, as he emerged from the shanty. "You crawl in now and I'll watch the fire."

"Sartin you kaint sleep longer?"

"No, I'm all right now."

Rankin went into the shanty and slept till daybreak. When he came outside he saw Alvin walking around the edge of the clearing, peering into the underbrush through a slight ground fog. A few minutes later he returned to the fire. "Good mornin Tom."

"Morning yourself! Why in tarnation didn't you call me?"

"No need Tom. I caught a few winks. Have some fresh coffee. Fred and them ought to be here instanter."

"That would be your younger brother, I suppose?"

Alvin nodded and at that moment both men stopped talking as they heard the rumbling of wagon teams approaching from the south. In the first wagon were the Partridge brothers, Fred, George and William, and Mary Elizabeth, Fred's wife, in addition to Lucia who had left the children with her husband's parents. Fred drove his team up to where Alvin and Rankin were standing and jumped to the ground. "Al, Lucia told us what happened, but don't you worry none. We'll find that boy, I vow."

Alvin was relieved. There were at least ten wagons filled with men and boys and more were expected.

"Where did you look yesterday?" Fred asked, taking command.

"Mostly to the north and east," Alvin said, waving his hand.

"What's to the west?"

"Low land. Medina Marsh some people call it. That's where I get our drinking water. Some springs."

"Seems to me, then, we ought to concentrate on that marsh to the west," said Fred, "and some of the men can go back over the ground you covered yesterday."

This was agreed and after the men had tied up their horses and oxen and had a bite to eat, they split up and headed for the big swamp. Water from melting snow was still standing in the pot holes, and within a couple of hours, many of the men were back in camp, their feet wet, their trousers spattered with mud. They drank more coffee and went back on different tacks, milling about, often following each other and uncertain about getting lost themselves. By late afternoon a sense of defeat had settled over the sugar camp, and most of the men living nearby had to leave. "We'll be back tomorrow if you need us," said Pickett. "Thar's no power on earth kin keep us."

Those who could not return alerted others. On the third and fourth day at least three hundred men and boys joined in the search and on the fifth day there were several hundred with scarcely enough room for all the teams and oxen in the clearing. By the end of the fifth day, most of the people were convinced that the child could not be found. It was reported that someone had seen three tracks of a boy's shoe in a mound of sand or ant-hill, and someone reported seeing tracks of an Indian pony, and another reported he had seen smoke coming from "the island", a small hill in the middle of the Medina Marsh. No one could remember who had seen the tracks, the sand hill or the smoke, but word spread among the people that the Indians had stolen Caspar Partridge.

On the morning of the sixth day only a few men, aside from the Partridge families, were on hand to continue the search. Tim Finney, a neighbor on Ball Prairie, finally spoke up and said, "Al, maybe them goddam Indians took your boy."

Alvin nodded. He was thinking of Lucia. She had privately expressed the same thought to him after her return to the sugar camp the second morning, but she had to be taken home that evening, almost on the verge of a nervous breakdown.

"There has to be some explanation," Fred insisted. "There isn't a spot big as a dollar we ain't covered. Don't you agree Tim?"

"Absolutely."

"It just goes to show you," Fred continued. "We're obliged to get these red skins out of this country and on to a reservation. Never know whose boy will be next."

"You better believe," said Pickett.

Late the following morning, the members of the Partridge families who had been sleeping in their wagon boxes and in the shanty, prepared to return to their homes on Ball Prairie.

"I'm going to stay a little longer," said Alvin looking at Fred.

"But I think you should come home with us," Fred insisted.

"No, I'll be all right. I just want to make another tour of the woods and pick up the sap buckets and stuff. You take the team and I'll walk home. Now for once, listen to what I say."

"Very well then Al. I'm only thinking about Lucia."

After the family drove off, Alvin went into the woods to collect the sap buckets, calling now and then to his son in a soft voice, almost as if he knew he would not be heard. After he completed his work, he decided to walk west to the springs. He knew there was a creek that drained the springs where he got his drinking water and the thought had occurred to him that perhaps his son, although only four years old, had managed somehow to wander this far west and drown. The other men had searched the area but perhaps the boy was caught under a tamarack windfall, or moss bank along the small creek.

Once he made up his mind to search the springs, Alvin felt a small sense of relief and he hurried on. When he reached the springs, he walked slowly around, peering intently into the clear bottom. He then continued west a few rods to where the springs joined to make the creek which flowed south. He turned south with the creek and followed the east bank, crawling on his hands and knees in some places to get through the alder brush. At one point he reached into the water to remove a mossy log and at another he lifted a dead branch of a tree from the water. As he continued south the creek became wider, and about a quarter of a mile below the springs he came upon a small pond, spruce and tamaracks hovering overhead, and below, an old beaver house rising three feet above the water level straight across the creek. He walked slowly along the east bank of the pond and finally crossed over to the west bank by crawling over the beaver dam, and continued to search along the west bank. The water was still crystal clear all the way to the bottom.

He finally retraced his steps to the beaver dam and was about to cross over to the east bank when he noticed that there was a deep hole in front of the dam where he could not see the bottom. Could it be possible that Caspar was down there, caught under the sticks of the beaver house? Without hesitation, he crawled back along the top of the dam and began to tear it apart, throwing sticks and logs in all directions, faster and faster. He began to perspire, but the pressure on his heart seemed to lessen now that he was about to solve the mystery of his son's disappearance. Within ten minutes he had removed the sticks above the water line and was already standing ankle deep in the icy water pouring over the dam. Suddenly he felt the dam breaking up under the pressure of the flowage and he jumped ashore just as the center washed out. A moment later the two wings of the dam began to crumble.

The short aspen logs, peeled by the beavers, the sticks, the twigs and grass used to insulate their house, now began to rise to the surface and flow down stream. Alvin expected the body of his son momentarily to surface with the debris and hurried below, but nothing appeared, and thinking he had missed it, he continued to run south along the bank of the creek, farther and farther, tearing his clothing, bruising his face and scratching his hands. Finally, he could scarcely breathe any longer, and then he tripped and fell flat on his face. Unwilling to rise, he buried his head in his hands and sobbed, "My son! My son!"

3

Earth, the daughter of Nokomis and the mother of *Ma'nabush*, also known as Hiawatha, made a special gift to the Menomini Indians when she guided *Ma'nabush*, out hunting one day, to a chain of wondrous lakes and rivers in the heart of Wisconsin. After the young hunter reached this place of great beauty, he made a big flat rock, colored black, on which rested a three-legged boulder. At the base of the rock ran a river called by the Menomini *Wapak'kase'pe*, which is to say, "the tomorrow river." *Ma'nabush* finished his day by building a ridge along the north bank of the river which he covered with dwarf willows. A few miles to the east the river joined the mighty Wolf, and here at the outlet stood six tall pines. When *Ma'nabush* passed this way these tall pines were people called by the Menomini *Wapak'kaini'u* or Waupaca Men.

For generations the Menomini had come to this lake country to tap the maple trees in spring, to hunt big game in winter. But in 1849 this scene of tranquility was forever broken when a party of landlookers from Vermont camped on the south bank of the river not far from a falls tumbling over the boulders along the ridge created by *Ma'nabush.* The strangers cut pilings and brush to make a lean-to shelter, and for a brief period of time people called this place "Vermonters Camp". But the Vermonters did not stay and the landlookers who came after them began to call it Waupaca Falls after a name they heard the Indians use.

William G. Caudle, who had been studying law in Milwaukee in 1849, heard about the future town site which was developing on the Waupaca river. He realized the time had come for him to strike out on his own, for it was important in the "Glorious West" as everyone was calling it, to get there first to get the most. Late in the fall, after the marshes around Horicon froze over, he left Milwaukee by stage for Berlin and crossed the ferry on Fox river to Strong's Landing. Here he hired an ox teamster to haul a load of supplies and tools thirty miles north to his destination on the Waupaca river.

With the help of some Indians and two white men who were there ahead of him, Caudle built a two-story log house that would serve as both office and living quarters. Here, like several other married men and bachelors, he spent the first winter alone. None of the men knew much about hunting and had it not been for the Indians, who were willing to trade a piece of venison for a knife or kettle, they might have starved to death.

The next spring Mrs. Caudle joined her husband, but after a few weeks in Waupaca Falls, she began to realize that the Glorious West her husband had been telling her about was in reality a lonesome and even dangerous place to live. Her sense of isolation was further heightened when rumors drifted into the settlement about a boy named Caspar Partridge who had been lost in the woods about twenty-five miles to the east and people were saying he had been stolen by the Indians. After that she heard no more about the tragedy until nearly two years later.

But the Indians had lived longer on the Waupaca river than the Caudles and this land was still, technically, their land. By the Treaty of the Cedars of 1836 the Menomini agreed to sell their lands lying between the Fox and Wolf rivers and move to the west bank of the Wolf which took in the future counties of Wood, Waushara, Waupaca and Portage. By 1844 most of the tribe had moved to the west bank and built villages, especially along the south shore of Lake Poygan, and here, every fall, the Indians received their annual payments from the government for the land they had sold. The coming together of all the Menomini bands, often a riotous affair, was called "payment time" and the place where the payments were made was called the "Payground". The Payground, located in Section 16 of Poygan township in Winnebago county, was also the place where Augustin Grignon conducted a trading post for the American Fur Company, and where the Catholics had established a mission church and school under the patronage of St. Francis Xavier.

After the Menomini moved to the Lake Poygan area, the early white settlers began to refer to the west bank of the Wolf river, where the Payground stood, as "the Indian Land" because it was the last of the Indian lands in southern Wisconsin Territory not yet ceded to the government. In 1848, by the Treaty of Lake Poygan, the Menomini agreed to accept reservation status and sell all their remaining lands, including their ancestral lands upon the Menominee river north of Green Bay.

The hitch in this arrangement came in 1850 when the Menomini refused to accept the designated site for a reservation. The Great Father in Washington city wanted his children to move to the Crow Wing river of Minnesota Territory, but after Chief Oshkosh went out there and looked it over, he returned, convinced that this was a burying ground, not a hunting ground.

Meanwhile, even though the Indians had not agreed to leave the "Indian Land" until a reservation had been found in Wisconsin, white settlers and landlookers crossed the Wolf river to the west bank and began squatting on future claims two years before the surveyors arrived. Thus there arose a period of nearly three years when the Indians and whites lived side by side both around Poygan and on the Waupaca river.

Pending their removal to a reservation, the Menomini continued to travel to the Black river country or north to the Oconto and Peshtigo rivers for deer hunting and trapping, but for those who did not wish to travel that far, their most favored hunting ground was the lake country on the Waupaca river.

There was a band of the tribe under Chief Rabbit presently encamped in the hummocks north of Shadow Lake, and a smaller band about a mile or so to the north. Isolated between these two Indian villages lay the white settlement overlooking the falls of the Waupaca river.

Nahkom, or "The Promising Woman", who had wintered on the Waupaca river for several seasons, was back again in the fall of 1851 accompanied by a boy of seven and two younger children, a boy and girl by a second marriage, in addition to an uncle,

Kosko'shekau, a sub-chief better known to the white settlers as "Big Peter". Nahkom's second husband, Tow-o-sa-ban, had gone with a party of hunters to the Oconto river that year and left his family in Kosko'shekau's care.

After a wigwam was completed on Shadow Lake, Nahkom's children ran in and out, shouting and playing games with the children of the nearest wigwams. Some of the older children even played with the children of the *Mo'hkoma'n,* or Long Knives, in the white settlement and learned words from each other, and the Indian children often stopped on their way home to beg for a piece of bread or candy.

Mrs. Caudle had given bread to these Indian children on several occasions, but one boy in particular fascinated her. She had mentioned him to her husband before, but now as she called to him for supper, she was determined to make him understand what was puzzling her. Presently she heard him tramping up the stairway on the outside of the building, stopping on the landing to brush the snow off his feet. As he opened the door, she hurried to embrace him.

"Bill," she said, scarcely able to supress her excitement, "I believe we girls have really stumbled on to something."

"We girls? What girls? You mean Theodora Thompson, the school teacher or Polly Ware?

But Polly's married, so that doesn't make her a girl any more, but of course there must be some nice Indian girls around."

"Stop teasing," she laughed, and went to the stove. She dished out venison stew, Indian potatoes and squash, and put the bowl on the table along with fresh bread and butter, coffee and cream. There was ample cream and butter available now that the Caudles had been to Berlin and bought a cow.

"It's odd you should mention Indians, because that's just what I want to talk to you about. That Indian boy I've been telling you about was here again today. He looks different than the other children, and just to get a closer look at him, I told him, or at least I motioned to him to come in the kitchen and I would give him some bread."

"You mean the one who talks English?"

"Yes, the one who points to his stomach and says 'me want bread.' "

"Did he come in?"

"No, he waited outside, but I got a good look at him before I gave him a sandwich and then he ran down the stairs like a cat."

Mr. Caudle had removed his coat and hat and was washing his hands in a porcelain washbasin which stood on a small bench under a window overlooking the forest and river. The roar of the falls could be heard in the distance.

"What's so odd about that? Seems you

mentioned before about a boy begging for food. There's a bunch of those Indians, you know, right down the path through the woods there near Shadow Lake. They've come back for the winter like always to hunt and trap."

"I know Bill. I've seen them and I know I've seen this boy before too, but seems to me he's grown. I'm sure of it. There's a change in him, and he's getting to look more like a white child. Today I mentioned this to Polly Ware, and also to Nellie Drootzer. She's American you know, but he comes from the old country."

"Yes I know Drootzer, or Druetzer, or whatever they call him. Used to be a lumberman. Now he tells me he's going to be a lawyer. Always talking about the time he was fighting the Seminoles down in Florida."

"Be that as it may, now let me tell you what I've got in mind. After seeing that boy again today, I'm convinced he is the lost child people been talking about since I come. And you remember what people said? They said he was not really lost and that some Indians stole him."

"You mean. . ."

"I mean that boy could be the lost child right down there in one of those wigwams."

"Which one?"

"The one I've been telling you about. He's got a small scar at both ends of his mouth, like he'd been burned or something."

"Oh him. He was here last year. I'm sure I saw him one time hanging around Judson's store waiting for a handout."

"It isn't just me Bill. Several of the women in the settlement have the same idea. He isn't as dark as an ordinary Indian. I won't swear he's white but there certainly is a resemblance between him and a white child. And he could even speak English, 'bread, me want bread,' he says."

"For heavens sake, every Indian child learns to say a few words in English. We're living pretty close together, you know. Too close in fact."

"Well, I didn't tell you," she went on, sitting down to the table opposite her husband, "but yesterday I mentioned my suspicion to Mrs. Boughton. That's Mike Boughton's wife."

"You mean the surveyor who lives north of the settlement?"

"Yes, she's a sister, I just found out, of this Pa'tridge who lost the boy. And today she got a good look at him too and now we're all agreed that maybe he is Pa'tridge's boy, Indian or no Indian."

The couple lowered their heads to say grace, and after they finished, Caudle looked at his wife in the lamp light and asked, "But how can you prove it? You just can't take him from the Indians and say, 'look'a here, him belong big white chief.' "

"Can if he isn't Indian. We'll get the sheriff after him."

"Sheriff? What sheriff? The sheriff we elected in this mixed up county isn't elected it seems. Some confusion in the law."

"Then you menfolks will have to go down there and take the boy because Maria Boughton wants to have a closer look at him. She swears there's a mark on his foot or something she will know him by. But he runs away from us soon as anyone approaches, like I said. Grabs the bread out of our hands and off he goes!"

"Well, if the rest of the men agree, I suppose we can go down there and take him, all right. We're citizens, although it still does not seem quite legal. I guess we've got about as many citizens here now as they've got Indians, but just how do you go about taking a boy away from someone who claims to be his mother? I know who she is. It's this Nahkom I met by chance the first winter I was here. Still, it seems like there should be some legal process for this."

"But if she isn't his ma, then what do you need a legal process for? Get this parson, Cutting Marsh they call him, who just moved to the settlement couple weeks ago, and have him explain it to the Indians. He speaks Indian they say. Or else maybe Dana Dewey can think of something. He's acquainted with the squaw I heard, and knows Big Peter they call him."

"Big Peter, my dear, helped build this house of ours."

"He did? I didn't know that. Anyway, as I was going to say, maybe Dana Dewey can talk this woman into giving up the boy peaceable like, and then there won't be any need for you to worry about breaking the law."

"Would you give up your future child peaceable like?" he laughed.

"But that's different. She's an Indian."

He shook his head and laughed again, eating heartily of the venison stew and dipping his bread in the gravy.

4

Nearly all the white men in the settlement of Waupaca Falls were assembled at the new frame house of Olaf Dreutzer, a Swedish emigrant, soldier of fortune and recently owner of a sawmill on the Big Eau Pleine river. Although none of the Yankees in the settlement had the money or the background of Dreutzer, they regarded him as an outsider and tolerated him mainly because he had made money and because he was married to a native American. Nor could they ever quite accept a man who believed in God but not his son and spoke the English language with a puking accent.

The air in the living room and adjoining dining room of the house reeked with tobacco smoke. The men had agreed to meet at eight o'clock on the morning of January 3, 1852, and after half an hour, about twenty men had assembled. They came in their mackinaws, buffalo coats and sheepskins, stamping the snow from their boots and apologizing to Mrs. Dreutzer for imposing on her hospitality.

"Nellie, vil you make coffee for the shentlemen?" Dreutzer asked his wife politely.

"Be glad to," she replied. "You men have important business to attend to. Go right ahead and I'll soon have coffee ready." As she closed the door to the kitchen, the house became a bedlam of loud talk. The men had gathered to discuss the matter of taking the Indian boy away from Nahkom, a woman of the Menomini tribe who was camped on the north shore of Shadow Lake. They could not say they wanted to arrest the boy, or his mother, nor could they say they wanted to recover the boy because there was no proof yet that he needed to be recovered. But they wanted to get their hands on him somehow so that the women could examine him.

"I say let's go down there and take him," shouted E.C. Sessions above the rest. "What do you think Sam?"

He was addressing Sam Ware who had been elected county judge in the first election the year before. "I don't know what to do," he replied, "but Polly says we got to do something."

"Well, Polly's right," shouted Alfred Woodward who owned two yoke of heavy oxen and a long breaking plow which he used for custom plowing among the new farmers.

"I've heard that boy talk English. Going by thar with my ox sled t'other day and he an' some boys jump on my sled and I ask him if he kin drive oxen and he says 'yes', and I give him the whip and he took it and he talked to them thar oxen and told 'em to 'gee' an' 'haw' plain as day."

"Shentlemen, shentlemen," said Dreutzer politely interrupting, 've must make decision. Ve must hev kommodant. Ven I vas fighting Indians in Florida ve. . ."

"Yes Olaf, we know," said Oliver Hibbard, "and you're right. We got to have a leader. You be the leader Olaf, and me and my brothers, Bill and Joe, we'll follow. We're convinced this boy be no Indian. I talked to Nahkom in sign language one day she was in our house and the boy be playing with our children and he calls out to my boy 'Henry' as plain as I can say it, and he can say 'yes' or 'no'. What do you think, Johnny, you're the sheriff?"

John Vaughan said, "No I'm not the sheriff, but I'll go along with the rest because I can't stand the thought of an Indian squaw raising a white boy. How would you like to have your boy raised by an Indian?"

"That's right," echoed several men, including Mose Buchman, George Ross and Ward Lent.

"If it was up to me," said James Thomas, "I'd wait for more help from Strongs

Landing. Bring up some gun-wagons and put the fear of God into these red skins. They'd soon hand him over."

"But Polly says we can't wait," Judge Ware insisted. "It's past New Years and the Indians might pull out any day now and then we'd never find the boy again."

"Should we bring any guns along?" asked Granvil Jones.

"I think not," said Dana Dewey. "If we come unarmed, they can't attack us."

"But vat eff Indians fight?" Dreutzer asked.

"They wouldn't dare," said Alfred Hitchcock. "They've made a treaty with the go'ment." Several men nodded in agreement.

"I hev terty-eight bull-dog," said Dreutzer, waving a small pistol he had taken from a drawer. He put it inside his pocket and laughed, and the others who saw him also laughed good naturedly.

"We better try to talk with them first," said Dewey. "I know Big Peter and Nahkom both. I was at a powwow they had for some Indian going to die and they was civilized to me. More than a year ago, calculate, but I haven't seen 'em since."

"Let's go then," Sam Ware shouted, "It's already past nine."

"What about the coffee?" one of the Dieter boys asked.

"No time for that now," said Ware. "It's

about a mile down there from here and there's fresh snow on the ground, so don't rush gentlemen. Save your breath.for the action if there is any."

A passing Indian had noticed earlier the unaccustomed meeting of Long Knives at the house of the big Swede and he knew this was no church affair since none of the men had their squaws with them. There was something about the way they looked at him as they entered the house that made him nervous. Perhaps they were preparing to attack the Indians and force them to leave before the hunting season was over. He hurried down the path to the wigwam of Chief Rabbit on Shadow Lake to report his suspicions. The chief did not like the news either and at once sent a runner to the band of Menomini camped on the north side of the settlement.

As the white men approached the encampment, they were greeted by dogs threatening them at every step. Most of the Indian males were out on hunting parties or attending to their trap lines this time of morning, and as a result the white men numbered as many as the Indians. On seeing the whites approach, several Indians ran back to their wigwams for their weapons, bows and arrows, spears and tomahawks, but no guns since the men with guns were out hunting.

"I wonder if they aim to fight," Sam Ware said under his breath. Dewey heard this remark and said, "That's impossible. Where's that preacher? He can talk to them."

"I'm here Mr. Dewey," said Cutting Marsh, slightly miffed at the reference to himself as "that preacher". He was a tall, commanding figure, a Presbyterian missionary formerly attached to the Stockbridge Indian reservation east of Lake Winnebago.

"Parson, tell these savages we want to see the chief," said Dewey. "Tell them we've come to take Nahkom's oldest boy. It does not belong to her."

Marsh grimaced at the reference to the Indians as savages but held his tongue. It was difficult to serve God on behalf of the white man and the red man at the same time, but he knew he had made his choice when he moved his family to Waupaca Falls a fortnight ago. He translated Dewey's instructions to the Indians.

On hearing this, Chief Rabbit emerged from his wigwam. Other Indians had also heard it, including Nahkom. The chief was baffled. What did the Long Knives want with an Indian boy? He looked across to the wigwam where Nahkom was standing. Noting this she quickly went inside and tied her oldest boy to her waist with a piece of rawhide and told the other two children to hide under a blanket.

When Marsh repeated the demand to hand over the boy, the Indians became excited.

"What's this?" one whispered. "What new tricks are the Long Knives going to play on us now?" Others could scarcely contain themselves in their fear and confusion and some began to jump up and down and to give war whoops, signaling other Indians in the area to come at once.

From the glances made by the Indians, Dewey and Marsh guessed at once where Nahkom lived. "She's over there," Dewey pointed. Led by Dreutzer, the whites formed a phalanx and marched through the Indians to surround the wigwam at about the same time as Big Peter came running into camp. He had been attending his trap line and was carrying a spear in one hand and three muskrats in the other. He looked questioningly at Dewey and wondered what his old friend had come for.

Dewey stepped up to him and said, "Look a' here, Peter. Smokiman have come to take papoose. You stole it when it was a small papoose. Two years ago in sugar bush. Him Smokiman's papoose. Scar on foot, and we are going to have him."

Big Peter appeared to understand the gist of this demand. He dropped the muskrats and said firmly, "No Smokiman papoose!"

"Oh yes he is Peter," replied Dewey, "and if you don't let us have him we are going right in after him. You understand that, don't you?"

Peter crossed the compound to where the

chief stood, touched him, and pointed at Dewey while repeating what he thought Dewey had said.

Dewey raised his voice for the chief to hear, "Yes sir, we're going to have him," and pointed at Nahkom's wigwam.

Hearing this, the chief was outraged, but uncertain what course to follow. He removed a tomahawk from his belt, a handsome weapon about six inches across the bit and a handle three feet long, all beautifully stained and varnished. He felt of it but dared not use it. He was frightened. How could he prevent the Long Knives from having their way without risking a small war? And what justice could he expect from a white society if one of their own people got killed? When would this humiliation ever end, he wondered? He raised his hand in the symbol for peace.

Dreutzer recognized this was the moment to act. "If any man will go in and keep the squaw from splitting my head open, I will take the child."

"Come right along with me," said Dewey, and he opened the door-flap of the wigwam. Nahkom, with her oldest boy tied to her belt, raised a hatchet and threatened to throw it at the intruders.

"If you throw that at me there's a dead squaw right here, for I'll kill you in a minute," warned Dewey, pointing his finger at the hatchet and at Nahkom. He spat on his hands and sprang at her, grabbing one wrist and dug his finger nails into the flesh as hard as he could. Nahkom had the hatchet raised with her other hand, but was forced to drop it under the pain inflicted on her wrist. The hatchet fell to the ground and she tried to pick it up.

"If you pick up that hatchet, I'll bung your eye right out," Dewey shouted. Dreutzer was temporarily immobilized by the struggle between Dewey and Nahkom, but with the boy still tied to the side of his mother, he suddenly reached for his pistol and pointed it at his head.

"*Kan! Kan!*" Nahkom screamed, reaching for her boy with her free hand. At that instant Big Peter entered the wigwam, carrying his spear, and was about to send it through the back of Dewey when he saw the pistol pointed at the boy's head. He froze, trembling with rage, and watched as Dewey cut the rawhide and picked up the boy.

"I've got him, I've got him!" he shouted, rushing outside.

"Let's take him to my house," said Dreutzer, "and ve send for to get Mr. Pa'tridge."

The white men moved off rapidly with their prize, while the boy screamed at the top of his voice and reached out with one hand to Nahkom. She was crying in a high-pitched voice too, wringing her hands and pounding her eyes with both fists. Two Indian women rushed to her side to prevent her from mutilating herself. She continued to cry and then other women began to cry and this set off a new round of barking from the dogs.

The chief immediately called a Council. After some discussion, it was decided that Big Peter should leave for Lake Poygan to inform the Black Robe, the Reverend Florimond J. Bonduel who was now in charge of the Catholic mission on the Payground, and to ask him to intercede on behalf of Nahkom's family. They were all aware that the Black Robe had accompanied the Menomini delegation to Washington in 1850 to beg the Great Father to let them remain in Wisconsin, and word had come back to the tribe how strongly the Black Robe had expressed himself on their behalf. He was their friend and protector now.

Father Bonduel heard the story that Big Peter had come to tell. Several of the chiefs who were available for an informal meeting held at the mission house, agreed that there was no time to appeal to the sub-agent of Indian affairs at Green Bay or to the superintendent at Sheboygan. The only thing that could be done on the spur of the moment was to write a strong letter, addressed to "whomsoever it may concern" in Waupaca, threatening the abductors with a civil action in a United States court of law.

Bonduel wrote the letter and signed his name with a great flourish of the pen.

Even though it was past midnight, Big Peter left at once with the letter and crossed the ice of Lake Poygan, following his own footsteps north through the forest in the light of the star-studded sky.

5

After the boy known to the Indians as Nigabianong was taken to the house of Olaf Dreutzer, several women in the village were called in to wash and examine him. "Let's get some water heated," said Polly Ware, going into the kitchen. "We'll wash him right here and get some of that Indian scrubbed off."

"I'll help," said Mrs. Sessions. The water was poured into a low stave tub made from an old whisky barrel. After washing the boy's body, the women unwound the two braids of hair and forced his head into the water. He cried and wriggled to avoid the punishment, but the women had their way.

"Caspar, my boy!" said Maria Boughton, standing back of the tub. Hearing this voice from behind, the boy turned and looked up to see where it came from.

"You see," she said, "he remembers his name. Isn't that sweet?" She handed him a stick of candy which he grabbed impetuously.

"Don't be afraid," she said, bending down to caress his cheek, "we'll have you cleaned up in a jiffy. We just want to clean you up and give you some clothes to wear like your mother used to make for you and then we'll give you something to eat."

Mrs. Dreutzer had been preparing a large plate of raccoon meat and potatoes. The menfolks could not resist the temptation to look in through the door at the bath arrangements but pretended not to be looking at the boy when his nakedness was exposed. After his feet were dried, Mrs. Boughton pointed and said, "You see, there's that scar. Not much, mind you, but there's some kind of a scar on his foot," pointing to the left foot. "He reminds me so much of Loretta. That would be his older sister, you know." The other women nodded and smiled.

"There can't be any doubt about it then, can it?" asked Mrs. Dreutzer.

"Indeed not," replied Mrs. Boughton. "Mike, I think you should start off at once and get down to Ball Prairie and bring Alvin back."

"Very well," Boughton said. He put on his light mackinaw, fur cap and wool mittens.

"Good heavens, Mike!" said Mrs. Dreutzer. "You just can't leave without something to eat along. It's forty mile down there and this is middle of winter."

"Oh, I can manage," he said with modesty.

"I'm used to being outdoors. At least I won't have to wade across Rat river this time of year."

Everyone laughed at the reference to Rat river because scarcely a person who had come to Waupaca had not had some amusing or near-tragic experience crossing this river which was without a bridge and seemingly without a bottom.

"No, I insist," Mrs. Dreutzer said firmly, and hurried into the kitchen where she made two big sandwiches of cold venison. She wrapped them in a cloth sack and also included a chunk of maple sugar she had purchased from the Indians the year before.

"You are too kind," said Mrs. Boughton. "I hope we can repay you Nellie."

"Not at all. I wouldn't hear of it," she said, handing the sack to Boughton. He stuffed it into his mackinaw pocket, put on his mittens while his wife went to the door to kiss him goodbye. "Do be careful now, won't you dear. Stop in Weyauwega if you have to."

"Not if I can help it," he said, followed by laughter all around.

It was already getting dark as he left the outskirts of the village and headed east.

Meanwhile, nearly all the white men in the community, men and women, came to the Dreutzer house during the afternoon and evening that day to have a look at the strange-looking boy. Some found a resemblance between him and someone they knew, or thought they knew, and some said his head wasn't flat in the back like an Indian, and his nose was different, etc., all of which further reinforced the general belief that this was not an Indian boy but the lost child of Alvin and Lucia Partridge from Ball Prairie. The fact that the boy was more than seven years old, and that Caspar Partridge would have been only five and a half years old, had not occurred to anyone because the boy was emaciated and suffering from malnutrition.

That evening Nigabianong was taken to the house of Silas Miller, a lay preacher and builder of the first grist mill. Dana Dewey, Miller and Sessions took turns watching him. The white men had made the change of venue in the false belief that the Indians would not know where the boy was in case they had any ideas of trying to recover him. But the Indians knew where he was.

The following morning Chief Rabbit, Nahkom and Big Peter came to the door of elder Miller. They knocked and when Miller opened, Peter presented him with the letter from the Black Robe at Lake Poygan. Miller asked them to come inside while he read the letter. When he finished, he smiled, but underneath the smile he was disturbed. A civil action? Against whom? Obviously it was meant for Dewey and Dreutzer, not him. He showed the letter to Dewey who almost exploded when he finished.

"Who is this son-, I mean who is this delegate of the Pope that thinks he can threaten us citizens? A tarnal foreigner! Ought to be run out of the country. Let's go over and see Olaf. He claims to be a lawyer now, or at least that's what he wants us to believe."

"Yes, I think that's a tolerable good idea," said Sessions who had just finished reading the letter.

Before anyone noticed, Nahkom had slipped into the side room where Nigabianong was playing with one of Miller's children. She picked him up and he clung to her like a rhesus monkey. The others looked at this scene of affection and wondered how they were going to separate them this time.

"Well, let's all go over and see Olaf then," suggested Miller.

"Agreed," said Sessions.

When Mrs. Dreutzer opened her door, she was amazed to see the mixed group of whites and Indians outside, not to mention Nahkom carrying the boy of the day before who was now wearing an old blanket over the hand-me-down clothes he had been given.

"We would like to see Mr. Dreutzer, Nellie," said Miller.

"By all means, parson, come right in. But what about the others? They can't stand out there in the cold?"

"Peter, you and Nahkom and the chief go inside," said Dewey. Nahkom's eyes flashed every time she was forced to look at Dewey, for the very sight of him affronted her.

Mrs. Dreutzer called to one of her girls and said, "Run over and get Missionary Marsh and ask him to come at once."

Dreutzer, smoking a long cigar, took the letter that Miller handed him and read it, and then reread it. A civil action? Was it possible? Yes, he supposed it was possible. Not that an Indian had a chance in hell to win a case in a United States court, but with this priest on his neck, perhaps it would be rather embarrassing to face a charge of kidnapping no matter how unjustified.

"Shentlemen," he said, "perhaps ve must not act too fast. I tink ve can gain obe-jek-teeve by taking different road. But ve must make sure dis is Pa'tridge boy. Ve must vait for dem to come. Mike must be der by now. *Ja ja*, ve better vait."

"What do you mean wait Olaf?" demanded Dewey. "Isn't that boy Caspar Pa'tridge? Mrs. Boughton said it was."

"*Ja-men*, I mean yes but, I tink dis priest could make trouble."

"But these Indians aren't citizens. We're citizens and what we do we do because we are citizens. Isn't that so?" Dewey demanded, looking to the others. Only Sessions nodded. Dreutzer took a long drag on his cigar, looked out the window at the snow forest, and finally said in a laughing manner, "But dey is persons, Dana."

"Not within the law, I wager. They haven't got no rights unless they're citizens and you can't call these savages people."

"But dey is persons, Dana, who the government acts as guardians to. Seems to me Nordvest Ordinance guarantees. . ."

"That's a long time ago," Dewey interrupted. "Andrew Jackson kicked the Northwest Ordinance right out the window with all the rest of this nonsense about Indian rights."

"Maybe so, but I tink ve should let the boy go now, at least vait till Pa'tridge comes."

By this time Marsh had arrived at the house. He took off his coat and hat and walked over to where Nahkom and the boy had taken a seat on the floor near the stove. He kneeled down and spoke to the mother and the boy in Chippewa, and they replied in Menomini because the two languages are similar. The conversation continued two or three minutes, everyone among the whites wondering what the pastor was talking about. Finally he got up and said, "I am sure this boy is not an Indian."

"Didn't I tell you!" exclaimed Dewey.

"But ve can't hold dem," said Dreutzer. "It vould be illegal."

"Yes, maybe so," said Marsh, adding

weight to the argument. "But perhaps we can ask them to stay in the settlement until the Pa'tridges get here." He turned to Chief Rabbit and asked him if he would be willing to wait. The chief and Big Peter exchanged a few words in a dialect which Marsh could not follow, and after a short parley, Peter turned to Marsh and said that the chief had been preparing to break camp and leave for Poygan, but if the Long Knives were willing to pay Nahkom's family three dollars for each day of delay, beginning today, he would stay.

Marsh translated this to the others.

"Money! That's all they can think of," said Dewey.

"I tink it is fair proposition Dana," said Dreutzer. "Who vil pay?"

"Not me by G-, not me I mean," said Dewey firmly.

"We'll work that out later," Sessions agreed. "But do we have their word on it?"

Marsh put the question to the chief. In reply he took a calumet from under his blanket and said he would smoke the pipe of peace to guarantee his word. He added that it was the white skins who spoke with a forked tongue and had hawk's fingers, not he.

Marsh failed to translate this entirely but assured the others that the chief would not leave.

The Indians returned to Shadow Lake. Nahkom insisted on carrying her Nigabianong all the way, and kept asking him if the Long Knives had given him anything to eat. "Oh yes, mother. The Long Knives kept calling me Caspar, and every time I looked up, they gave me more to eat," and he giggled, happy in the thought of a full stomach.

6

Mike Boughton found the Partridge families attending worship service in the district log school house which was being used on Sundays by the Free Will Baptist congregation. "May I interrupt the services," he called out to the pastor from the door. "I have news of the missing boy. I mean Caspar Pa'tridge."

"By all means," said the pastor, nonplused in the middle of a heavy sermon on the dignity of man. The Partridges recognized the voice and everyone turned to see who the stranger was. As he walked up to the front he turned and said, "Alvin, we've found your son. At Waupaca. Found him yesterday among the Indians."

The news electrified the congregation. The pastor realized it was useless to continue his sermon and gave the benediction. As soon as he had finished the congregation was on its feet demanding to hear the details. After

Boughton had finished, Alvin said, "We'll go at once Mike. I'll take the geldings."

"I think it would be better if we both went," said Fred Partridge. "I'll take my team too."

"All right!" said Alvin excitedly. Lucia held a handkerchief to her eyes and began to cry in relief and happiness. Men in the audience crowded around them, offering to do anything that might be helpful. "How about you Wash?" Alvin asked, looking at Washington Manuel, a friend and close neighbor on Ball Prairie.

"I'm ready to go Al."

"Get a couple of men and meet me at my place at noon." Turning to Boughton, he said, "You better stay with father and rest a day."

"No Al. I'm going back with you. I know the road and I can sleep in the sleigh box if you bring some extra hay and blankets."

The Partridge families returned to their farms, Fred having agreed to come to Alvin's place and join him there with more men. Not a moment was wasted and by noon the party was under way. Lucia packed warm clothing for her son and sent along a big basket of food and coffee for the men.

The two teams made good time and shortly after dark they crossed the Wolf River on the ice and stopped in Fremont to rest and feed the horses. After leaving Fremont, there was no packed road across the marshes to the west and two men with lanterns went ahead of the horses to pick out the best ruts in the snow. The rescue mission reached Waupaca at midnight and stopped at the first house where a candle was burning in the window, the log house of Oliver Hibbard overlooking Crystal River. Hibbard directed the party to the house of Dreutzer, unaware that the Indians had returned to Shadow Lake earlier in the afternoon. When Alvin arrived at Dreutzer's he was disappointed not to find his son there and insisted on seeing him at once despite the late hour.

The men from Ball Prairie were given quarters in different log houses, and stables were found for the two horse teams. Since the Boughtons lived two miles north of the settlement, the Partridge brothers were invited to stay at Dreutzer's and Mrs. Boughton and Polly Ware had come to help prepare supper for the men.

As soon as he had completed his social obligations to his guests, Dreutzer went to the house of Cutting Marsh and awakened him and the two men walked by aid of a lantern down to Shadow Lake to bring back Nahkom and the boy. The fires in the wigwams were burning brightly at this late hour, as if the Indians were expecting trouble.

Big Peter emerged from Nahkom's wigwam when he heard the strangers approach. After Marsh explained his mission, Peter disappeared into the wigwam and not long after Nahkom, the boy, and Peter, were ready to leave. The boy was again dressed in an Indian blanket and his hair was braided, but he was wearing wool socks in his moccasins as well as wool underwear, mittens and a stocking cap the white women had given him.

Oil lamps borrowed from several homes in the community burned brightly in the Dreutzer home to provide ample light for the special occasion. Alvin waited impatiently as Nahkom entered and slowly began to remove the boy's clothing and arrange the two braids in his hair.

"But that's not Caspar!" he exclaimed, incredulously.

"It must be, Al," said Mrs. Boughton. "Look at his foot there. Take off his moccasin on the left foot and look at it. It's your boy all right. He's changed, but he's yours. Yes it is."

"Come here son," said Alvin, holding out his hand.

The boy hesitated, but with a stranger holding out his hand, perhaps he was going to offer him something to eat, and he went over to him. Alvin looked at him, trying to find a connective link with the past, but shook his head.

"Didn't I tell you Al," said Mrs. Boughton. "He still understands English. Walked right over to you when you spoke to him."

"Well I vow," said Fred, "he looks like his sister Lucinda."

"Just what I said," Mrs. Boughton agreed. "Just like Loretta."

"Here son, let me feel of your head," said Fred, holding out his hand. "I want to talk to you Caspar. It's been a long time. Don't you remember me Caspar? You used to come over to our place and play on Sundays with your cousins."

The boy smiled on hearing the stranger use the magic word which surely meant that someone was going to bring him something to eat. "Me want bread," he said, looking at Fred.

"Listen to that now will you!" said Fred. "He speaks English after all this time with the Indians. That's pretty good, young man. Remarkable boy, Al. Here, let me feel of your head now." He ran his fingers through the boy's hair around the braids, feeling of the contour of the skull. Everyone watched with intense interest because it was already established that Fred had knowledge of phrenology and could determine character traits indicated by the configuration of the skull.

After he finished, Fred looked at the others and said, "I believe this is Caspar all right. No doubt about it. He's a little gant but nothing three square meals a day can't cure. He's yours Al."

Alvin looked at the boy again and then at Nahkom. She was watching him closely, not missing a flicker of his eyes or inflection of his voice, trying to determine what he was thinking. It seemed to her that he, at least, was not so sure this was the son he had lost.

"Maybe he looks like him to you," said Alvin, "but I just don't know what to think. Parson, what do you think?" he asked, turning to the missionary.

"Well sir, I have been in the habit of noticing the modulations of the Indian voice, and when the boy answered my questions yesterday it appeared to me that his mother tongue was English. I asked him a question in Indian and he answered in English 'no sir' as plainly and fully as any white child ever did, and I have never known an Indian child among the Menomini, Fox, Sac or Chippewa to make an answer in that manner. I examined his right foot where there's a scar which he told me was caused by his little brother cutting him with a knife. This Indian woman here pointed to the corners of his mouth yesterday when I was talking to her and she said the scars on the mouth were caused by *mis-quo-sho* which means smallpox and I understood her to say that her first husband also died of smallpox. She now has a second husband who is wintering on the Oconto River, but I don't think those scars on his mouth were caused by smallpox. I'm a physician, you know, as well as pastor."

Alvin nodded, but said nothing. Comments were being exchanged among the other people and finally Fred raised his voice and said, "Let's take him and be done with it. This is Caspar and this woman hasn't got a right in the world to keep him. In fact we ought to bring her before a court for hiding him all this time."

Meanwhile, several of the men from Ball Prairie had been reading the letter which Bonduel had written from Lake Poygan.

"Well, don't you agree?" Fred asked impatiently.

No one seemed to agree with him except his sister.

"Well, what did we come here for if we didn't come to bring Lucia's boy back?" he demanded angrily.

Washington Manuel, who had driven with Alvin's party to Waupaca, said, "If we can't all agree on this, Fred, I don't see how we can hold the boy, or this woman. Perhaps if Lucia were to see him she. . ."

"Why of course, Wash!" interrupted Fred. "Why didn't I think of that? We'll just take him down to Lucia and let her decide."

"Are you shur-r Indians agree?" asked Dreutzer.

"Ask them, parson," Fred said.

Marsh translated this request to Big Peter and Nahkom. She agreed no harm could come of this, since she was going in that direction shortly anyway and if the Long Knives wanted to give her family a ride, it would be better than walking in the snow, but only on condition that she would be paid the three dollars promised her for delaying her departure, and another three dollars for the second day.

"I'll pay her," Fred assured everyone, "and here's a five dollars down." He forced the money into Nahkom's hand while Marsh interpreted the arrangement.

Looking at the others Fred said, "Reminds me. After we get down home we'll have to have an interpreter. Ask this big Indian here if there is anyone available around there."

Marsh translated this to Big Peter who replied that William Powell, the government interpreter, whom the Partridges had met nearly two years ago, was still at Winneconne Settlement. When Alvin heard this he said, "Fine, I'll drive by way of Winneconne and see if I can't get him to come over to the house."

"Then let's get some sleep before we turn back," said Fred. "For the sake of the horses, I think we better not start out until Tuesday morning, early. It's a fer piece as we used to say."

Everyone laughed, anxious to restore tranquility in a delicate situation clouded with doubt. It was two o'clock Monday morning before supper was finished and the men from Ball Prairie went to their separate quarters. Marsh explained to the Indians that they should report back on Tuesday morning. Nahkom picked up the boy and the Indians filed out of the house. Alvin watched her as she went, wondering what Lucia was going to say. To Alvin the boy looked Indian. He was not the sweet, curly-haired boy he had lost, and his heart sank in despair once again.

All day Monday the women in the settlement cooked and baked to make up baskets of food for the two sleigh-loads of people returning to Ball Prairie. Nothing like this had ever happened before, they agreed, and nothing like it was apt to happen again. Alvin and his men were out in the stable currying the geldings, inspecting their shoes and the sores under the collars. He had brought along a special ointment to sooth the sores and he went back five times that day to apply it to his pets. He was only too glad to be out of the house for a spell because every time one of the women caught his attention she wanted to assure him that the boy was his and he need have no doubt about it because a woman's intuition was seldom wrong.

7

Nahkom, her three children and uncle, Big Peter, and Washington Manuel rode in Alvin's sleigh on the return trip, while three of the men who had come in Alvin's party transferred to Fred's sleigh. After stopping an hour in Fremont to rest and feed the horses, the two parties separated. Fred took the same way back as he had come through Winchester while Alvin drove south via Orihulla on the ice of the Wolf river, and crossed the two lakes, Poygan and Winneconne, on the ice to where William Powell lived in Winneconne Settlement. The settlement, lying on the east bank of the Wolf river, was mostly Irish, and since Powell, a mixed blood, considered himself a citizen and not an Indian he also lived there.

Alvin had met Powell two years ago when Caspar was first lost. He had gone to him for help and he had also given him handbills to tack up around the Payground offering a reward of $2000 for any information leading to the recovery of his son. But nothing ever came of this.

It was already dark and the temperature dropping rapidly below zero when Big Peter guided the teamsters to Powell's house. After a brief discussion, Powell realized something extraordinary had arisen and at once invited the travelers inside. He sent an Indian out to take charge of the horses and feed them in the stable. It was too cold for them to stand outside even with a blanket on, and they still had two more hours of travel before reaching home.

While Nahkom loosened the clothing of her children and rubbed their feet, Powell's cook, an elderly Indian woman, began to prepare a big kettle of soup made of wild rice and walleye.

Alvin described the events at Waupaca although he was not familiar with the details of the abduction by the Waupaca mob, and after he finished, Powell turned to Big Peter and the two men talked quietly in Menomini. Finally, Powell turned to Alvin and said, "Is this your boy, Mr. Pa'tridge?" nodding towards the child known to the Indians as *Nigabianong*, meaning the "Setting Sun".

"Well sir, I'm not entirely sure it is our boy and that's why I would like my wife to see him because a mother ought to know if a father doesn't," he laughed guardedly.

Powell only smiled and said, "Then you want to take him to your house if it is agreeable to the Indians?"

"Right."

"All right, Mr. Pa'tridge. I'm sure it will be all right with them and I'll come over later tonight. I want to make some enquiries around the Payground. Seems to me I've seen this boy before and this squaw too. Big Peter, of course, I know well."

While the visitors were waiting for the soup, Alvin described the ordeal he and his wife had gone through after losing their boy nearly two years ago. The fish soup was soon ready and the Indians were served on the floor, while the three others ate at the table.

Washington Manuel, anxious to get started, went out to hitch up the team and brought them around to the door. Since the Indians still had on their blankets, they were ready to leave and all climbed back into the sleigh box. The temperature was still dropping and by the time the party reached the Partridge farm two hours later, there was danger of frostbite to the feet of nearly everyone, especially Nahkom and the children who were too tired to get out and exercise.

Lucia was waiting for their arrival and came to the back entry with a lamp in hand, followed by Sport who bounded ahead to smell of the horses. Alvin called from the sleigh, "Get these people inside Lucia where it's warm while I unhitch." He had already dropped Washington Manuel at the nearest point to his own farm.

As the Indians got down slowly from the sleigh box, Sport approached, his hair on end, barking angrily. "Get back, Sport!" Alvin shouted. The dog backed off. And now, instead of going directly into the house, the Indians went to the stable to relieve themselves and Alvin drove the horses into the stable, unharnessed them and put their blankets on. He then escorted the Indians into the house. Sport followed on their heels, growling, and bounded through the door ahead of the strangers, aware he was not welcome, and hid behind the kitchen stove.

"There he is Lucia," Alvin said, pointing to the young Nigabianong. Lucia began to help Nahkom unwrap the children, while her own children watched, completely fascinated by the tattered clothing and dusky faces of the strangers. Nahkom removed Nigabianong's blanket and scarf, straightened out his braids, and turned him around to face Lucia.

"But that's not our Caspar!" she said, her voice rising, at the same moment that Sport growled from behind the stove. Turning to Alvin, Lucia said, "Where is *our* boy? I thought you said he was our boy!" She looked at the other Indian children and to the door and said, "Aren't there any more?"

"I'm afraid not, dear."

"But that's not our Caspar!" she pleaded. The boy's eyes, numb with cold, suddenly came to life. There was that magic word 'Caspar' again and he looked at Lucia and said, "Me want bread."

"But you shouldn't have your hair braided if you're Caspar," she protested, looking at him in unbelief. Finally she got up and went into the pantry to butter a slice of bread. Noting the pleading looks from the other two children, she went back and buttered two more slices for them. She turned to Alvin and said, "Did you think this was our boy when you first saw him?"

"Frankly, no, but sister thought so and so did Fred, and all the others in Waupaca seemed to think so, and finally we agreed to bring him down here for you to decide. I'm willing to believe it if you are. He's changed. There's no doubt about it, but he's nearly two years older and living with the Indians all that time would change anyone. He's hungry all the time for one thing."

Neighbors who had been waiting for Alvin's return, now began to arrive and despite the cold, the house was soon filled with the curious and well-meaning who had come to examine the long lost child. Many of these same people had searched for him two years ago and seemed visibly relieved that he had now been found.

Lucia became increasingly nervous amidst

all the talking and exclamations. She sent her children to bed and prepared to make supper for her husband and the Indians. Nahkom, still wearing an old Indian blanket, remained behind the boy and watched jealously as one white squaw after another came over to touch him or caress his cheeks. This was *her* Nigibianong, she thought, and it was not their right to touch him.

"Oh that's your Caspar all right," said Jane Manuel who had come to help Lucia cook supper for the two families.

"I agree," said Mrs. Isaiah Pickett, crowding into the pantry. "All you got to do is look at those little hands. Just like his grandma, Mary Elizabeth. Takes after you in his eyes, Lucia, and after his pa around the mouth. That set chin, you know."

Lucia made an excuse to get out of the pantry. "What are we going to do Alvin?" she whispered amid all the loud talk. Everyone keeps telling me this is our boy and I just can't bring myself to believe it. Of course, having his hair braided and all that does make a difference, but still. . ."

"I wish it was our boy," Alvin replied, "and perhaps he is, but what if he isn't? Perhaps this squaw would be willing for us to adopt him and give him a decent home. He seems pleasant enough but he looks like an Indian to me."

"I know, but then he would grow up with

our children and if he isn't our boy, I would not like that. I know I could never be satisfied. What did Fred say and why isn't he here?"

"He told me he had some business to attend to when he got home and not to expect him for a couple of days. I imagine our sister-in-law will be here any minute ready with more advice."

Lucia went to the woodbox to fill the kitchen stove. Alvin stopped her. "Let me do that." She looked up at him and picked up the hem of her apron to wipe the tears from her eyes.

After they had eaten, Nahkom's younger children's eyes began to close and Nigabianong too was nodding. More blankets were laid on the floor near the stove and Nahkom covered him with her blanket. Lucia went to a bedroom and came back with a pillow, but the boy was already asleep. At that moment Mrs. Fred Partridge and three neighbor ladies entered. Since the front door to the house was blocked by snow, the company came through the back entry where milk pails and other utensils were stored.

"Why Lucia honey! Is that Caspar?" asked Mrs. Partridge. "Why don't you put him to bed with the other children, or at least in a bed?"

"I just haven't the heart to take him away from the squaw. She watches me like a hawk and I guess she thinks I'm going to steal him from her."

"Well, my dear, someone will have to tell her because Fred told me for a fact before he went to bed tonight. . .dead tired you might know. . .that he had found Caspar. Felt of the bumps of his head and everything."

"I know Mary Elizabeth," Lucia protested, "but the bedroom downstairs is filled with coats and hats of our company. I just can't. . ."

"Maybe so, but it does seem a little strange, your son sleeping on the floor with Indians."

Further discussion about the propriety of letting the boy sleep on the floor was halted by the arrival of William Powell. Everyone who caught a glimpse of him wondered what he was doing here. Most of the people were aware of his official capacity and even more aware of his mixed blood, and someone was asking him to talk to the boy and someone else was asking him whether Nahkom would sell the child. He was not sure where this suggestion came from. Was it Mrs. Partridge? After some effort the boy was awakened and Powell spoke to him and his mother for several minutes in Menomini.

Finally Powell got up where he had been crouching on the floor and drew Alvin and Lucia aside. "I've been talking to the people at the Payground and they swear that boy belongs to Nahkom. And she says he was born at payment time in 1844."

"Are you quite sure?" Alvin asked.

"There are no records, but the Indians are agreed that he is her son but there seems to be some confusion about who the father is. I was also talking to the sub-agent for the Bureau of Indian Affairs who just happened to be at Cowen's trading post when I passed by there and he said if you can't prove your claim to the boy you should release him soon or there could be trouble."

Alvin looked at Lucia. She nodded her agreement, unwillingly it seemed, but with a look of sad resignation in her eyes.

"Would you mind keeping the Indians here overnight?" Powell asked. "It is so cold that it would be risky for the children to be out in this kind of weather. And they have no ponies as you know. Would you be willing to bring them back to Winneconne with your team tomorrow or day after as soon as the cold spell breaks?"

Alvin again looked at Lucia and she nodded. Alvin said, "Then you better tell Big Peter here what the arrangement is."

"Very well," said Powell. The conference between them broke up and Powell remained a few minutes, talking with acquaintances in the crowd of people, and finally found his coat and hat while signaling to Big Peter to follow him outside.

The last of the visitors left at midnight.

Alvin, who had driven a team of horses nearly fifty miles that day and had been on hand to greet the many people who came in that evening, was numb with fatigue. Lucia was overcome with both fatigue and nervous frustration. She went to the children's room and pushed the bed to the wall to make room on the floor for the Indian family, and made no effort to part the boy from Nahkom who carried him into the bedroom.

The next morning Lucia heated water to bathe the young Nigabianong. He was not as badly in need of a bath as she had imagined, but his hair had been braided and she wanted especially to wash and comb out the braids. Nahkom protested, since she had just braided the hair after the boy was returned to her from the Long Knives in Waupaca, but when Lucia offered the boy bread and butter covered with apple sauce, she relented. After the bath, Lucia thought the boy's hair was a bit curly and seemingly reddish in streaks. She gazed at the emaciated body and sighed. The other Partridge children watched intently as these operations were in progress. Throughout the day they attempted to play games with the Indian children, but since they spoke no English, there were often lapses in the games and the conversation.

Despite the continued cold, people kept coming from far and near, all intent on getting a glimpse of the lost child, and all intent on supporting the myth of plausibility in favor of the Partridge paternity.

By Wednesday evening, Alvin and Lucia were fairly well convinced that this was not their boy. "He doesn't act like one of us," said Alvin. "There is something strange, something Indian in the way he moves."

"And frankly he doesn't look like our children, I don't think, no matter what the others say," said Lucia. "Loretta keeps telling him he's her brother, but she was only five and a half and I wonder how much she really remembers except that fight they had up in the sugar bush. I think you better take them all back to Winneconne tomorrow. We just can't keep them here any longer, or I'll lose my mind with that Indian woman sighing and moaning every time I touch that boy."

The next morning Alvin told Big Peter to prepare to leave and the Indians seemed relieved despite the cozy warmth of the house and all the good food they had eaten. On the way across the prairie Alvin wondered over and over whether he was doing the right thing. He knew Fred was going to be angry but he was sick of having Fred tell him what to do, too. It had always been that way, ever since they were children back in Trumbull county, Ohio.

At Winneconne Settlement Alvin shook hands with Big Peter and waved goodbye to Nahkom and the three children. The Indians then crossed the ice on the Wolf and walked over to Nahkom's sister living in a small log house near the Catholic mission. When relatives learned that Nahkom's family had returned they gathered at the log house to congratulate her on her safe return and her son's miraculous escape from the hands of the Long Knives. Obviously, they reasoned, she still retained some of her Medicine Dance powers, or why had the Great Spirit rewarded her with such a happy outcome? It was true that the Black Robe had written a letter, and people said he had occult powers, too. Despite these assurances, Nahkom wanted to go over the mission with Nigabianong and thank the reverend missionary for his help in saving her boy.

"But mother," the boy insisted, "we must bring him a present."

"Hush child, you know we have nothing to give him. We are too poor. You have some new clothes from Waupaca, it is true, but look at your mother. The same blanket for ten years."

The boy shook his head sadly, wanting desperately to give the Black Robe a present which he knew was the custom of his people.

Father Bonduel received Nahkom and the boy, and in his halting Menomini, he told her how happy he was that they had returned, and also how happy he was to have been of service to her. It was only through the mercy of Jesus Christ and His holy mother, the blessed Virgin, that this had been made possible.

Nahkom accepted the assurance of his good will and thanked him with tears in her eyes. Overcome by the sight of his mother's happiness and the memory of his own frightening experience in Waupaca, Nigabianong broke away from her and ran outside to a small coop where the Black Robe kept a few chickens. He grabbed a big rooster and plucked three colorful feathers from its tail and returned to the house. Passing a wash stand in the entry he took a towel and wound it around his head to make a turban after the manner of the Potawatomi chiefs.

To Nigabianong, the rooster feathers were eagle feathers, the most sacred symbol of the woodland and plains Indians. His mother had told him many stories about the meaning of the eagle feather, but the one he liked most was the one about the grandfather who lived in the middle of the forest with his grandson. At an early age the grandfather told his grandson to put an eagle feather in his hair and later when the smoke of the grandson's pipe turned into pigeons he knew that he would one day become a great hunter and brave warrior.

But the eagle feather was also the symbol of loyalty, and the oath of blood brotherhood was sworn in its presence. Aware of all this, the young Nigabianong went to the room where his mother and the Black Robe were waiting for him and handed the reverend missionary one of the feathers and asked him to insert it in his hat. Father Bonduel obeyed his young admirer, and by this gesture he knew that the boy was adopting him into his totem and would share all that he ever possessed with him, even to life itself.

The boy then attached a second feather to the turban he had fashioned from the towel, and the third he threw into the flames of a wood stove nearby and watched it burn. No one spoke through this simple ceremony.

"*Ah sah,*" Nahkom muttered, and taking her boy by the hand, she walked out without another word.

8

George Daken, "rimes with bacon" he was always telling his customers, was a drummer for the Grant Clothing Warehouse at 156 East Water Street in Milwaukee and at the moment he was intent on reaching the village of Oskhosh before dark. He was driving a cutter behind his favorite mare, Bessie-Belle, following the Old Lake Road north between Fond du Lac and Oshkosh, a distance of twenty miles. All the Earth around was smothered in snow, and the great, aging willow trees on the banks of Lake Winnebago bent under the weight of the ice and cold. Through the willows to the east of the road he could see the vast expanse of snow-covered ice, and here and there a blanket shelter where an Indian, peering into a big hole chopped through the ice, waited to spear a sturgeon.

The temperature on this late afternoon in February hovered around ten degrees above zero. It was not that the drummer was cold, since he was snuggly wrapped in a bearskin coat, his head and ears covered by a beaver cap and his hands encased in dogskin gloves, the cuffs of which reached to the sleeve of the coat to keep the snow and cold out. A buffalo robe covered his lap, and under the robe, on the floor board, glowed a charcoal foot warmer.

But this was the first time he had been this far north in Wisconsin, and he had been told both at Wade House in Greenbush where he stopped two nights ago, and at the Badger Hotel in Fond du Lac the night before that he would have to cross the Fox river on the ice to reach Oshkosh. The float bridge which replaced Webster Stanley's ferry in 1849, was not in use in winter, and the thought of crossing over on the ice made him uneasy. He encouraged the mare, gently, and tried not to think about the road ahead. A bit of doggerel he had once memorized came to mind.

'A stranger preached last Sunday
And crowds of people came
To hear a two-hour sermon
With a barbarous sounding name.
'Twas all about some heathens
Thousands of miles afar
Who live in a land of darkness
Called Borriboola Gha.'

A land of darkness, he thought, and now the darkness was closing in on the Old Lake

Road too, but not on 'Borriboola Gha'. Presently he felt a dip in the road which brought him to the embankment leading down to the ice on the river. "Steady now, Bessie girl," he said, tightening the reins lightly. The mare responded, picking her way down the slope and, once out on the ice, she broke into an easy trot.

Daken had been told that he would find a livery stable behind Oshkosh House, a few doors up Ferry street from the river on the east side of the street. He decided not to register first but to go directly to the stable to make certain there was room for his mare. He drove down an alley alongside the hotel and found the stable by a light burning feebly through a window. He got down from the cutter, moving stiffly for a moment while holding his knees, and then straightened up. He threw a blanket over the mare, but did not tie her because she had walked up to the double doors of the stable, waiting impatiently to be admitted, the hair in her nostrils frozen, ice and snow clinging to her belly and fetlocks.

The office of the livery stable was in a room at the left of the double doors where the light in the window came from. Daken walked in and found the hostler dozing in a homemade Morris chair, his hands folded over a big stomach. The chair had no cushion and the sleeper was using a loose bag of oats to sit on and several empty grain sacks draped over the back for a head rest. An oil lantern hung over a table in the middle of the room, and around the table were two mate's chairs, two stools, and three spittoons stained from top to bottom with tobacco juice. The floor was littered with chaff and oats.

On the outside wall of the office was a small stove and to the right, half way between the brick chimney and corner of the room, was the window first seen from the alley. There were two bunks, one above the other, clinging to the opposite wall. They were covered with straw ticking, old blankets and badly soiled pillow cases made of flour sacks which had been washed and bleached to remove the brand names.

In one corner of the office stood a rolltop desk. This was the private area of the hostler, for it was his responsibility to keep the books and turn over cash receipts to Monoath Griffin, owner of the hotel and stable.

The hostler was by now somewhat awake and heard the stranger introduce himself. "Daken's the name, rimes with bacon," he said, reaching out to shake hands. "Can you take care of my mare?"

Without getting up, the hostler shook hands and said, "My name's Bill LaFramboise. That's French for razzberry and it don't rime with nothin," he laughed, just as he always laughed, hard and loud, his great stomach quivering like calf's foot jelly. But he quickly added, looking up at Daken, "But I'm a Downeaster myself. Bedford, Mass. So don't get me mixed up with these French Canucks around here from the Upper country or whatever the hell they call it. They used to think they be runnin everything in these parts, but no more they ain't. Not by a damn site. White man's ataking over this country."

William LaFramboise, better known along lower Ferry street as "Guzzleguts", reached both arms into the air and stretched, exhaling loudly and filling the air with a blast of whisky breath. "Must have dozed off," he drawled, wiping his eyes. Suddenly he eyed Daken. "Did you say you had a horse?"

"Yes sir. I'll be staying a couple of days. From Milwaukee. Selling drygoods."

"Impossible! This place be chock full, mister. Choreboy's shoveled more manure out that manure hole in the last three days than ever before."

Daken was taken back. Nothing like this had ever happened to him before in two years as a drummer, first in northern Illinois and now in Wisconsin.

"Full up, I tell yah," LaFramboise continued. "Come along and I'll prove it to you. I should be beddin down the cattle soon anyway." He unhooked the lantern and opened the door leading to two long rows of stalls, picking his way gingerly down the middle of the floor to avoid stepping into the manure heaps behind the horses and oxen. He held up the lantern and turned to Daken. "Like I said, all taken, Mr. Bacon."

"Daken."

They squinted at each other in the light a second, and then both laughed and in that laugh there was instant friendship.

"Well now, look'a here, Mr. Daken-Bacon, I could just put that mare of yourn in the gangway next agin the wall. Choreboy walks back to fill the mangers thar but he kin manage, I calculate."

"Just fine, sir. My mare at least can eat and if she wants to sleep she can sleep standing up."

"That's as much as any horse can do, I say every time," said LaFramboise, and both men laughed again. "Bring her in then and I'll fetch a pail of water. Wouldn't give her more right now."

Daken was relieved and hurried out to unhitch the mare. As he led her into the stable, she tossed nervously, rumbling through her nose as she eyed the other horses. While the stable boss came with the pail of water, Daken unharnessed and covered the mare with the blanket again and fastened it under the neck. As he was leaving, he petted her gently on the flank. "Good ol' Belle girl!" He turned to LaFramboise. "How much?"

"Two Yark shillings, hay and oats overnight."

Daken reached into his pocket. "Here you go."

"Thank you sir! That's the way I like to do business. And if I may say so that's a mighty fine lookin mare you got thar. Here's the one I drive," he said, pointing to a gant-looking roan. "She ain't no pertikeler beauty to boast on, but you get to the bottom of a hill with a load on, she's thar I tell you! And over here be two teams from out of town. Come all the way down from Waupacy up thar in the woods some'ers."

The two men returned to the office. Daken took off his bearskin and sat down to warm his hands over the stove a minute. "Tell me, sir, how does it happen there are so many people in town?"

"Ain't you heard? Big trial commencen in the morning. People acoming in from all over. Buttrick, Ed Buttrick, he's the judge. Had to rent the Methodist church to hold court. Biggest damn pow-wow since I come here five yar ago. No four. No by God, it's 1852 and that's five. My choreboy will take my place tomorrow 'cuz I'm agoing to church early for once," he chortled.

"What trial, sir?"

"Not really a trial. Sort of. Maybe. A test case between two women claiming to be the ma of the same boy. One's an Indian squaw and t'other's the wife of Alvin Pa'tridge. He lives north of town a few miles. Drives a span of chestnut geldings. Mighty fine drivers too. One of the best in the county if you ask me. Morgans. But I'll bet they got some Aye-rab in 'em too. Wife's name is Lucia. You see them thar Pa'tridges lost a boy nearly two yar ago. Up thar in Clayton township, east of Winchester. Lost a boy in the woods when they was sugaring. Never found him. Someone said the Indians stole it."

"That must have been horrible for his parents," suggested Daken.

"Yep. Caspar be his name. Caspar Pa'tridge. That's Al's boy. Been here a number of times, him and the misszus."

The hostler left the office and went into the tack room to find a bottle of redeye he had hidden in a sack of oats. He returned and handed the bottle to Daken who politely refused, saying, "I've taken the pledge, sir."

"No!" La Framboise roared. "Well, I'll wipe my chin for you then," and he lifted the bottle to his own slightly swollen lips and afterwards corked it, saying, "Well sir, it be this way. Indian family up north thar by Waupacy had three children arunning around and abegging from the settlers like always. And one of the boys talked English, people said, and someone said it must be a white man's boy. So then word got around it might be the Pa'tridge boy, and this person, whoever he was, asked the boy straight out if he knew Al and Lucia and he said he did. Them fellers in Waupacy surrounded the wigwam and took the boy prisoner and sent Mike Boughton to fetch Al. Some trip in the middle of winter. Forty mile one way, calculate. So Al and his younger brother Fred and some of the neighbors drove up to Waupacy and I heard they had quite a time atrying to take the boy away from the squaw. The boy refused to talk English any more and kept atalking Indian to the squaw just like he belonged to her. Well, that's what people said, but you hear so many things, depending on who's doing the talking, or lying maybe."

"So the boy wouldn't talk English?"

"That's what they said. Just pretended not, and then they said the Indians rubbed bear grease all over him to make him look more like an Indian."

"Then it wasn't the same boy who was lost two years ago?"

"Well now, it beats all! The boy Al and Lucia lost was a bright, right handsome lad. His pa had him here once or twice. That was before he got them geldings. But I ain't seen the boy now for couple years of course and I didn't get a chance to see him when the Pa'tridges brung him down from Waupacy few weeks ago. Some feller was in here last night and he said he'd seen him. Said he be lank and miserable lookin just like it be half starved.

Leave it to them Indians! They got ten dogs arunning around the wigwam and nothing to eat themselves."

"Then what?"

"Tarnation, my friend, that boy they said was so damned dirty and what with that squaw alooking on like a mare watchin her first colt, and amaking signs to everyone that boy's hern, why—ah, Al and his wife guessed it might not be Caspar after all. When they brung it down to Ball Prairie I heard someone washed its head and when they combed the hair it got curly and a neighbor boy said if it be Pa'tridge's boy he'd know it by a curl in his head, and damned if that curl warn't thar, but Al and Lucia kept thinkin it wasn't thar boy and the neighbors and Fred kept telling them it be."

"Then Mrs. Partridge didn't think it was her boy?"

"That's the trouble. When this squaw and this man they call Big Peter and the Indian children kept talkin in Indian to the boy, Lucia said maybe they should stay overnight, and they stayed couple of nights I guess and the neighbors was acoming and agoing, acoming and agoing. But Lucia still not sure, mind you, and finally a day later she told the Indians to leave, and take the boy, and that made the neighbors madder than hell to think she'd give a white boy to the Indians. Now I hear they've changed thar minds. Fred swore up and down it be Caspar, and of course, Fred's the boss in that family. Second of Wakeman's boys. So couple weeks ago Fred went to Winneconne with some neighbors to fetch the boy and they come with a constable and a court order. Quite a time finding them. The squaw and the boy had beat it back into the hills around Pine river, but they tracked 'em in the snow. And Fred made Bill, the youngest brother, swear out the complaint. Bill ain't got no assets, you see. Lives with his pa and ma, so if the Pa'tridges lose the case, they think no one can sue Bill for damages."

"So they're going to hold trial to find out whose boy it is?"

"Should be interesting. I heard them Indians and half-breeds got witnesses lined up from here to Neenah to prove the boy belongs to the squaw. Even Chief Oshkosh is in town. Of course that Fred Pa'tridge just could be wrong this time. He thinks he knows everything. Always right, you know. I dasen't say nothing when he's around much. Usually keeps his horse here."

There was a pause in the conversation and Daken got up to leave. "Is the hotel full?" he asked.

"Not sartin, but if it be, come back and take the top bunk here," LaFramboise said, waving at the bunks on the wall.

"That's mighty kind of you, sir," said Daken. He put on his coat and cap and opened the door. "See you tomorrow, or sooner if I can't find a room. Many thanks just the same." He left, happy to have found a place for his mare but hoping desperately he would not have to spend the night in a stable bunk which, from experience, he knew was probably crawling with bedbugs or lice. He walked to the cutter, emptied the charcoal burner in the snow, picked up a valise in one hand and sample case in the other and hurried up the alley to the front door of Oskhosh House. The air was almost too cold to breathe now.

9

The county commissioner for Winnebago county, Edwin L. Buttrick, pounded his gavel on the plain kitchen table before him and said, "Owing to the illness of Judge Jedediah Brown, I have been appointed to hear the suit of William Partridge vs. Nahkom, a female of the tribe of Menomini Indians. A writ of *habeas corpus ad scititious* issued by Judge Brown in January last has been served on one boy child alleged in the complaint to be Caspar Partridge, son of Alvin and Lucia Partridge, lost since April 19, 1850." He nodded to a tawny, rag-muffin boy of about seven or eight years who was sitting between Sheriff A.B. Cooley, law enforcement officer for Winnebago county, and Constable Kendrick Kimball. "Counsel may call his first witness."

Commissioner Buttrick, a rather young man for the grave responsibility suddenly thrust upon him, was well aware of the Bible story about the two mothers who claimed the same child. He had mentioned to his wife that he wished he had a solution as simple as the one proposed by King Solomon. But this was a court of law, he had told her, and judgment would have to be based on the evidence of sworn testimony, not on whim.

Trial was being held in the First Methodist Episcopal Church located on the northwest corner of Church and Division streets in Oshkosh. Counsel for the two parties had actually appeared earlier at the Court House to commence proceedings on January 20 but owing to the great concourse of people flocking to the county seat to attend trial, a continuance was urged by both sides and trial was rescheduled for February 12 to allow time to find larger accommodations. The commissioner then made arrangements with the elders of the Methodist Church to rent their building and, by holding court morning, afternoon and evening, he hoped to hear the case in two or three days, thus holding down the extra expense to the county. James Densmore, editor of the weekly *Oshkosh Democrat*, was employed to record the testimony in the absence of the clerk of court.

On Thursday morning, February 12, every inch of space in the church on both sides of the center aisle was taken as well as extra chairs along the walls of the nave. The gallery at the rear was likewise crowded and groaned under the unaccustomed weight of the crowd. From the gallery, Mrs. Buttrick watched her husband with keen interest, and in a nearby pew Father Bonduel was watching the proceedings.

There were two wood-burning stoves to heat the church, one in front of the door leading to the sacristy at the right, and another at the left, both surmounted by long, black pipes rising high into the ceiling where they were joined and extended back to a brick chimney. Though the temperature was uneven, the air was heavy with the smell of wigwam smoke from the Indians and stable manure from the boots of the white men.

The witnesses subpoenaed by the court were not actually segregated, but it appeared that most of the white men and their families were in front at the right of the main aisle, and the Indians, mixed bloods and traders with their Indian wives at the left. Everyone kept his hat and coat on, and most of the Indian women sat huddled in gray cloth blankets or shawls. Several Indian men had on buckskin trousers and fringed leggings, with blankets over their shoulders, and three of the chiefs present wore black worsted suits which they had used on a trip to Washington City in 1850 to visit their Great Father.

The witness chair was placed in front of the chancel in the main aisle at right angles to the audience and facing the commissioner who sat in a high-backed Jacobean chair at the right of the front pews. The chair, ordinarly stood in the chancel but had been moved to the main floor for the benefit of the court.

Counsel for both sides shared a small table near the door of the sacristy on the left. They stood with backs to the chancel during examination in order not to obscure the commissioner's view of the witness or that of the audience. There was scarcely any room for them to move about.

William Partridge, seated with other members of the big Partridge clan in the front pews, was the first witness called by Leonard P. Crary, counsel for complainant. The witness placed his hand on the Bible and was sworn. "State your name and address."

William Pa'tridge. I live in town of Vinland with my folks."

"Are you the petitioner in this complaint?"

"Yes sir."

"Tell us about it."

"Well, my brother Alvin lost his boy. I wasn't here then, but I seen him once before he was lost and I think that's the same boy," pointing to the seat where the boy sat next to the sheriff.

"No further questions. Your witness," said Crary, turning to Jackson Whitney, counsel for defense.

"No questions on cross, your honor, but I

reserve the right to recall," said Whitney.

"I now call Mrs. Lucia, I mean Mrs. Alvin Partridge," said Crary. The witness removed her hat but kept her coat on. She walked to the chair with dignity, was sworn in and sat down. It was noticeable that she was rather dark complexioned. "Tell us about yourself, Mrs. Partridge, your background I mean."

"I was twenty-nine years old last July, and I've been married nine years to Alvin, my husband. We moved up from McHenry county."

"How many children do you have?"

"Four. Loretta, the oldest girl. She was seven last July. And Caspar, a boy, five years old last May, and Lucinda, a girl three years old last December, and the baby. But we lost our boy."

When was he born?"

"May 24, 1846. McHenry county."

"When was he lost?"

"April 19, 1850."

"Tell us about it, please."

"We were making sugar that spring five mile north of the home place on the timber forty in town of Clayton. It was on Friday morning, I remember, when we went to the sugar bush and took our children too. I mean the three older ones because the baby hadn't arrived yet. We had not been in camp more than an hour or so when we missed Caspar. We called to him, and my husband called louder and louder and we went among the trees and footpaths and through the brush there, but all of a sudden it seemed like the forest..." she stopped and clutched her handkerchief, twisting it to keep from crying. "All of a sudden it seemed like the forest had swallowed up our little Caspar. My husband then went to the neighbors to get help."

"Were there any clues?"

"We found some tracks which I think were his because he had lost one shoe that morning, and the print of one shoe was found in an anthill near a big swamp, I mean to say, I think they were his shoe tracks. I didn't see them. People come from all over to search and they made a circle and looked for a week."

"So you never heard anything more of him?"

"First we heard was on Sunday the fourth of January last, when we were in church, just a few weeks ago. We heard he'd been found among some Indians in Waupacy county."

"Then what?"

"Well, then the men, I mean Alvin and Fred and some neighbors hitched up two teams and started off through the snow for Waupacy. They brought the boy back."

"Is that boy in this court room?"

"That is the child," she said, pointing to the boy sitting between the sheriff and Constable Kimball. "And I have no doubt that he is mine. I think his color changed, but his feet, ears, nose and shape of his face appear natural."

"Was there any birth mark or scab on the boy you lost?"

"At first I thought I detected a scar, but it was so small it was not plain to be seen. I thought his hair at first very thick, but it looks more natural now than it did when they first brought him down from Waupacy. His hair was brown when he was lost. When he was brought to me his hair was in two long braids, just like the Indians, and we washed and combed it and it seemed much lighter than before. It was matted and filthy at first, and the water he was washed in became discolored. Couldn't see the bottom of the tub. I heard the women in Waupacy washed him too but that squaw must have used something on him because he sure was a mess. I remember I washed his feet and the feet was white, not colored like the rest of his body. He has now some scars on each corner of his mouth and on his stomach, and four under his chin, and one on his side. He said, or at least someone told me he said, the scars was put there by something the size of his little finger which he called *medicine.*" She paused. "By the way, I wanted to say that my oldest daughter thought this was her brother when he was first brought to our house, and the school children who visited, too."

"Objection," said Whitney. "The questions assumes a fact not in evidence."

Both Crary and Whitney turned to the court. "Well gentlemen," Buttrick began. "I realize the hearsay nature of this testimony, but I'm going to allow it in order to give the broadest possible scope to this examination. I'm sure you both agree we want to get at the truth in this and if what the girl thinks has any bearing, even though not in evidence, it won't hurt to hear. I'm stretching the rule book, I realize, but you may continue Mr. Crary."

"Thank you, your honor," said Crary. He nodded to Mrs. Partridge to continue.

"Well, what I started to say was that he said the white folks wanted to skin him, and make a white child of him but he dared not admit in front of my children that he was already a white child."

Here Buttrick intervened. "How do you know what the boy was thinking, Mrs. Partridge?"

"That's what they told me he said."

"Who told you?"

"Some people. I forgot who."

"That is all," said Buttrick, nodding to Crary.

"No further questions. Your witness," Crary said, turning to Whitney.

"Mrs. Partridge," Whitney began, "when this boy in court was brought in your house in January, you say you recognized him?"

"Yes sir. You see when they first brought him in he was muffled up and I raised my voice, I guess, and said 'that's not my child' but as soon as he got warm and his muffs was taken off I thought him my boy. The child has been at Sheriff Cooley's or at Kimball's place and I've gone to visit him, I think, eight different days."

"Did you speak to him?"

"I heard him speak some words in English. He was just four years old when he was lost, you know."

"Mrs. Partridge, when your boy was lost, were there any scar marks on him?"

"Yes, there was a scar from a small cut."

"Where?"

"Small scar. And his toes turn out too. He's round shouldered and has not got a flat head behind like an Indian and I think he looks like his grandma."

"Have you any idea how long it would take to forget the English language or how long it would take to learn Indian, Mrs. Partridge?"

"I told Mr. Powell, that Indian trader, I told him I thought this was my child."

"Did Mr. Powell ask you, and I quote, 'Do you and Mr. Partridge claim this child?' "

"No, he did not. Powell come to our house. You see the child was first brought down from Waupacy by my husband and Fred and the neighbors and Alvin went to Mr. Powell's place first because he's the government interpreter and he's supposed to know about people around the Payground. After they stopped at Powell's house, they brought the boy to our place on Ball Prairie that same evening, I mean this squaw and this boy and two other children and someone called Big Peter. Later that night Mr. Powell come to our house and said he had just come from the Payground and got the facts and he was sure the boy was not the one we lost. We didn't know what to say, so next day or day after Alvin took the boy back to Winneconne. But I think it a shame I can't have my boy now."

"How long was the boy actually at your house?"

"Not two days, actually, but we just couldn't manage it any longer, and the Indian woman clung to the boy just like it was hers and we didn't want no trouble with the Indians my husband said."

"Who took the boy then?"

"The squaw."

"But you admit, Mrs. Partridge, that when the boy was first brought in to your house that you did not think it was yours."

"Yes, on account of it being disfigured. And that Indian woman being with it and me not really having a good chance to look at it."

"But you must have looked at it, as you say, when you washed it."

"All I know is I was awfully upset that

night. So many people around. And here was my boy and those Indians acting like they owned it and I didn't have a right to touch him." Tears gushed to her eyes and she hurriedly used a handkerchief.

"One more question. Is it true, Mrs. Partridge, that you or your husband offered to buy the child?"

"That's a lie!"

"That is all," said Whitney.

"I now call Alvin Partridge," said Crary. In her confusion, Mrs. Partridge could hardly find her way back to her pew and she was assisted by her husband who then returned to the stand.

"State your name and address."

"Alvin Pa'tridge. Live in Section five. Town of Vinland."

"How big a place do you have, sir?"

"Well, when the census taker come around last time I had forty acres of improved land and 129 acre unimproved. Cash value of my place would be $1200 and also $100 worth of machinery, two horses, two milk cows, three heifers, and three pigs, altogether worth $267."

"Raise any crops?"

"Yes sir. Two hundred eighty bushel of wheat and two hundred bushel of Indian corn last season."

"Your honor," Whitney objected, "this is irrelevant."

"Very well," said Crary. "Is that boy over there your boy, Mr. Partridge?"

"It is."

"Can you tell us how your boy was lost?"

A year ago last spring we were makin sugar on a timber forty. One day me and my family, three children, the youngest wasn't born yet, and after we been there about an hour, Caspar was missing. I started looking and after some time I called on the neighbors to help me. More than a dozen of us searched all around. Second day we sent out a general alarm and as many as a thousand people were out looking and we searched for six days and all we found were some tracks in a little mound near the sugar bush. I also heard some Indian pony tracks were found. We designed to examine every foot of ground and some of the company remarked that not a spot big enough for a dollar had been missed. There's a big marsh or swamp eighty rods west of the camp and the tracks I mentioned were leading off that way, sort of."

"Then you made a thorough search."

"Certainly did. The day after we stopped searching we heard he had been seen among the Indians."

"What did you do then?"

"I asked Mr. Caldwell, the trader who lives over by Winnebago Rapids to make a search and he told me he would and he went across Rat river where the Indians were making sugar that year."

"But he didn't find him?"

"No sir."

"When did you first hear the, that is, a certain boy, had been found?"

"Well, my brother-in-law, Mike Boughton, brought word down to us on Sunday fourth of January last. We started out the same day for Waupacy, and found him there. Some friends had kept him. I thought he was our boy. I examined him but he did not look natural to me, though. He was frightened and crying all the time. I told the people his feet and hands looked natural. But the Indians were unwilling to give him up. Later they agreed to allow the boy to come with us if the family come along too. That boy is ours, I tell you. I was present at its birth."

"Thank you Mr. Partridge. Your witness."

"Is it true, Mr. Partridge," Whitney began, "that you were spying on the Indians at the Payground in October last and the year before?"

"Objection," said Crary.

"On what grounds counsel?"

"Your honor, no proper foundation has been laid."

"Over-ruled. I am interested in knowing what measures the witness took to find his son. You may answer Mr. Partridge."

"I wasn't spying. I was just looking for my boy."

"And you were at the Payground two different times?"

"Why yes, I went in October 1850 first time, and in October 1851 the second time."

"And you also posted a reward for the boy. Two thousand dollars as I recall. It seems rather extraordinary, Mr. Partridge, that you mixed freely with the Indians at the Payground on two different occasions and also offered a generous reward, and yet no one ever came forward to claim the reward or gave you the slightest clue to the whereabouts of your son."

"Objection, your honor."

"Sustained. Strike the last."

"Did you ask Mr. Powell if the Indians would sell the boy?"

"No, I did not have a chance to keep him. I took him back next day to Mr. Powell's place."

"Do you understand Menomini, Mr. Partridge?"

"No sir."

"How do you know this child in court speaks English?"

"I'm convinced he do, but have not conversed with him except through an interpreter. He refuses to talk English. But I heard him say 'yes', and 'no', and 'don't cut the skin.' "

"Don't cut the skin?"

"Guess he said it all right. No one was

around who understood Menomini at the time."

"But if you don't speak any Menomini, you really could not be sure whether he was talking English or Menomini, could you?"

"Objection."

"Sustained."

"That is all."

"Gentlemen, it's past noon," said Buttrick. "We will recess for one hour." He banged the table and started out through the back way via the sacristy. The white men and their wives began to move to the rear doors. The Indians crowded around the heater on the left side of the nave, and Nahkom watched as Sheriff Cooley prepared to take the boy out for lunch. She had understood nothing of the testimony because the white man's law did not provide simultaneous translation from English into Menomini. But Nahkom had not missed a single glance of the other woman toward the boy. She had wondered, if there was any doubt about whose boy it was, why the honorable judge had not taken the boy's pants off and looked at his penis? That would have been a possible solution, for she was certain that there was still a mark on it from the time he was born. His grandmother, following old custom among the Menomini, had pinched it between the nail of her thumb and forefinger and the child had screamed like it had lost its manhood. But the old woman meant no harm, only to leave a mark on the penis to keep it from growing too large and the future man too proud. Nahkom realized she had not not made an examination of this area for a couple of years now, but even assuming the mark was still there, she knew that the inscrutable Americans would never accept this kind of evidence.

10

At two o'clock in the afternoon, Commissioner Buttrick emerged from the door of the sacristy, took his seat in the Jacobean chair, blew his nose loudly and said, "This court is now in session. Call your first witness, Mr. Crary, if you please."

"I call Mr. Frederick Partridge," said Crary. "Tell us what you know about this boy."

"I knew my brother's boy before he was lost. Next time I heard of him was when Mike Boughton come down from Waupacy. We drove up there and they asked me if the boy was my brother's and I examined him a long time, feeling of the bumps on its head and all, and I concluded in consequence of the bumps and shape and everything that it was my brother's boy. When we were getting ready to take leave, he exclaimed more than once, 'don't cut the skin!' I also heard him say 'yes sir', and 'no sir'."

"If the Indians had stolen the child, as you

seem to suggest, what was their motive?"

"Revenge."

"Revenge?"

"Why yes sir. It goes back to the fall of 1849. There was a canoe on the Wolf river above Winneconne there somewheres. My brother found it on shore and as there was no one claiming it he used it for a trip to Oshkosh. When he got back he turned it over to Caldwell, the Virginian. Mr. Caldwell said he knew who the owner was and would deliver it to him, but instead of that he sold it to another man and told the Indians that Pa'tridge had stolen it and sold it for whisky."

"But how do you connect the defendant, Nahkom, with that?"

"Simple. Mr. Caldwell has been seen in her company, and she's an Indian, like the rest of them, with an undying thirst for revenge and stealing white children has been one of the most terrible ways of revenging the wrongs inflicted on them by their white neighbors."

"Objection, your honor, please," said Whitney, his voice rising.

"Sustained. Mr. Partridge, you will confine yourself to facts, not opinion."

The witness glared at the commissioner and nodded. Crary saw the hostility and said to Whitney, "Your witness."

"I have no questions on cross, your honor," said Whitney, "but I would like to point out the similarity of testimony between this witness and the previous one, both agreeing on the same English words allegedly used by the boy but neither making any effort to explain what was meant by 'don't cut the skin'."

There was growing disturbance in the church among the white spectators during the testimony of the last witness. Buttrick realized he could no longer ignore it and said, "I will have no more of this disturbance. It has also been intimated to me that insinuations and charges are in circulation in this community in relation to myself, to counsel on both sides, and the officers having this matter in charge which, if true, would consign us all to the penitentiary. I wish to say to the ladies and gentlemen here, that if they would extend the same charity to us that they would expect under similar circumstances it would be a great deal more creditable to themselves and much more pleasing to us. You may continue, counsellor."

The audience grew quiet.

"I call Mrs. Maria Boughton," said Crary.

"My husband's a surveyor in Waupacy county and I'm a sister of Alvin Pa'tridge. We live above the Falls. I have known Caspar, calculate, since he was a baby and I have no doubt the boy in court is my brother's."

"When did you first talk to the child?"

"First time on third day of January last. I

asked him if he had ever lived with Alvin Pa'tridge, and he bowed. I asked him if he had an uncle Philip, and he bowed. I asked him if he had an aunt Sarah, and he bowed. I asked him if he had such an uncle, and named one of the neighbors, and he shook his head. He had no such uncle. I asked him if he had a sister, Loretta, and he bowed."

"Thank you Mrs. Boughton. That is all," said Crary. "Your witness."

"If someone spoke to you in a questioning manner in a language you did not understand," said Whitney, "what would be your natural reaction Mrs. Boughton?"

"Me?"

"Yes. Would you not shake your head or nod?"

"Objection," said Crary.

"Sustained," said Buttrick.

"Thank you Mrs. Boughton," said Whitney.

"The prosecution rests, your honor," said Crary.

Opening for the defense, Whitney called Edward F. Sawyer to the stand. "Tell us what you know, Mr. Sawyer."

"I'm from Winneconne Settlement and I've seen this woman called Nahkom many times and the boy too since February 1850. He was brought down to Cowen's trading post. Indians was makin sugar on Rat river that year."

"That is all," said Whitney. "Your witness."

"Mr. Sawyer," Crary began, "I would like to hear more about your version of the arrival of this child at Cowen's place. How are you so certain about it?"

"I'm certain because Cowen brought this child to his house just after I come down from Shawano Lake that year. We had a good deal of sport about him and called it a half-breed."

"What do you mean?"

"Well, my attention was called to it because its features was more like a white child than an Indian."

"That is all," said Crary.

"I now call Mr. George Cowen," said Whitney.

"I live on the east shore of Winneconne marsh," said Cowen. "I do some fur trading. My wife's a Menomini, a descendant of the Gauthiers from Mackinac. I heard about Pa'tridge losing a boy two years ago, but I brought that boy over there by the sheriff to my place in February. He had a hurt on his breast. His mother showed it to my wife and asked if she could cure it."

"Could she cure it?"

"There wasn't much she could do."

"That is all. Your witness."

"I have no questions," said Crary.

"I call Mrs. Rosalie Dousman," said

Whitney. "Tell us what you do and what you know about this, Mrs. Dousman."

"The last several years I have been teaching at the mission school on the Payground, in the girls' school, and I live nearby. Before that I taught at Green Bay, or Shantytown actually."

"How long have you known the defendant?"

"Since 1847, and the boy since I first met his mother. They have been to my house on the Payground. She called him 'son' and he called her 'mother'. I have fed this boy and he sometimes calls me 'grandmother'. All this before the Pa'tridge boy was lost, and if I may say so, I think it is an outrage to suggest this boy is not Nahkom's."

Before Crary could object, Buttrick said, "Time's up. We will recess until seven."

11

During the recess between the afternoon and evening sessions of court at the church, the janitor had been busy lighting the big chandelier which hung from the high ceiling of the nave, as well as the solar side lamps around the walls of the chancel and in the gallery. Although the lighting was dim, the spectators found it almost brilliant as compared to the light from the candles or rag ends dipped in tallow fat on a saucer which they used at home.

The janitor was throwing more wood in the big heaters when Commissioner Buttrick walked through the door of the sacristy and declared court in session. "Cáll your next witness for defense," he said, nodding to Whitney.

"I call Mr. Augustin Grignon."

An elderly man, carrying a cane, approached the chair with caution. He was dressed in American-style trousers, vest and blouse, a black cravat with high collar under a frocked coat. A gold watch with a chain of braided human hair protruded from the fob pocket of the vest. Since the witness spoke only French and several Indian dialects, there was a slight delay as Whitney waited for the appearance of an interpreter, Mr. A.H.L. Dias, an immigrant from Lower Canada who had recently opened a tobacco store in Oshkosh. Whitney turned to Dias and said, "Ask Mr. Grignon to tell us something about himself and what he knows about this boy."

Dias took a pinch of Scotch snuff and began to question the witness and after a couple of minutes he turned to Whitney and said, "Messieur Grignon say for me to say that his grandparent, Charles de Langlade, was the first white man to settle in Green Bay or in Wisconsin. He say he has been operating a trading post on the Payground for many years and he has known this Indian woman since the day the boy was born. He say the boy was born the same year messieur Jones made the first payment at Lac du Poygan in 1844."

"Thank you Mr. Dias and express my thanks to Mr. Grignon. Your witness," Whitney said, turning to Crary.

"No questions."

"I now call Louis Porlier," said Whitney. "How long have you known the defendant, sir."

"For nearly twelve years. In 1844 she came

to my trading post on Lake Butte des Morts and got cradle-bands. I have seen this child with the mother, but never took particular notice of it. I think it is her child. I know it was with her before the Pa'tridges lost their child. If the Indian woman lost any children since 1844 I would have known about it because her band of Indians always came to my trading post for funeral clothes."

"Can you swear this child in court is the same child she got the cradle-bands for?"

"No."

"That is all. Your witness."

"Mr. Porlier," Crary began, "I recognize your name as one of the oldest in Wisconsin history. Since you are of French-Indian descent, I note by a copy of the *Green Bay Advocate* for June 28, 1849 that you and your children shared, with other mixed blood families, in a special appropriation of $40,000, authorized by Congress for their benefit. Is that correct?"

"Yes sir."

"In other words, you have a certain obligation to the full-blood Menomini, don't you?"

"No obligation. The mixed bloods will not share in the annuities at payment time in the future because we have chosen not to move to the reservation on the upper Wolf river. That is our privilege according to treaty. We are citizens."

"I see. No further questions."

"I call Mr. Amos Dodge," said Whitney. "Are you acquainted with the defendant, Mr. Dodge?"

"I presume I am acquainted with this woman, but I do not know any particular name for her."

"Then you have seen her?"

"Yes yes, of course, I've seen her for the past five years."

"What about the boy? Did you ever talk with him?"

"Yes, and just a few days ago he could not understand or speak English."

"Then you speak Menomini?"

"I get along."

"That is all. Your witness."

"Mr. Dodge," said Crary, "have you had any talk with the Indian mother, and if so did you ask her who the father of this child was?"

"Yes sir. At first she refused to answer me."

"Then what?"

"Next she told me it was Caldwell's, she believed."

"She believed? Which is it?"

"Well, I said she said it was her husband's child."

"Then you are contradicting yourself."

"No, I have never said that she contradicted herself about who the father of this child was."

"Didn't you say she had lied to you?"

"I never said she lied to me about who was the father of it. I said I asked her who her husband was and she said she meant, quote, 'her other husband'."

"Who?"

"Caldwell."

"That is all," said Crary.

"I now call William Powell," said Whitney. "Tell us what your role had been in this affair, Mr. Powell."

"I have known the defendant for nearly a dozen years, and the boy since 1848. When the Pa'tridge child was lost, Mr. Pa'tridge came to me and asked if I would go up the Wolf river with him to make some enquiries among the Indians. I could not go at the time and got Caldwell to go in my place. After this child was brought down from Waupaca Falls a month or so ago they brought him over to my place. I was at Mr. Pa'tridge house late that night, too. A great many ladies and gentlemen were there. They asked me to see if the child could speak English, and I spoke to him and he said he could not. Someone, I don't remember who, but think it was Mr. Pa'tridge, requested me to ask the Indian woman if she would sell the child and Nahkom's reply was 'who ever heard of such a thing as selling one's child? Not all the money the Pa'tridges own could induce me to part with him.' The Indians were fixing to go back to the

Payground that night, but it was cold and I asked Mr. Pa'tridge to keep them over night, and to bring them to my house next morning, which he did. This is the same child, Nahkom's child, I knew in 1848."

"That is all. Your witness."

"No questions," said Crary.

"I now call Chief Souligny," said Whitney. Again there was a delay as an interpreter, William Johnson, was called to the stand. "I believe Mr. Johnson speaks Menomini," said Whitney to the court. "Mr. Johnson, ask the witness if he understands the nature of an oath." Johnson turned to the chief and after a moment said, "He professes to be a Catholic now, and says he knows the meaning of a Christian oath."

"Very well," said Buttrick, "swear him in."

Souligny placed his hand on the Bible and was sworn. A man in his late sixties, a long, weathered face, brown as a smoked carp, he had lost an eye in the campaign against Black Hawk in 1832 fighting on the side of the Americans under General Dodge. He was wearing buckskin trousers and jacket, a red blanket over one shoulder and an eagle feather from a headband. In his left hand he held a large pipe of redstone richly decorated with feathers of birds and ornamented with ribbons of many colors—the great Calumet of the Indian people, symbol of peace.

Without being questioned by counsel,

Souligny, still on his feet, turned with a gracious movement to the court and began to speak, stopping at the end of each sentence while waiting for the interpreter to translate.

"My friends," he began, "we want peace, you want war. If you will study the history of our tribe in relation to our conduct with you and of your consideration for us, it will be sufficient to ascertain the truth of what I am about to say, and which is as clear as the rays of light that shines upon our eyes. This great domain you live in belongs to us by right of conquest. Then we were powerful and you were weak. Nor did you possess a single foot of ground on which to plant your corn. You sensed this weakness and your government came to ask us, as a favor, whether we would sell some of our lands near Green Bay for the Stockbridge and Brothertown Indians who had to leave New York state to make room for the Long Knives. Whether by blindness, whether from natural goodness, we consented to this and that day marked the beginning of our downfall. Children of nature that we are, we did not know, when we signed the treaty, all the ruses and detours of a people who call themselves civilized. But if I myself had not been a madman, I would have been able to avoid the great sorrow which now weighs upon my people.

"O that the powerful wind of the West might carry my voice all the way to

Washington to ask Senator Dodge, who was our commander in the Black Hawk war, if my language, in all that I say, is the truth or spoken in malice. Following the treaties which we made with your government we were plundered in nearly all parts of our land, even those lands where the ashes of our fathers and our children repose. We have religiously observed the terms of these treaties because we revere the Great Spirit, our *Kitchimanitou*, and because we love equality and justice. But you have not reciprocated.

"In all the treaties that we have made with the President of your government, our Great Father in Washington city, we are urged to become civilized, to educate our children in your ways, to give up hunting and become farmers, to worship the Great Spirit of the Christian religion with love in our hearts, and to pray and sing His praises.

"Seriously, if you look for the motive which prompted the Partridges and their virtuous associates from Waupaca into this unhappy quarrel between us, is it not the result of greed, to get rich at our expense rather than the mere possession of the young boy who they so unjustly claim as their own? Yes, they know, at the bottom of their heart that the son of Nahkom, who is also my grandson, is not the son of that pale-faced American woman sitting over there.

"By all that I have just said, it is evident

that not only do the Long Knives wish to take our land away from us, but even the money which the government has agreed to pay us for the land, or rather for the gift of it. You oppress us. You wish to exterminate us, and in order to succeed, you will stop at nothing whether it violates the treaty directly or indirectly.

"If we protected you when we were numerous and strong, and you were weak and without resources, would we be stupid enough to attack you now that you have grown strong and we as weak as young shrubs whose tender bark in spring is nibbled at by the young rabbits of the forest?

"It is therefore utter nonsense, devoid of all common sense, which blames Nahkom for having stolen the child of Alvin Partridge, as if the Indian mothers of our tribe, with scarcely food enough to feed their own children, would take on more children born of American mothers. Yes, I repeat, it is a trick, unworthy of the people and even the name 'American' with which you glorify yourselves. How about it, warrior chiefs and nobility of our tribe, have I not told the truth?"

As Souligny finished speaking he turned to the Indians in the audience, waiting for an answer and Chief Oshkosh spoke up and said, "Of course you have told the truth."

The nature of this testimony and response from Chief Oshkosh was a deviation from the rules of the court, but Crary made no objection. The spectators too were amazed. No one had ever heard an Indian, much less a chief with an eagle feather in his hair, express himself so eloquently.

"Your witness," said Whitney, slightly overcome with emotion.

"Before he leaves, I would like to ask the chief where he saw Nahkom and this child," said Crary. Johnson turned to Souligny and explained the question and after a brief exchange, he turned and said: "He says the mother made sugar, spring before last, at Poygan, on the Indian side, that is, the west side of the Wolf river about twenty miles from Rat river, and that she and the boy were on the west side of the Wolf at Poygan the entire sugar time. He says the child's name is O-ah-ka-hah, after the thunder. He remembers the time he was born. A small pole or post is driven into the ground when a child is born. He says that post can still be found if anyone wishes to look for it."

"You mean it has the boy's name on it?"

"No, this post is driven into the ground when a squaw is about to give birth, and she hangs on to it with both hands, squatting and bearing down to aid in delivery."

"Thank you, Mr. Johnson, and express my thanks to the chief if you will," said Crary, forcing a slight smile.

"I now call Chief Carron," said Whitney.

The witness was one of the mixed bloods who appeared in court wearing a French surtout and a soft plug hat. He said he was a Catholic and was sworn in like the others.

"I am called Carron by the whites, but I am really Claude Carron, orator of the Menomini nation. My ancestor was Thomas Carron," he continued, "also known as Chief Tomah. I went to Washington two years ago with Chief Oshkosh and the others to serve as the speaker when we asked our Great Father, President Fillmore, not to send our people to Crow Wing river."

"What is your relation to the defendant?"

"I have known her for eighteen years and I have known this child two years. It talked good Menomini when I first saw it."

"That is all. Your witness."

"Do you know how many children Nahkom has?" asked Crary.

"No, I do not remember much about this child either. We never talk about children except when they are sick."

"No further questions."

"I now call Koshko'shekau, also known as Big Peter," said Whitney. Turning to Johnson, Whitney said, "Mr. Johnson, I understand this witness is not a Christian. Would you ask him if he understands the nature of an oath?"

There was a brief discussion with the witness and then Johnson said, "He understands an oath and that a falsehood would be killing his body and soul. He appeals to his grandfather, the Great Spirit, and to his grandmother, the Earth, for the truth of what he is about to say."

"Is that agreeable to the court?" asked Whitney.

"I'll accept that," said Buttrick, "but he need not put his hand on the Holy Bible."

"Yes sir," said Johnson. The witness was sworn according to these circumstances and took the chair.

"Ask him what he knows about this child," Whitney said.

Johnson turned to the witness and talked for several minutes and then addressed the court. "He says he was at the Payground when the child was born and he has known it ever since that time. Nahkom has made sugar, he says, where he has and he has seen her at every sugaring time for the past several years. He says he ought to know who the child is because Nahkom is his niece. When the child was taken by the white settlers in Waupaca, the witness went on foot many miles through the snow to the missionary on the Payground to get him to write a letter in English addressed to the white men in Waupaca. He is not sure what the letter said but he thinks that the missionary threatened the whites there with a civil action if they did not release the boy at once."

"That is all," said Whitney.

"No questions," Crary said.

"I now call Nah-tum-pe-mo-na," said Whitney, enunciating each syllable carefully. An Indian woman about thirty-five years old was shown to the chair, her hands partly hidden under a faded blue cloth blanket. Underneath she wore a skirt and blouse of broadcloth, a loan from Mrs. Dousman. She wore no jewelry or other ornaments.

Turning to Buttrick, Whitney said, "I understand, your honor, that this witness is also not a Christian."

"Ask her if she believes the Great Spirit will punish her for wrong doing."

"Yes your honor." A brief exchange followed between the interpreter and the witness. Spectators in the audience were again intrigued by this dialogue and listened attentively to the melodious but gutteral tones which were filling the church with strange, no doubt evil vibrations issuing from the depths of the ancient forest. The white men instinctively wondered how to push these unseen forces back into the forest and stifle them before they could do any harm to the American Dream which was to cut down the forest primeval and bring the light of Christian civilization into the clearings and across the prairies and mountains. Was it not true that these people of the forest were also a "degraded race?" For these were the words of the editor of the *Oshkosh Democrat*, the very man recording the trial who a year earlier had written that the American Indians were incapable of improvement "and found so by centuries of experience and the sooner they died out the better for them and for the others."

The interpreter turned from the witness and said, "She says she does not believe the Great Spirit will punish her for wrong doing, although she is not entirely certain what one means by 'doing wrong', sir."

Buttrick leaned forward. "You mean the Indians don't know the meaning of sin?"

"Well no, your honor, there is really no suitable word for it in their language. Isn't that a Christian conception?"

At this the spectators in the audience began to whisper, so loudly in fact that Buttrick could no longer ignore it.

"There will be order in this court," he shouted. Any more of this disrespect will be dealt with firmly. I hope that is understood." He then turned back to Johnson and said, "Tell the witness, then, that we expect her to tell the truth. The Indians do have a word for truth I believe."

"Yes, your honor."

Crary interrupted. "Your honor, I don't see how we can accept the credibility of this witness. She is not a Christian and she does not know the meaning of sin and apparently has no fear of eternal punishment."

"I appreciate your sentiments, counsellor," said Buttrick, "but if I were to apply the same rule to the other witnesses," nodding in the direction of the white men, "we would not have many who could qualify either. Whether or not this witness is a Christian is not the concern of this court. I am here to enquire after the fact, not the private belief of the witness. You may proceed. Mr. Johnson."

Johnson turned to the witness and explained what the honorable judge had said. She nodded her agreement and bowed slightly, her black eyes flashing in the light of the lamp on the table. After further questioning, the interpreter said, "She says she is an older sister of Nahkom and has lived together in the same lodge since they were children. She says she knows this child is Nahkom's because she suckled it herself and because of this it is half her child and she ought to know whose child she suckled. The child was sick with smallpox two years ago at Winneconne. It got hurt some years past on the breast when his mother fell from a horse."

"I see,' said Whitney. "I believe that is all."

Buttrick looked at his watch. It was past 10 o'clock in the evening and the church was growing cold because the janitor, trying to save on wood, had not fired the stoves for more than two hours.

"It's late," said Buttrick. "This court is adjourned until ten o'clock tomorrow morning." He knew he could just as well have said nine o'clock in the morning, but Justice, balancing her delicate scale with a blindfold over her eyes, was urging him to delay, as long as possible, the melancholy account of events past and the ominous threat of events future.

12

Nahkom, the defendant, was the first witness to be called when court reopened at ten o'clock the following morning. Although the mother of three children and probably over thirty, she was fair to behold and, like many of her people, bore a marked resemblance to Caucasian women. She wore a purple shawl over her shoulders and underneath a full-gathered skirt and waist of broadcloth, the same dress her sister wore the day before on loan from Mrs. Dousman. Her black hair was neatly parted but held together in back by a bead fillet, otherwise she wore no other jewelry or ornaments.

The day was Friday, February 13, and the weather outside was cold and threatening. Witnesses and spectators entering the church were coughing and spitting more than usual. But despite the cold, the church was again filled. LaFramboise, the hostler from Oshkosh House, was back in a different pew but near a spittoon. Farther up front he could see George Daken who had found a chair along the wall on the right of the nave. Daken realized by now he might just as well give up trying to sell much on this trip to Oshkosh. All he had heard the day before concerned the trial and the "lost child". Prospective customers were less interested in what he had to sell than of convincing him of the waste to the taxpayers of holding court for "a bunch of wild Indians," as one of them expressed it.

He got a glimpse of the child now and then when people in front moved their heads or hats. The child was rather small for his age, he thought, and seemed dwarfed in the pew next to the big sheriff. Seen from this distance, it was difficult to get any single impression of him except that he was swarthy and thin. It was the attitude and bearing of the boy that attracted him the most. He never twitched a muscle, and the expression on his face remained unchanged no matter who was talking. Only a child trained by an Indian, he thought, could appear this detached. Perhaps he was half Indian, although none of the businessmen on Ferry street he had talked to even hinted at this possibility because this would have been a denial of the Partridge paternity.

The moment had come for trial to resume. The commissioner opened the door of the sacristy and walked over to the Jacobean chair and sat down. He pulled a big red handkerchief from his pocket, and blew his nose. The audience recognized the signal and waited. "This court is now in session. Call your next witness, Mr. Whitney."

"My first witness today is the defendant, Nahkom, who is not a Christian, but through the interpreter here I understand that she believes the Great Spirit will punish her if she tells a lie. Is that satisfactory?"

Buttrick looked at Crary, who nodded casually and said, "I imagine so, your honor." There was a ripple of laughter, since none of the white men believed in a Great Spirit.

Nahkom was hugging the shawl around her shoulders, but she relaxed a bit when she looked at the boy less than fifteen feet away. Their eyes met but neither made the slightest sign of recognition, for love among the Indians manifested itself by the extremely tolerant attitude that parents had for their children and the respect they had for the individuality of each child. It was true that Indian children were not always at home, especially the boys. They went from wigwam to wigwam, scrounging and playing, but whether they spent the night in their own wigwam or with an aunt or grandmother was all the same because there was group responsibility here and relatives bore part of it. Had not Nahkom's sister suckled Nahkom's child? It made no difference whether the milk came from her own breast or her sister's, for it was the milk of human affection.

Nahkom's mind flashed back over the past several years, and even weeks since the Long Knives had so brazenly attempted to take her Nigabianong away from her at Waupaca Falls. She remembered it all too well. She had just prepared some muskrat tails in ashes for roasting, and the boy and his younger half-brother and sister had come in, smelling the freshly-roasted tails. They finally were allowed to fish the tails from the ashes and break open the skin, hard as a shell from the heat, and suck on the small bones inside. Nothing tasted better and they were forever demanding more.

And she remembered the nights the white trader had come to her after her first husband died, and made love to her without the doe skin with the hole in it between them. He wanted to caress her body the way the Great Spirit had made it, he had said. But her first husband, and her second husband had always made love to her with the doe skin between them.

And in the long evenings, when the smoke rose lazily through the flap in the dome of the wigwam, she recalled the stories she had told her Nigabianong who in the ceremonial feast of bear meat had been given the alternate name of O-ah-ka-hah, meaning the thunder. She herself was a *Mete'w* or member of the

Lodge of Mystic Rites, the repository of health beliefs, and she had attended the annual rites of the lodge since her initiation as a teenage girl. Now she had been hoping that her second husband would initiate her favorite son into the mystic rites when all these incredible events occurred—events beyond her comprehension and control. Was she losing some of her magic powers? Perhaps she and her second husband had failed to carry the sacred "bundle" on some occasion or had neglected a particular sacrifice to the spirits of the underworld. Someone was obviously witching her and she realized she would have to see a shaman to combat the witch.

But how fascinated her son had been with the stories she told him, especially the story of the birth of Big Rabbit, *Ma'nabush*, and how the red-headed woodpecker told Big Rabbit, who had changed into a man, to slay Flint-Rock, and how the flakes fell in all directions from Flint-Rock and that was how the Human Beings got the flints to make fire with.

Johnson, the interpreter, was addressing her. She snapped out of her reverie. He had been asked by Whitney to ask whether she claimed to be the mother of the child and if so, where he was born. They talked back and forth in a spirited manner but subdued in tone. Finally Johnson said, "The Indian woman says that she is the mother of this boy. He was born on the Payground, she says, at payment time seven years ago, and next fall he will be eight years old. She says she has always lived around Lake Poygan since the boy was born. She says wherever she plants her corn is her place of residence and for the last seven years she has made her residence at the mouth of Little river in Waupaca county. Three years ago she went north to the Oconto river and was gone five months hunting."

"Who took care of the children?"

"I was just coming to that. She says her father, whose name is Au-sin, wintered that year on Rat river and she left the oldest boy, I mean the boy in court here, she left him with her father. When she came back from the Oconto country she went to get the boy with George Cowen's team of horses. She knew nothing of a lost child and the first she heard of it was when the white men took her child away from her at Waupaca."

"That is all. Your witness."

"Mr. Johnson, would you please ask the defendant a little more about her family," said Crary.

The interpreter turned to Nahkom and after some discussion he said, "She says her first husband, Pi-ah-wah-tah, is the father of the child in court. He was a full-blooded Menomini and she says she is a full-blooded Menomini. Her second husband is

Tow-o-so-ban and she has two children by him."

"Mr. Johnson, please ask her what she told Mr. Dodge," said Crary. After a brief exchange, Johnson said, "She says that she told Mr. Dodge the child belonged to her 'other husband', meaning Caldwell. But she says she did not know Caldwell was a white man."

"What? Are you sure you are interpreting this witness correctly, Mr. Johnson? I can't believe any Indian would not know a white man from a red man, even in the dark."

The audience laughed and Buttrick pounded the gavel for order.

Johnson talked briefly with Nahkom and turned back to Crary. "She seems confused, and I find it a bit hard to follow her line of thought. She said she had seen the trader at different times at the Payground where he has traded at payment time, but is not acquainted with him."

"Not acquainted? Are you sure this is the meaning she has in mind?"

"Well, she pretends not to know him very well any more. Let's put it that way."

"I see. At least that makes better sense. That is all."

"I now call Chief LaMotte," said Whitney. Since he was a Catholic and spoke English, he was sworn in without the aid of the interpreter. "Tell me, sir, what is the derivation of your name? It sounds French."

"I am called LaMotte and I am a descendant of Sieur de laMotte Cadillac, one of the founders of the city of Detroit."

"I see. Tell me what you know about this child."

"I have lived at Poygan for eight years, after removing from Green Bay. Four years ago Nahkom visited my place at Poygan and she brought this child with her. I remember it so well because it was on a very warm day and the child was wrapped in a blanket, like a coat. He appeared very white in complexion, I mean as compared to a full-blooded Menomini. But I often thought about it afterwards and laughed to myself because for some strange reason his mother had him wearing this blanket around him on such a warm day, and leggings too as I recall. But I knew the boy before the Pa'tridge child was lost and if I had known that any Indian stole a child I would have gone and made him give it up."

"By what authority?"

"I am the second chief of the Menomini and generally recognized as the leader of the Catholic band. I served under Colonel Stambaugh in the Black Hawk War and am also one of the signers of the Treaty of Poygan in 1848."

"Under which the Menomini have agreed to leave this part of Wisconsin very soon, I believe," said Whitney.

"Yes sir. They're movin to a reservation on the upper Wolf."

"Good riddance," someone mumbled in the audience.

"Order!" shouted Buttrick. "I will have no more of these interruptions." Everyone knew who made the remark because it was followed by a loud sizzle of tobacco juice striking the side of a spittoon.

"That is all."

"I have no questions," said Crary.

"I call John L. Williams," said Whitney. After the witness was sworn, Whitney said, "I understand you are the son of Eleazer Williams, the missionary to the Brothertowns, I believe."

"Yes sir."

"How long have you known the family of Nahkom?"

About five years and I've seen the child frequently at Winneconne, I mean around the Payground."

"When sir?"

"I don't remember seeing it before Mr. Pa'tridge lost his boy though."

"But I thought you said you did see him before."

"Yes, three years ago at Poygan Payground. What I mean is I did not notice him positively till last summer."

"That is all Mr. Williams. Your witness."

"No questions," said Crary.

"Gentlemen, and ladies, it is time for dinner," said Buttrick. "I am getting hungry." The audience laughed respectfully. "We will adjourn for one hour."

13

As the white men moved outside for the noon recess, pushing ahead of the Indians, LaFramboise was one of the first to reach the board walk. He waited for Daken. Snow banks lay on both sides of the walk and there was little room for anyone to stop and visit. As Daken approached LaFramboise he said, "Are you going to eat or feed horses?"

"No sir, Mr. Daken, I'm not afeeding a thing today except myself. Choreboy can do something for his keep. Let's find a place to eat."

"Oshkosh House is good," said Daken.

"Nah, they charge too much. Let's go down to the Grub Saloon just beyond the hotel. Uncle Sherwood's place. He's a steward on the *Badger State* in summer and moves into town for the winter. He really knows how to roast wild prairie chicken."

As the two men turned south on Ferry street off Church, LaFramboise said, "I heard someone say Caldwell, Arch Caldwell I mean, will be on the stand this afternoon. That feller always give me the fan-tods. He's one of them Indian traders and you kaint trust one of them further than a horse trader," he laughed.

The two men found the Grub Saloon and were followed in by other customers, many of them spectators at the trial. LaFramboise and Daken ordered prairie chicken sandwiches and coffee.

"Got to hurry, my friend," said LaFramboise, "or someone will jump our claim to a church pew. Will you be able to stay the rest of the trial?"

"No, I'll have to head back for Milwaukee in the morning after I see a customer tonight."

"When you be back, calculate?"

"In spring I suppose after the ground dries up."

"By that time you'll probably know how the case come out. If Buttrick doesn't decide for the Pa'tridges, thar'll be hell to pay I tell you."

Daken nodded, although by this time he did not believe that the boy belonged to the Partridges. The two men rose to pay for their lunch, and Uncle Sherwood, in white apron and longhorn mustache, took the change and thanked them. They hurried back to the church.

* * * * *

Oshke'hene'niw or Young Man, a younger brother of Chief Oshkosh, was the first witness called for the defense in the afternoon and since he was a Catholic convert, he was sworn like the others who were presumed to be Christians.

"What can you tell us about this child?" Whitney began, looking both at the witness and at the interpreter.

Johnson, the interpreter, talked a couple of minutes with the witness and then said: "He says he has seen Nahkom and that child over there by the sheriff over the past seven years. First time was at the first payment made at Lake Poygan in 1844 when Colonel Jones was the agent in charge of distributing the annuities. The witness acted as chief to inspect the list of people who were entitled to the money under the terms of the last treaty. The night of the same day the list was drawn up, this child was born, and arrangements were made the next morning to pay the child's share out of fractions. There is no doubt in his mind that this is Nahkom's boy. He also remembers that she made sugar two years ago at Poygan."

"That is all."

"Would you ask the witness," Crary began, addressing the interpreter, "where Rat river is? Is it on the so-called Indian Land?"

Johnson turned to the witness and talked a

moment and said, "No, it is not on the Indian Land because Rat river lies east of the Wolf river and his people were supposed to remove to the west bank of the Wolf by the treāty of 1836."

"Then she was trespassing."

"The chief says he knows where Rat river is. It is not on the Indian Land. Nahkom made sugar at Rat river seven years ago, the last time, but two years ago she made sugar at a place fourteen miles from Rat river."

"Then she must have been trespassing seven years ago."

"The chief says it sounds a bit foolish to him, since his people have been making sugar on Rat river for a hundred years. He says that was all Indian land once. Now it is your land, but what did the Indians get for the land? He says they got payment time when everyone gets drunk."

Buttrick intervened. "I'm sorry, Mr. Johnson, but the clerk will strike that last, beginning with 'that was all Indian land once.' "

"Yes, your honor."

"No more questions," said Crary.

"I now call Archibald Caldwell," said Whitney. There was an undercurrent of whispering as the witness approached the stand. Everyone knew him as a "squaw man," or white man married to an Indian."

"How old are you Mr. Caldwell?"

"Forty-six."

"Any family?"

"My wife Susan. She's a Menomini. I got five children."

"I understand you helped the Menomini around Neenah during the smallpox epidemic there some years ago."

"Sure. Lots died, but I did what I could."

"You were in danger yourself, were you not?"

"People needed help."

"When did you first become acquainted with the defendant?"

"In January 1844 at Winneconne. Her husband Pi-aw-wah-tah, died dat spring and I made his coffin. At payment time dat year I saw Nahkom wid a child in a cradle, but I can't swear dis is dah same child or not. But it is dah same one I seen her wid since every payment time."

"When did you first notice the boy?"

"My attention was first called to it in 1844 by dem fellers jokin me about it being my child. I been every year at dah Payground and traded with Nahkom too. Saw the boy in 1848. I heard Mr. Pa'tridge lost a child and he asked me to look for him."

"And you found no one?"

"No sir."

"That is all. Your witness."

"Mr. Caldwell, have you ever had any discussion with Nahkom relative to this child at any time?" asked Crary.

"No sir."

"Did she ever tell you who the father of the child was?"

"No, she never told me her husband was not dah fadder. None of Nahkom's friends ever spoke to me 'bout who dah fadder was. Dey all know me."

"Do you get along with the Indians?"

"Of course. And I always found der chiefs to be honest."

"I imagine every trader in this state would swear that the chiefs are honest," replied Crary, followed by a burst of laughter from the audience. Buttrick banged his gavel.

"That is all," said Crary, a slight smile on his face as he watched Caldwell leave the stand.

"The defense rests, your honor," said Whitney.

"Gentlemen," said Buttrick, looking at Crary and Whitney, "I would like to see you in chambers, please." The three men went into the sacristy and the sheriff closed the door. After ten minutes the door opened and the men returned. Buttrick looked at his watch and then up at the waning light in the big windows of the church, and said, "It's nearly candle lighting. Court will convene at seven o'clock this evening."

As LaFramboise and Daken came out together, people were rushing to get to their appointed places in life. Daken said, "Well, what do you think the court was talking about behind that door, sir?"

The hostler spit out what remained of a cud of chewing tobacco he had nursed most of the afternoon, splattering the clean snow with a streak of brown. "Think hell! I'm not paid to think. I told you that Caldwell give me the fan-tods! He set thar in court amaking out like he might be the father, and that thar squaw asaying she wasn't acquainted very well with that person. She knowed him all right. The question is, did she know him under her blanket? If she did, then she must have a brat hidden in the timber some'ers, 'cus that thar boy in court be Al's and no tarnal Indian."

The two men hurried down Ferry street to the livery stable behind Oskhosh House, dodging back and forth between pedestrians, some coming from the Grub Saloon and some going to the stable to look after their horses and oxen. LaFramboise and Daken reached the stable just ahead of several other men who had attended the trial and were now preparing to return to their shanties and "improvements". LaFramboise knew all the men, most of them new settlers who had established pre-emption claims on Ball Prairie northwest of Oshkosh.

"Guzzleguts, who you bettin on?" one of the men asked as they stopped for a moment in the stable office to hear their own prejudices discussed but not denied. The question came from Tom Rankin, one of the neighbors who had helped Alvin Partridge hunt for his boy two years ago. "I'm beginning to think Caldwell is the father of this boy and if he is, seems like Al ain't got too much rights to him."

"Rankin, you must have turpentine in that one eye of yourn," LaFramboise shouted. "That boy ain't no Indian I tell yah! I been livin in this here country longer'n you and can tell the difference."

"But what if he's half Indian?" Rankin asked. "I'll bet that's what all the hush-hush was about when Buttrick and them two lawyers went to the preacher's room."

LaFramboise threw some kindling into the stove and got down on his knees to blow into the grate, mumbling, "Damn choreboy, kaint even keep the fire agoing." He blew lustily on the coals a minute and got up slowly, hitching his big stomach upward and readjusting his suspenders. He turned to Rankin: "If that child be the squaw's, how come the boy didn't give his ma a sign or somethin when she was alooking at him? He set thar like he never see her before."

"But that's the Indian way, they tell me," said Rankin.

"Indian way my foot! Now look'a here Rankin. You on our side or thar side? That boy be Al's boy and it takes the rag off the bush to hear you atalking this way. You sound like them half-breeds in court who trade with the Indians and talk sweet to gain thar favor. What you got to gain?"

"But the boy looks a little Indian to me," said Rankin, shifting nervously on one foot to the other.

"How can it if it be Al's boy?" LaFramboise demanded. "You heard Al's wife, didn't you? And Fred too. He knows all about those bumps on people's heads. We kaint let a white boy be raised by no Indian, my short-horned friend. He'd never go to church or nothin. We got too many hard cases in this country already and if them Indians get the boy, no tellin what they'll make of him. Maybe torture him. My ol' man used to tell about the white boy the Indians stole down Ohio way, or Pennsylvania, or some'ers back thar. Hung him by his thumbs and beat the livin whey out of him. Made him promise to kill a white man and take his scalp. Imagine that? But thar's no tellin what these savages aim to do. I heard they be fixin to go on the warpath if that boy ain't give over to the squaw. Let them come I say! Most of us got a squirrel gun."

"Would you shoot at one?" asked Rankin.

"Me? I'd admire to. Right between the eyes," said LaFramboise, pointing at the center of his forehead. "And I'd watch him jump ten feet in the air!" He raised his arms like he was about to fly through the ceiling, and everyone laughed at the thought of this spectacle.

"It don't seem fittin though," said Rankin.

"Now look'a here," said LaFramboise, pointing his finger at Rankin's chest. "If you keep beatin the drum for these here Indians we'll just find you an ol' squaw and you can start amaking sugar on Rat river yourself."

"Right!" Isaiah Pickett shouted, laughing loudly.

Rankin sensed the hostility behind this facade of humor and said, "Well, I'm not the judge. Let him decide."

"That's better, you ol' claim jumper you," said LaFramboise. "If I didn't know you better, I'd say you looked a little Indian yourself." Everyone laughed.

"But why didn't Lucia keep the boy then, I mean in the first place?" asked Rankin politely.

"Goddamit Tom!" interrupted Pickett, "Lucia couldn't make up her mind and Al warn't so sure hisself with that squaw hanging around all the time."

"It beats the hell out of me, too," said LaFramboise, shaking his head. He left the office to go into the tackroom for a jug of whisky. As he returned he twisted the cork off the jug and handed it to Rankin. "Here, this will put hair on your chest, you Indian!"

"It sure will," roared Pickett over the

laughter of the others. Everyone took a drink from the jug except Daken who asked to be excused, and the men shortly left to hitch up their horses and oxen.

14

After eating supper at the Grub Saloon, LaFramboise returned to Methodist Church. Although court would not convene for another thirty minutes, the pews were already filling up, and the Partridge clan and their friends from Ball Prairie and Waupaca were taking their usual seats up front on the right.

The Indians, not allowed in the saloons, had no place to go between court sessions except to the livery stables and they welcomed the opportunity to return to the church to keep warm and nibble on dried venison and cold boiled potatoes.

Nahkom was in the front pew at the left which was somewhat obscured from the boy she claimed as her son. He was seated as usual next to the sheriff on the right side of the nave.

The court commissioner opened the door of the sacristy promptly at seven o'clock and walked to the Jacobean chair and sat down while blowing his nose.

"Call your first witness in rebuttal, Mr. Crary, if you please."

"I call Mrs. Polly Ware," said Crary. A witness subpoenaed from Waupaca, she was sworn in, her head held high which accentuated her cheek bones and sharp eyes. She wore a flounced satin dress barely visible under a cloth coat, and hid her hands in a big fur muff. Perched gaily on the side of an upswept hairdo she wore a new hat purchased that very day in Oshkosh.

"Tell us all you know about this case, Mrs. Ware," said Crary.

"My husband and I come to Waupacy Falls in 1849, one of the first ones there. But I'm not much acquainted with Nahkom although have seen her and the child at the Falls. She told me the cause of the scars on the boy was caused by *esko'te'w* which a gentleman present said was the Indian word for 'fire', and she pointed to the stove when she said it. I spoke to the child in English, and Nahkom cuffed it when it answered me in English."

"Where was the child at this time?"

"At Dreutzer's place. I went there to wash it. He was very dirty with what seemed to be lampblack and grease. My hand and wrist was crocked very much in washing him. And while I was washing him he said, 'give me some water'. When washed, I called two physicians to see the scars on him. There was one scar on the ankle and one of the breast about an inch and a half from the collar bone, perfectly round, about the size of a shilling. He is quite round shouldered but nothing peculiar about his breast. About the same as any child. One a little fuller perhaps, but that's common with children. I've raised a number myself. Well, what I was going to say was that I called him 'Caspar' and he looked me full in the face."

"That is all. Your witness."

"Mrs. Ware, how many Indians have lampblack handy?" Whitney asked, "and what kind of physicians are you talking about? I'm amazed to learn there are two physicians in a settlement less than three years old."

"Well, there's the reverend, I mean Missionary Marsh. He cures people. And someone else who says he's a doctor."

"But who is probably a quack," suggested Whitney.

"Objection!"

"Sustained."

"That is all, Mrs. Ware." As she left the chair, she glared at the defense attorney.

"I call Mr. Oliver Hibbard," said Crary.

"I'm from Waupacy Falls too," said Hibbard. "Seen the boy here in court when I was teachin school at the Falls last year and Nahkom come with this child one day into my school room and wanted to sell venison and I told her to 'puck-a-chee'—that's Indian for to leave—and she left, evidently offended. The next day when I came back from dinner I saw this child settin in front of my school house and he said, 'I'm no Indian papoose. Indians carried me off,' and he made motions with both of his hands."

"You distinctly heard the boy say he was no Indian papoose?"

"Yes sir."

"Did Nahkom ever tell you she was the mother of the boy?"

"No. She told me she had only three children and these she had in my house frequently. The one she called the oldest is not the child here in court. It is, I think, a year or two older than this one, full as white, and his hair is somewhat curly and he squints some. I used to see this child often. Never seemed to have any particular guardian. Ran around to different wigwams."

"So you think there is a fourth child in the family?"

"Yes sir. I heard my wife ask her how many children she had which included this boy and at least three others who were present. Nahkom, by signs, said she had three and pointed to two small ones, and to another, a little taller and heavier than this one in court, and of about the same complexion. I never heard her designate this boy as her own."

"That is all. Your witness."

"Mr. Hibbard, do you speak Menomini?" Whitney asked.

"No. The conversation between Nahkom and myself was more particularly by motions. When I asked her how many children she had she put up three fingers. I can swear positively that she told me that this child here in court was not her child and she said that more than twice. She told it to me the same way she told me a thousand other things."

"Do you understand Indian sign language, Mr. Hibbard?"

"No, I mean we made motions."

"What kind of motions?"

"Well, you know."

"No, I do not know. Please describe how you talked with the defendant."

"Well, I can't right now."

"Well, Mr. Hibbard, if you can't right now, how could you understand 'a thousand other things', as you put it?"

The witness flushed and began examining his finger nails.

"You are excused," said Whitney, who could scarcely disguise his disdain for him.

"I now call Dr. James Ladow," said Crary. "Have you examined the boy in court, sir?"

"I examined his foot this morning and found a scar about half way between the heel and toe, on the instep. Scars frequently go down, that is, change places."

"Anything else?"

"I examined the boy's hair and thought from the appearance of the hair and skin that they were colored or stained. You see the skin is composed of three layers, and the middle layer is what gives color. If you make an application that will stain the layer lying below the scarf skin, the stain so communicated will last for years. It is a physiological fact that stain once produced on this second skin, though it may have been done in a short time, will sometimes remain a lifetime. If the arm is bared to the sun six weeks, a stain is sometimes produced that cannot be removed for years."

"What can produce a stain, doctor?"

"Many substances. An application of nitrate of silver will make a white man almost as dark as a Negro. I have seen several cases of this where the application was taken internally. Sometimes change of habit will produce a change in skin too."

"That is all. Your witness."

"Dr. Ladow, what in your opinion caused the scars which you refer to?" asked Whitney.

"I cannot state whether the scars were caused by eruption or by external applications, most probably external injuries. On one side of the breast bone the chest is much higher than the other on this boy. This might have been caused by injury, or by hereditary descent. I might add that I do not believe the child a full-blooded Indian child."

"That's interesting, Doctor. You do not believe he is a full-blooded Indian. Conversely, then, he could not be a full-blooded white child either, could he?"

Crary jumped to his feet. "Objection, your honor. Counsel is leading."

"Sustained."

"That is all."

"I now call. . ." Crary began, but was interrupted by the court. "It is getting late again, gentlemen," said Buttrick, "and this court will stand adjourned until tomorrow morning at ten o'clock, God willing." He banged the gavel.

15

The morning session of court in the Methodist Church on the third day of trial was taken up with rebutting testimony by the prosecution but before the first witness was called there was a stir on the right side of the aisle. The child had just been brought in by the sheriff and led to his customary pew along the east wall. People in the front pews who had a clear view of him at once noticed a change in his appearance. His face and neck, seemingly greased, had taken on a more swarthy complexion. His hair was uncombed and his hands and face were in need of soap and water.

Members of the Partridge clan began to whisper over their shoulders. Someone had deliberately painted or put grease on the boy to accentuate what were presumed to be his Indian features. The mumbling grew louder in the audience and indignation mounted. Presently Mrs. Alvin Partridge stood up to address the court.

"Your Honor, I think something is happening to that boy that ought not to happen. He left here last evening washed and combed and he comes back this morning unwashed and greased besides. I would be thanking you if you would take the boy out of the hands of the sheriff and give him to someone else to take care of."

Nahkom, who was seated at the left, recognized the voice of Mrs. Partridge and so did the other Indians. They had heard it the first day of the hearing, the rather high-pitched voice of a woman who had suffered much since the loss of her son nearly two years ago. The Indians did not understand what she was talking about now, but they knew it concerned the boy because the commissioner had turned to look at him.

"I see what you mean, Mrs. Partridge. Something indeed has happened to him." He turned to the sheriff. "Mr. Cooley, where have you been keeping this boy?"

"Hank Kimball's been keeping him home most of the time. He's been down to my hotel too, and I've had him out riding in the cutter."

"Well, wherever he's been, he will have to get better care. Understand?"

"Yes, your honor."

Mrs. Partridge was still standing, waiting for Buttrick.

"In whose hands do you feel he should be placed Mrs. Partridge?"

"I have no choice, your honor, but I'm willing for him to go anywhere except to Mr. Cooley's."

Buttrick thought for a moment. He wondered if it would be advisable to turn the child over to Mrs. Partridge. It could ease the pressure he was under from the white community.

"Well, would you be willing to care for the boy, Mrs. Partridge?"

Several women in the audience nodded in agreement as if to help Lucia make up her mind. The Partridges conferred briefly among themselves and finally Alvin arose to say, "We would, your honor."

"Very well. But bond will have to be posted of $2000."

Alvin glanced at Fred, and when he got his nod, he said, "Yes, bond will be posted."

"Very well then. It is strictly understood that this action can in no way influence the jurisdiction of this court over the boy. Is that clear Mr. Partridge?"

"It is, your honor," said Alvin as he and his wife sat down.

The Indians were wondering what the Long Knives and the honorable judge had been talking about. Powell, the interpreter for the tribe, thought the Indians should be told. He raised his hand to Buttrick and when the latter nodded, he rose and said, "Your honor, the Indians are not aware of what is going on. I believe they should be informed."

"By all means. Will you tell them?"

"Yes sir." He turned to the Indians. When Nahkom realized the implications of the court's decision, she sighed audibly and bent forward in the pew, pulling at the corners of her shawl. The Long Knives had confronted her son with a pistol at Waupaca the first time, and they had come a second time, like dogs, tracking her through the snow to Pine river, and now they were about to separate her from him a third time. Suddenly she felt a sharp pain in the pit of her stomach caused by an unspeakable fear such as a hunter gets when he loses his way in the woods. Her heart beat more rapidly and she began to perspire and a few seconds later she had to urinate. She got up and hurried out through the sacristy door at the left and went to an outhouse standing in a snow drift back of the church.

Surprised by her action, Nahkom's sister jumped up and followed her, and a second later Mrs. Dousman went out. The boy, who was in his customary place at the side of the sheriff, straightened up when he saw Nahkom disappear. His eyes darted to the sacristy door and up at the sheriff. The sheriff patted him on the shoulder, but his eyes continued to scan the door and then shift abruptly to the

Partridges because he understood what Powell had said in Menomini. He knew he was now to be taken away from the constable's house and sent to live at the house of the Partridges where he had spent two nights several weeks ago. He wondered if the new squaw would feed him as well as the constable's squaw. After the first day or so when he was brought to Kimball's he had eaten like a glutton. Furthermore, he liked the comparative warmth of the white man's house, with the big stove and a chimney where the smoke escaped instead of circling hazily around the inside of the wigwam and out through a flap in the roof. He remembered all too well when the wind shifted that the smoke in the wigwam would not escape through the flap in the roof but would drift in a cloud over the fire. At times like this there was nothing to do but leave or lie flat on the ground.

The white men began to snicker when they saw Nahkom rush out and Buttrick again pounded the gavel for order. "This is still a court of law here, ladies and gentlemen, and we will wait a few minutes to hear what has happened. I hope it is nothing serious. While we are waiting, Mr. Cooley, please take the boy out and clean him up."

"Yes, your honor." The sheriff got up and took the boy by the hand and stalked down the center aisle. The Indians on the left continued to stare ahead, but the white men swung around for a closer look at the celebrated 'lost child'. To save time bundling the boy's feet, the sheriff picked him up and carried him down the snow-covered street to a hotel. Fifteen minutes later the two returned and again there was an exchange of glances among the white women, nodding approval.

At that moment, Nahkom and her sister and Mrs. Dousman returned and took their seats. Nahkom walked somewhat bent, trying to hide her face as much as possible behind her shawl. After she sat down, she remained motionless, staring straight ahead.

"I now recall Alvin Partridge," said Crary. "Tell me a little more about the events that followed after this boy was brought down to Winnebago county from Waupaca, Mr. Partridge, please."

"Yes sir. When I got to Mr. Powell's place at Winneconne Settlement, I asked him if he knew anything about the boy and he said he was acquainted with Nahkom and knew she had some children by her first husband, and that she had lost some, but he did not know how many. He did not know all her children I mean. He knew she had two or three on the annual payment roll, but when he asked Nahkom what the age of this child was she said it was born at Poygan at the first payment."

"Did you ask Mr. Powell when he came to your house if he would ask Nahkom how much she would take for the boy?"

"There was no conversation by my neighbors, myself, or my wife about asking Nahkom what she would take for the child. And neither did Mr. Powell ask me if I claimed the child."

"That is all. Your witness."

"Mr. Partridge," said Whitney, "can you tell me for certain which foot your son had a scar on?"

"No, not quite, but we used to talk about it at home and said if the boy were ever found we'd know it by the scar."

"Nothing else? A rather strange way of identifying a child you have allegedly known for at least four years, wouldn't you say Mr. Partridge?"

"Objection!"

"Sustained."

"Now I ask you one more question. Just what agreement did you make with Mr. Powell after the boy was brought to your place from Waupaca the first part of January last?"

"The agreement with Powell was, when I took the Indian family to my house, that I was to take them back if we were satisfied the boy was not ours."

"Then you brought the boy back to Powell's place at Winneconne of your own accord because you did not believe him to be yours. Is that correct?"

"Leastways at first."

"Then you changed your mind?"

"Yes."

"Why?"

"All kinds of reasons."

"That is all."

I recall Mrs. Partridge," said Crary. "When did you first come to believe this was your boy, Mrs. Partridge?"

"At Mr. Kimball's place couple weeks ago. I told the boy he was my boy and if he wanted to come and live with me he must put his arms 'round my neck and kiss me and he did so. Since then he has called me 'ma'. I put my finger on a knife in a picturebook and asked him what it was and he said 'knife'. I told him Loretta was his sister and he might talk as much English as he pleased to her. He smiled and said 'good morning, Loretta.' He wanted Amelia Lucinda to sleep with him and pointed his finger and said, 'Amelia. . .sleep.' She did not incline to be still and he said to her 'lie down, Amelia', and he pointed to the stove close by and said 'Amelia, say stove.' "

Here the court intervened. "Mrs. Partridge, do you know which foot has a scar on it?"

"The left foot, about an inch long, near the top."

"Do you or your husband have Indian blood?"

"No sir."

"That is all."

"I have no further questions, your honor," said Crary. "The prosecution rests."

"Do you have another rebuttal witness, Mr. Whitney?" asked Buttrick.

"Yes, your honor. I call Joseph Revoir to the stand."

A former blacksmith hired by the government to assist the Indians, he once operated a shop on the west bank of the Wolf river opposite Winneconne Settlement. "How long have you known the defendant, Mr. Revoir?" asked Whitney.

"For seven years, and this child here used to come into my shop every day, it seems. I knew it before Mr. Partridge's child was lost and I even remember the first time I saw him he was tied up in bands and slept in my shop. I have seen him every year growing up. Two years ago in February I was discharged by the government and I made a trip to the other side of Lake Poygan to buy some maple sugar and there I saw this child again. When I came back to Winneconne I met Mr. Partridge who said he had lost a child and was looking for it among the Indians."

"Are you positive Mr. Revoir?" asked Whitney.

"Positive. And that boy talked Menomini. I even used to play with him when I had time and he always talked Menomini to me."

"That is all. Your witness," Whitney said, turning to Crary.

"Did you ever try talking to this boy in English?" Mr. Revoir.

"It never occurred to me because he never used it otherwise."

"And you say you understand Indian, I mean Menomini Indian?"

"Certainly, good enough to get along."

"I see. That is all."

"Defense now recalls Mrs. Rosalie Dousman," said Whitney. After she took the stand he said, "Tell us once again what your relation to the defendant is, please."

"From the year 1847 we have had an aunt of Nahkom for a servant in our house, and for four years the grandmother of Nahkom has had a wigwam in our yard at the Catholic mission on the Payground. I have fed this boy often. I know he is the same child I knew at the mission. He's a sickly, weak child."

The court intervened again. "What about his breast bone, Mrs. Dousman?"

"Nahkom showed me his breast one time. One side was fuller and higher than the other. Another time she said to me that she almost killed her boy when she fell from a horse and he got hurt very badly. This was three years ago before I ever heard about the loss of the Partridge child."

"Thank you, Mrs. Dousman," said Buttrick. "You may continue Mr. Whitney."

"Thank you, your honor, I have no more

questions. Your witness," he said turning to Crary.

"I have only one question," said Crary. "Can you tell me what name the Indians give to this boy?"

"I do not pronounce his name well because I do not speak Menomini although in Chippewa, which I do speak, I would pronounce it as Ka-ma-ya-kah."

"Mrs. Dousman, how is it that you who have been teaching in a mission school for Menomini children these many years do not speak their language?"

"I am not teaching them Menomini, but English. Since I am familiar with Chippewa, which is the mother tongue of the Menomini, I can make myself understood, but I do not pretend to be an expert. The name Ka-ma-ya-kah naturally would be Chippewa. I believe the same applies to similar names in French and English if I'm not mistaken."

"*Touche*," said Crary, a faint smile on his lips. "The child obviously has as many names among the Indians as a three-tailed bashaw. That is all."

The audience laughed and Buttrick banged the table for order.

"The defense also rests, your honor," said Whitney, shaking his head in disgust at Crary's final remark.

In an effort to wind up the trial that day, the court had allowed testimony to run through the noon hour and it was now nearly two o'clock. "This court is now adjourned," said Buttrick, "and judgment will be pronounced on or before March six." He banged the gavel and immediately the Partridges moved towards the pew where the boy was seated. A lively discussion was heard among the members, all trying to ingratiate themselves with the boy.

Nahkom looked on in dazed silence, unable to move, until finally Mrs. Dousman took her by the arm and led her out.

"Before we start home, Alvin," Lucia was saying, "we must stop and buy this young man a new pair of shoes and some wool socks and pants too, and when we get him home I can fix a new coat from that old coat of yours."

"But Lucia, honey, I've got an old coat home that's just the thing," said Mrs. Fred Partridge. "Don't you fuss. We'll make him look like a proper gentleman. What are you having for supper tonight? Why don't we all stop at father's place on the way out and have supper with the folks?"

"Good idea," said Fred, and everyone knew this was an excellent idea. They began to file out of the church and return to the livery stables for their teams. Alvin and Lucia, accompanied by the boy, broke away from the others to have coffee and cake at Oshkosh House. The boy was the center of attention and the Partridges were enjoying their new-found popularity. “He ain’t ours to keep yet,” Lucia told friends wistfully, “but I am sure Mr. Buttrick knows by now whose boy it is.”

16

Edwin L. Buttrick left his law office in downtown Oshkosh later than usual that evening and returned to his house in Algoma village, across the Fox river. His wife was waiting for him, seated in a rocking chair near a window of the kitchen, reading the new thriller "Two Years Before the Mast". She looked up and smiled happily as he bent down to kiss her.

After he had hung up his coat and hat, he noticed the fire in the kitchen range was down. He went to the woodbox and found two sticks of burr oak and slid them into the firebox. Gazing momentarily into the coals he turned to his wife and said, "That's me in there, burning in hell!"

"Ed, darling, I *do* wish you wouldn't use language like that. If anyone from our church ever hears you. . .but I know right away what's bothering you. It's that decision. But you've heard the evidence. You've watched that boy in court and now you should be able to make up your mind. I just feel so badly for Lucia. She lost her boy and now she's got a chance to have another. . .I mean, her boy again."

"There you go! Her boy? How do you know it's *her* boy? You must have changed sides a hundred times and now you're leaning to her side again."

"Not leaning, Ed," she giggled, "just reclining."

"Then if I don't agree with you, you'll be upset."

"Ed dear, you must do what *you* think is right."

"And what is right? All I know is that if I don't agree to turn that boy over to them they'll crucify me."

"You mean the Pa'tridges?"

"Of course. Now they're going around town and meeting after church up there on Ball Prairie, threatening to raise a militia to keep the boy if my decision doesn't favor them. I never should have given them temporary custody. But I wanted to be fair, I mean to the Pa'tridges, but of course that wasn't being fair to the Indians either. Was it? I just wasn't sure what to do. You know that. The heat was on and I simply felt I had to give into all these people glaring at me in court all the time."

"I know Ed. Ever since she got that boy

home, Lucia has been indulging him something awfully, they say. I even heard he is being massaged with some sort of white ointment to make him look more white."

"That's understandable, but to raise a militia, that's something else!"

"But how can they? They're civilized people and have to respect the law."

"My dear, out here in Wisconsin there isn't much law to go on yet."

"Poor Lucia, though. She's never recovered from losing that child. I can see it in her eyes. They've got a new house but that's no substitute for a lost child. And just imagine what that poor woman went through. It's the woman who suffers the most."

"Women always say that."

"I don't care what you say. Just imagine. Going to bed at night wondering and wondering what might have happened to your child. Wondering if he had been eaten up by wild animals or drowned, or stolen by the Indians. And if he wasn't stolen, think how that boy must have cried and cried till he couldn't cry no more. How awful!"

"But if he was crying, someone should have heard him."

"Think of it," she said, unconsciously shrugging her shoulders.

"Yes, but that's a memory now and we have no control over memories. What I'm faced with is a decision which I'm supposed to be in control of. I thought Judge Brown would take up the matter in circuit court but you know what he said after he got on his feet again. He said, " 'Ed m'boy, that decision is your consarn, not mine. You heard the evidence and I didn't. I could read it but I'm not going to. I'm not telling you whose boy it is,' he says, fiddling that walnut shell in his pocket like he's always fiddling, but he says 'I'm telling you, Ed, be a man.' Easy for him to talk. Be a man! I've got the whole town on my neck already simply because I allowed those Indians to testify in a court of law. You heard what they said? They said the Indians were outside the law because they weren't citizens. Imagine! Not citizens!"

"But some of them don't want to be citizens, I've heard."

"I wouldn't blame them. But that's neither here nor there. What I'm saying is that boy never belonged to the Pa'tridges."

"If you feel that way, then stick to it."

"Then we can kiss Oshkosh goodbye. I wouldn't get any more legal business here. Too bad too because this town is really going to boom before very long. The government surveyors like Ellis and the rest are telling people that the timber stands thick as hair on a dog all the way up the Wolf river to Shawano lake. There's money to be made here. Bags of it."

Now was the moment, he thought. He went

to his coat and removed a sheaf of papers. Returning to the kitchen table, he threw the packet down and said, "There's the decision! All fifteen pages of it. I worked on it all day today and yesterday. Went back over the entire testimony word for word, and. . ."

"And you think the boy belongs to the Indians."

"Of course."

"But you can still change it."

"Change it! You mean you want me to award the child to the Pa'tridges?"

"It just seems so awful to think of giving that little boy back to the Indians. He has such an interesting face. He should get a Christian education and be brought up proper."

"Now you're evading the issue. It's not my job to educate this child. My job is to decide who his mother is and I say the weight of the evidence favors the Indian woman."

"In what way?"

"Well, you heard Amos Dodge. His testimony was positive and he's a white man, too. Then take the testimony of Mrs. Dousman, for instance. Do you think she was lying when she said she had known this child before the Pa'tridge child was lost? She's been teaching in Catholic schools for Indian children for years. I'd rather doubt my own grandmother."

"Just because she's a Catholic doesn't make

her any better than the rest, and you know it. She got married pretty young, you know."

"Now what's that got to do with it? She's raised a family of upstanding children, by her own efforts, because I heard her husband didn't have much when he died. No, Mrs. Dousman is what I call nice people."

"Even if her grandmother was an Indian?"

"O my Lord! When you say that, I feel like moving right back to Vermont. These Indians are people and just because some of them don't think like Christians doesn't mean they're not included in God's plan for us all. You know I've never taken to this 'noble red man' stuff that Cooper's been peddling, but the fact is God made us different. He also made us equal in his own sight."

"Equal? I'd like to see you with an eagle feather in your hat, like that chief had in court." The thought of it made her laugh. Buttrick went to the woodbox to fill the stove again, banging the lid down as he finished. It was always his way of giving vent to a provocation. She jumped up from her chair and threw her arms around him. "Oh, Ed, I love you so, and I want you to do what you think is right, but you know I'm not interested in what's right. I'm interested in helping Lucia."

He held her to him and kissed her. "By the way, what are we having for supper?" he asked.

"I shouldn't feed you at all, I declare. But I must say this time of year is not easy to find anything fresh. I got a steak of sturgeon which some Indian brought in to the market, and we'll have soup of Indian corn. That ought to catch your fancy, Chief Huggin-Bear. And I've fresh rolls, and tea to drink."

"No desert?"

"Wild plum jam on your rolls is all. But tomorrow morning we'll have buckwheat cakes covered with fresh maple syrup I bought this morning from one of the Pa'tridge boys."

"You what?"

"I suspected you weren't going to award that child to the Pa'tridges, and now that the final decision is coming up, I thought if I bought something from them today, they might. . .oh, well, you know." She turned to the stove to prepare supper. As she put the water on for tea, she said to him, "Now Ed, while I'm making supper, you can set like a judge and give me the gist of your decision."

He scanned the pages, written in blue ink, long hand. "Well, let's see now. I go back over the case and tell how they hunted for the boy without success and then twenty months later, how a child is found in Waupaca where Alvin's sister lives. The attention of the people is attracted to him by his intelligent appearance and the fact that he knew a few

English words and appeared to be a sort of *nullius filius. . .*"

"*Nullius* what?"

"*Nullius filius,* that's Latin for a boy seemingly without a mother wandering from wigwam to wigwam. The child is taken by the whites, scrubbed and interrogated. No English words could be got out of him though he talked Menomini with all the fluency and gutteral emphasis of a native."

"But how can you say no English words, Ed? Mrs. Boughton and some others said they heard him say some English words."

"What words? Same words every Indian boy learns out begging among the white settlers. They're not stupid, these children, and this one is a sharpy. Furthermore, the Pa'tridges were continually talking about a mark on him and a scab on his foot and they couldn't even agree on which foot is was. On the other hand Nahkom gave birth to a child at Lake Poygan in October 1844 and more than a dozen Indians and whites said they had seen this boy with her many times."

"But how can you say it was her child? The Indians don't have to be baptized and there's no record of their ages."

"But a lot of white folks don't have any records either."

"Very well then. What else you going to say?"

"I'm going to say that though Alvin

Pa'tridge swears positively and in so many words he is the father of the child in dispute, his evidence must be based on a comparison between this child and the child he lost. And what is the evidence on this point? Caspar Pa'tridge leaves his family a round-faced, curly-haired white child, well versed, for his years, in the English language. At the expiration of a little more than twenty months a boy is brought forward with straight black hair, a thin face, a tawny skin, and who talks an unknown tongue and is said to be the same child. Why, it just doesn't make sense. The testimony of Mrs. Dousman, on the other hand, was direct and pointed, and the fact that this child has been living among the Indians for a number of years was corroborated by the testimony of Dodge, Caldwell, Cowen, Grignon, et cetera et cetera."

"But the testimony of Mrs. Pa'tridge is corroborated, if that's the way you want to put it, by Mrs. Boughton and Polly Ware and others."

"Not one of whom understood a word of the Menomini language! In other words, the evidence of impressions is balanced against the evidence of facts."

"What facts?"

"Well then I go on to say that the fact that Alvin and Lucia Pa'tridge voluntarily surrendered up possession of the child to the

Indian mother and after two or three weeks the writ of habeas corpus was sued out by William Pa'tridge, the brother of Alvin, is strong evidence to suggest that Alvin comes to the conclusion the child is his rather from the well-meaning but injudicious declaration of others than from the conviction of his own judgment based upon an examination of the child himself."

"I think I know what you mean," she commented.

"But another thing, certainly it must have occurred to more people than myself," he continued, "that it was mighty funny that the writ was not sued out by Alvin, the father of Caspar. And even Bill, Al's younger brother, didn't seem to know his name was on the complaint at first. Fred just went ahead on his own and did it."

"But it seems to me, Ed," she said without turning, "that some of those witnesses were a little mixed up, the Partridges included, and even Nahkom for that matter."

"You mean contradictory."

"Well, yes, both. Half the time they didn't even answer the lawyers' questions. Weren't you supposed to see that they did?"

"Not me, dear. I figured Crary and Whitney realized some of their questions were being evaded, or that the witnesses contradicted themselves, but they were too polite to bear down in cross-examination. Whitney especially. And what's more, I don't think that Johnson man was a very good interpreter for the Indians either, especially when Nahkom took the stand. But there's something else I haven't told you."

"You mean you been holding out on me?" she laughed.

"Well, I just thought it could wait. You remember a couple of witnesses hinted that the child is a mixed-blood, and Caldwell himself admitted in open court that he had been joked about it among the traders. Well, now, after that time I called counsel for both sides into the sacristy, I told them I wanted to see Arch Caldwell in my office before I made up my mind on this. When we got together finally, he admitted that he kept trading goods as Winneconne and that Nahkom had a wigwam close by and that he had had criminal conversation with her and believed that child was his. He's a squaw-man, you know."

"What's that?"

"A white man living with an Indian."

"A white man living with an Indian? How interesting! Ed, what if a white woman had an Indian for a husband," she giggled, "or if I had an Indian brave for a husband. What would that make him?"

"It would make him rich because he could trade you off for six white horses."

Quick as a flash, she dipped water from the pail and threw it at him. He leaned over his papers and yelled, "No! No! This is the only copy I've got."

She rushed over and kissed him. "Tell me more about this squaw man."

"All I can say is he's from Virginia and talks like a Virginian, dem and der, but can't even write his own name as I found out when I notarized a mortgage for him."

"But you never told me about this meeting with Caldwell."

"I couldn't. Privileged information. There were hints, as I said, from other witnesses about the mixed blood of the child. Even Dr. Whats-his-name said he did not think it was a full-blood Indian. And this from a prosecution witness. But Crary and Whitney were both too polite to question Caldwell about it at the trial so that's when I decided to have a talk with him in private."

"But that still doesn't prove it is *his* child," she said, tossing her head in disdain.

"Anyhow, I leaked this information out, thinking if the Pa'tridges heard about it they might not be so upset after they heard my decision."

"I wouldn't count on it, my dear. It's the others who won't hear of it."

17

Tim Finney ran most of the way from the Winnebago county court house down to the livery stable behind Oshkosh House. He burst into the office where he found LaFramboise working at his roll-top desk, writing out collection notices.

"Get me a horse fast, Guzzleguts," Finney ordered. "I got to get out there ahead of the sheriff."

"Get out where ahead of the sheriff?"

"Buttrick just give that Pa'tridge boy to the Indians. Sheriff Cooley will be on his way out to Al's place to fetch him, and I aim to warn the neighbors. I know damn well they ain't going to put up with it."

"When did this happen?"

"Just a few minutes ago over at the court house. Buttrick called Whitney in and was waiting for Crary and then Crary didn't come because Whitney forgot to tell him or somthin, but Buttrick waited for Crary and when he come he give his decision. Said the boy belonged to the squaw. I just happened to be in the court house and heard it from the clerk. Saturday afternoon, you know, and not many people around. My birthday too, twenty-seventh of March."

"What you aimin to do, Tim?"

"Get me a horse and I'll explain later!"

"I wouldn't be too hasty, Tim. 'Course you can have my horse but don't kill it." He went into the tack room and found a Mexican saddle and the two men returned to the barn to saddle the roan.

LaFramboise said, "Last time Al Pa'tridge come here was just before the trial and there was two teams here from Waupacy and they come down to testify for Al, and they said Al would pay their expenses, and he ain't come near this place since. I just heard from a feller up the street he never even paid the hotel bill for them people from Waupacy."

"I don't give a hoot in hell, Guzzleguts," Finney replied impatiently, backing the roan out of the stall.

"Maybe so, Tim, but someone's going to give a hoot and next time it'll be your turn. Al's been telling around town how much money he made last year, and all about that new house he's built, but now I heard he stayed with friends in town during the trial and when he left he didn't even give them a piece of maple sugar."

"Whose side you on, Guzzleguts?" Finney shouted, as he mounted the roan and started off at a gallop. At the end of the alley he turned north on Ferry street heading for Ball Prairie.

Half an hour after Finney left, Sheriff Cooley came to the stable. LaFramboise was currying a horse for one of his customers. Now he wanted to tell the sheriff about the unpaid bills but realized his insolence in the church during the trial had not gone entirely unnoticed and he had better not say anything to him about the money he had coming from the Waupaca people.

"Guzzleguts, what are you lookin so sad for?" Cooley asked.

"Kaint rightly say, sheriff, but I'm not feeling good. Must be the bloody flux acoming on."

"Ah, come on, you ol' brick. Help me get the harness on my horse and you'll feel better. I'm in something of a hurry."

"Sheriff, you always believed that boy belonged to the Indians, didn't you?"

"Why yes, of course, I knew it from the start. Didn't you?"

"You know damn well I didn't. But now I'm not so sure any more. And a lot of other people I know are beginning to wonder since they begin paying Al's bills."

"That's life, Guzzleguts. Reminds me of this editor of the *Democrat.* He comes up to me one day during the trial and says it was an outrage on the people—I'm not sure what people he was talking about—but he says it was an outrage on the people to bring that boy in court looking dirty and I told him right to his face that it was a greater outrage for the people to claim it when it wasn't theirs to begin with."

"You said that to Densmore?" LaFramboise blinked in unbelief.

"Yes sir-ee, and I was right too. I'm on my way out to Al's place to pick up the boy and turn him over to the squaw, his real ma."

"All alone?"

"Why not? I've got a court order here," and he tapped his coat pocket.

LaFramboise was speechless for once. He scratched his seat and hurried to hitch up the horse, torn between what he knew to be his duty to warn the sheriff and his fear of the consequences if he did. He wanted to tell the sheriff to drive like the wind if he was going to beat Tim Finney, but he stood there, the wind oozing out of him, and avoided the sheriff's eyes.

"Be back shortly, I calculate," said Cooley over his shoulders as he drove off in his buckboard, humming the *Irish Washerwoman.*

LaFramboise closed the barn doors and went back to his office where he tried to concentrate on his book work, but the thought of what might happen to the sheriff haunted him and he finally got up and went to the tack room for the jug of redeye. He sat down in the Morris chair and the more he thought about the events of the past few weeks, the more he drank. Life used to be so much less complicated than it was now days, he thought. The country was going straight to hell, what with all these newfangled inventions like the steam engine and the reaper, and people moving out West by the tens of thousands to look for gold in California, pulling up their roots from the New England stone piles and causing mischief, lynching each other and not paying their goddamn bills. What was the world acoming to?

The choreboy came into the office on his way home in the evening and finding the hostler asleep, lit the lantern and hung it over the card table. Four hours later LaFramboise was awakened by a loud voice which he recognized as the sheriff's. It did not seem like more than a few minutes since he had left.

"Open them barn doors, Guzzleguts!"

"Comin sheriff, comin," LaFramboise called back as he straightened up and took a deep breath. He walked unsteadily from the office into the stable and lifted the cross-bar on the two big doors. The sheriff drove his rig in and stepped down. The horse was wringing wet.

"Guzzleguts, you got anyting to drink?"

"Nothin but redeye."

"Then give me some."

LaFramboise went back to the office for the jug while the sheriff unhitched and led the horse into the stall and threw a blanket over. When LaFramboise appeared with the jug, the sheriff grabbed it and seemed about to empty it, but finally lowered his arm and said, "There's mischief afloat, I tell yah, Guzzleguts. Mischief, hell and damnation. I don't know what's going to happen but first thing tomorrow morning I'm going to see Buttrick on official business even if it's Sunday."

"What happened?"

"Well, this is what happened, if you want to know, and you might just as well know because it will be all over town before church tomorrow morning. I got out to Al's place and I said I had a court order to take that boy back and turn it over to the squaw on the other side of Winneconne there. Al, you know, had posted that $2000 bond. So when I come with my court order, Al looks at it and then he says, 'if you're fixen to take that boy, wait for me 'cuz I'm going to hitch up my team and drive to town to see Buttrick.' "

"What for?"

"Nothing. It was just a stall. Before he got them chestnut geldings hitched up, here comes two wagons filled with fellers from 'round Ball Prairie. One of them told me privately they had all congregated north of Al's place there at Mikesville Corners after Tim Finney went 'round, just like Paul Revere, soundin the alarm. Elisha Brown was driving the lead wagon with them fast-walkin brindles of his, and he comes into Al's yard and says, like he don't know what's happening and he says to Al, 'what's the sheriff doing here?' and Al, he says 'he come to take my boy.' And Brown says, standing there in the wagon box holding the reins on those brindles and all them other fellers standing up ready to jump down, Brown says, 'Sheriff, I wouldn't take that boy if I was you,' and he turns to the other men and they all nod. I didn't see any gun on them but they had at least ten men in each wagon box and I realized I'd been outflanked as badly as Santa Anna outflanked them Kentuckians at the Alamo. Then Brown says, innocent like, 'You willin to give up that boy now, sheriff?' and I said, 'well, if that's the way you fellers want it, there ain't much I can do,' and Brown said, 'no there haint.' So I give the boy back to Al. Then Brown says, 'now Al ain't responsible for that $2000 bond he posted, is he sheriff? You just returned that boy of your own free will, didn't you?' And all I could say was 'I suppose so.' What else could I say? I wasn't about to shoot anybody. I didn't even have a gun." He paused, and then said, "I feel like vomiting."

"Oh hell sheriff. Come in my office and take

the load off your feet."

The two men went into the office and the sheriff sat down in the Morris chair, deeply dejected.

"Let me fix you a hot sling," said LaFramboise. "I ain't got no rum here but this redeye will do with hot water and sugar." He poured hot water from a kettle and stirred the glass before handing it to the sheriff. "This will hold you till I get a bite to eat for us. I'm fryin some beans and I've got fresh bread and butter I just bought from a woman lives south of the bridge."

"Mighty kind of you, Guzzleguts," said the sheriff. He took the proffered glass and sank into silence, staring absently into the light of the lantern. LaFramboise set the round table and the food was soon ready. The beans were dished directly from the frying pan onto the plates, and the two men sat up to the table.

"Don't feel so bad sheriff," LaFramboise said, "You did your duty, I vow."

"Duty hell, Guzzleguts! I should have gone out there with an armed posse. And damn those sonsabitches straight to hell! I never felt so rotten in my life, standing there all alone and being made a fool of by a bunch of Yankees calling themselves Americans, and then one of them says through the side of his dirty mouth, 'Sheriff, you ain't about to get 'lected, come 'lection time, 'cuz you're an Indian lover.' I liked to have swung at the baggage-smasher, but he was standing there in that wagon box and all the others heard it and laughed."

"I'm sorry, sheriff," said LaFramboise. "I know most of them fellers and I can't figure what's come over them. What they did was wrong. What do yah think Buttrick will do now?"

"He could hold them in contempt of court."

"What's that?"

"Why, ah, he could fine them and force them to turn over that boy to the squaw and if that didn't work he could send them all to the calaboose."

"But he won't do that, I suppose."

"No, I don't suppose he would. The brave citizens of Ball Prairie would rise up in arms and come for him with a rope, I suppose. But Al isn't going to get by with this, I vow. He owes the county the cost of the trial plus the $2000 bond he posted, and he better turn that boy over or I'll see him in hell! We still got laws in this country."

At that moment both men stopped to listen as a horse galloped up to the barn doors and a voice rang out. "Guzzleguts, it's me!" It was the choreboy. He had been riding bareback and slid down from his horse and rushed into the office.

"Oh you, Mr. Cooley! I didn't know you was here."

"Calm yourself, son. What's the trouble?"

"Sir, we live south of town, you know, me and my ma. And I was in bed atrying to get to sleep when I heard a team go by and someone acrying. I pulled on my britches and ma said not to go out there, but I slid out in the dark and followed that team down the road a piece, the old lake road to Fond du Lac, and I swear I heard that Indian boy acrying 'cuz I heard him cry once when he was at Kimball's place."

The sheriff stood up, once again the law officer, and said, "How long ago did he pass your house?"

"By the time I caught up and got back, and then got my horse out of the barn, must'a been a hour. Awfully dark."

Whose team was it you saw, son? Chestnut geldings?"

"Looked like brindles. Not sure though."

Both Cooley and LaFramboise knew that Elisha Brown owned a span of brindles which were recognized as one of the fastest walking teams in Winnebago county, a fact which Brown never failed to mention to anyone who wanted to listen. There was little chance of catching up with them and it was fairly certain that the abductors would avoid Fond du Lac and pick up a stage to Milwaukee.

Word of the abduction reached Mrs. Dousman Sunday morning at the Catholic mission church where Father Bonduel was celebrating mass. Mrs. Dousman went at once to the wigwam of Nahkom's sister where Nahkom was waiting for the return of her son. When she saw Mrs. Dousman coming she knew at once from the look on her face that she brought bad news. Nahkom listened quietly and tried not to cry, but her heart was breaking. "*Neki'qs! neki'qs* (my son! my son!) she began to wail, pulling at her hair and walking distractedly around the wigwam fire. Finally she sat down in front of the fire and began to sing the Indian lament for the dead in a high-pitched tremolo, her body swaying to and fro.

18

Three days after the abduction, the principal chiefs of the Menomini bands were assembled for a Council on the Payground. Among those present were Oshkosh, Sha'wanno of the Shawano Lake band, Carron, LaMotte, Big Peter, uncle of Nahkom, Souligny, grandfather of Nahkom, Kinepoway, also known as "Looki-at-him", Aime'tah, the ancient one, chief of the Little Chute band, Wi'skeno or "Cut-Nose", Chiko'tam or "Laughing Hyena", chief of the Oconto river band, and Asha'wani'pinas, chief of the Peshtigo band.

Also attending the Council were William Powell and Archibald Caldwell. The latter was included in the Councils of the chiefs because he was married to a Menomini and because he was a friend who had once shown great compassion on their people.

The Council was being held in a hogan and the chiefs were seated according to grades of rank and totem affiliations. They were here to discuss the recovery of Nahkom's son and to hear what Captain Elias Murray, Indian agent at Sheboygan, had written in a letter addressed to Chief Oshkosh.

Most of the chiefs were without funds, a fact made all too evident by their tattered blankets. But a fire burned in the center of the circle to warm the hogan and also to provide coals for those smoking *kinnikinick*, the scrapings of the dried red willow bark. While two of the chiefs still smoked the traditional calumet, the others had bartered theirs for cheap clay pipes and household necessities. The Long Knives were anxious to buy the calumets, not for purposes of peace and prayer, but for conversation pieces and museums. To the white man it was unthinkable that an ordinary piece of stone, carved into the shape of a long pipe resembling a tomahawk and decorated with feathers, could be considered sacred. But neither could the Indians see what was so sacred about a black book which the Long Knives put their hand on when they swore to tell the truth and seldom did.

At the moment, Powell, the interpreter, was translating into Menomini from the letter Murray had sent. "It states here," he began, "that he hopes the Menomini will not retaliate against the white man for the loss of Nahkom's boy and he appeals to everyone to avoid using violence to redress a violation of the laws of the land."

"What laws?" LaMotte asked with irony in his voice. "The same law that now protects the Partridge family from being sent to jail for the abduction of our son?"

A general murmer of assent was heard.

"Another thing," Powell went on, "he says he has reported the case to the Indian Bureau in Washington and he still hopes he may be instructed to restore the child to his mother."

"Then he knows where it is?" Chief Oshkosh asked eagerly.

"He does not say. Everyone I talked with believes that he is in Illinois, but the sheriff in one state can not go into another without the proper legal papers."

"We understand that," Oshkosh said impatiently. "What else does the agent of our Great Father say?"

"He says he is not ignorant of the fact that the Long Knives want your lands, but he has written a letter to the editor of the newspaper in Oshkosh and told the poeple that if they will exercise a little patience, their wishes will be accomplished for them."

"For them!" Oshkosh grunted. "What about us? It's the same old story. The Long Knives take the turkey and give the Indian the owl."

Powell shrugged and said, "I suppose so."

"Then it doesn't sound like we can bring

any action against the Partridges in a court of the Long Knives," said Oshkosh.

"I'm afraid not, and even if you could, you would probably never get a white jury to convict them."

A long pause followed. The chiefs lit their pipes while their women brought in tea and a kettle of dried venison cooked in maple sugar and bear oil.

"What else does he say?" Oshkosh asked.

"Well, there is a report here about a meeting held in Neenah sponsored by Fred Partridge and Jim Dolson, and they, I mean the people at the meeting agreed to pass some resolutions and to warn the Congress of the United States that their families were not safe any more with Indians still around. In one resolution it also says here that the Partridges were justified in resisting the decision of the court and securing forcibly those rights which could not be secured by an appeal to the law of the land."

"In other words," said Oshkosh, "they have two sets of laws around Neenah now, one they support when they win, and another when they lose. Our great hero-rabbit, *Ma'nabush*, couldn't do better than that."

At that moment several dogs began to bark outside, but they did not jump at the stranger who approached. He was George Cowen, owner of a small trading post on the Winneconne marsh.

"May I come in?" he asked politely in fluent Menomini.

"Enter friend," said Oshkosh. Cowen bent down to enter and took a seat near the low door. "I have news," he said. "I have just come from Oshkosh where I had my horse fed at the livery stable behind Oshkosh House. The hostler, the one of the big stomach, told me that the family of Alvin Partridge packed up and left Winnebago county."

"Left? Left where?" Oshkosh asked, leaning forward.

"For Illinois, or somewhere."

"When did this happen?"

"I'm not sure. Packed everything they could into two wagons and pulled out. The hostler saw them driving down Ferry street just after dawn, the chestnut geldings in the lead. The mob on Ball Prairie thought that because the sheriff handed the boy over to the Partridges, that Alvin wasn't liable for the $2000 bond. But Buttrick issued a bench warrant for his arrest and instead of facing that, he deeded his farm over to his father, Wakeman, and took off early this morning, like I said."

"What about Fred?"

"He is still here, but I also heard that Mr. Crary, their lawyer at the trial, wasn't paid for his services and has slapped a judgment against both Alvin and Fred for nearly $300."

There was a sense of relief and unbelief in

the sudden turn of events. Finally Souligny, the one-eyed warrior spoke: "Yes, I can see it now. The Partridges took the law of the Long Knives into their own hands. They defied their government and when they did that, they stepped outside the sacred circle."

"There is an old saying," Powell said, " 'the guilty flee when no man pursueth.' "

"The guilty may flee but when will we get our boy back?" Oshkosh interrupted. "His mother makes herself sick with singing and grief. Her sister tells me she cannot get her to eat, and the way she looks I am beginning to wonder what is going to become of her. I must do something for her, but what *can* I do?"

To cover his confusion, he waited for his pipe bearer to light his pipe. No one else spoke. Finally Powell said, "Captain Murray expects you to be ready to leave for the reservation on the upper Wolf river in June."

The chiefs heard this announcement in silence. They did not want to leave Lake Poygan but it was either the upper Wolf or Crow Wing and none of them had any desire to move into hostile territory surrounded on one side by Chippewas and on the other by the Sioux. Oshkosh smoked his pipe out and then said, "This Council is concluded. I imagine it will be the last one on our Indian land. The Long Knives are too many. We are too few."

19

The cold north wind, gusting and uncertain, raced in streaks across Lake Poygan while the waves pounded savagely at the banks along the south shore. Farther out the white caps forced the thousands of geese and goldeneyes and gadwalls to look to the reeds and rushes around for a place to rest from their long overflights between the frozen north and the warm south.

Reversing the course of nature, another flight but not of wild fowl was preparing to move north in the face of the wind on this first November day of 1852. These were the Menomini Indians, more than fifteen hundred men, women and children who had assembled at Winneconne to embark in their birchbark canoes and move up the Wolf river to their new home in northern Wisconsin, the home reserved for them by their Great Father in Washington City.

Altogether the several bands of Menomini

in Wisconsin numbered nearly twenty-five hundred souls, but some were members of Chief Keshena's band who would move down to the reservation directly from the Menominee River country north of Green Bay. Other bands would move to the reservation from their present encampments on the Wolf, the Waupaca and Embarrass rivers, joining the canoe flotilla at Mertin's Landing or farther north at Grignon's sawmill below Mukwa.

Since the water level was down this time of year, two to six men could paddle the canoes, depending on their size. It was not the paddling against the current that would cause the difficulty, but the cold wind, the nights spent ashore without shelter, and lack of food that would cause the most suffering. The Indians had pleaded with the agent of the government to delay the trip until spring, but the agent was impatient. The Indians must go now or lose their option to the upper Wolf river reservation.

The children at the Catholic Mission on the old Payground had been sent home several days ago when rumors began to circulate that the departure date, after six months of waiting, had finally been set. And when the day came for the families to report at the river bank at Winneconne the people looked at their wigwams and log cabins and small frame shanties and were saddened because they had come to love this place of the lakes and marshes. Where else had *Kitchimanitou* arranged a better balance of nature between the fields of planted corn, the wild game, the ducks, the fish and wild rice?

George Daken, "rimes with bacon" he was still telling his customers, had just finished his breakfast in the small dining room of the Hamlin Stagecoach Tavern on the east bank of the Wolf river at Winneconne. He had arrived the night before by stage from Oshkosh in response to a letter from a new customer who was opening a store, since Augustin Grignon was getting ready to close the American Fur Company post on the Payground. With the Indians gone there would be no one to buy peltry from and no one to sell cheap goods to.

Daken walked into the lobby and over to a bay window facing west across the river. He had heard from a waitress about the impending departure of the Indians and when he looked across the river he could see that they were waiting to load their canoes. The several bands, somewhat isolated from one another, were stretched along the west bank more than two-hundred yards north to south, some with rolls of reed matting, some with big bundles made of deer hide or bags made of bearskin. Scattered overall were axes, bucksaws, kettles, kitchen ware, and weaving heddles packed into split basketry and birch bark buckets. Here and there, resting against a bundle was a bow and arrow kit, an old flintlock rifle, spear or warclub. And running everywhere were dogs, barking at random, some trying to sneak up to a bundle in search of food.

Beached along the shore lay birchbark canoes, some small and some twenty-four feet long, but nearly all overage. Loading operations were being handled by the young Indians and the women. Most of the older Indians, waiting for the signal to board, sat on the embankment, clutching their ragged blankets to escape the fury of the wind. The children, who could not sit still, were teasing the dogs or making up games, shouting and laughing, obviously excited about the prospects of a future which held no terror for them.

"Good morning, Mr. Daken," said the inn-keeper, C.R. Hamlin, as he approached the window from another door. "What are you watching? The Indians?"

"Good morning, mine host," Daken joked, "Yes, I'm looking at that scene across the river."

"Did you ever see such a sad-looking sight in your life?"

"No, can't say as I have. Where are they going?"

"Well sir, they're leaving this part of the state. Moving to a reservation. Way up the

Wolf river. I'm not acquainted up that way but I heard from the priest it's above Shawano Lake, wherever that is, about sixty miles as the crow flies, but much longer following the river which I understand is crookeder than a cork screw."

"Is there a village or anything when they get there?"

"Not a shanty as far as I know. They'll have to dig right in, and I'll bet there'll be snow on the ground before they get there. Don't understand why the government didn't get on this earlier. The Indians were supposed to leave last summer, in June you know, then the government agent said no, it would be in the early part of fall and here it is, the ground frozen and geese flying."

"Say, who are those two white people walking through the crowd to the left there?" Daken asked, pointing. "The man looks like a clergyman and who is the old white woman?"

The old white woman isn't entirely white. That's Mrs. Dousman, Rosalie Dousman, who has been teaching the Indian girls at the mission school, and the Black Robe—that's what the Indians call him—that's Bonduel, Florimond Bonduel. He's the man in charge of the mission on the Payground, the St. Francis Xavier Mission they call it."

"Where's he from?"

"I believe he said his home is in Belgium. Came to Milwaukee in 1837, he told me, and held mass in Solomon Juneau's house, first time in Milwaukee. He was in Green Bay later and after the Indians got moved over to Poygan, he came here."

Father Bonduel could be seen carrying baggage and arranging it in heaps by the canoes along shore. It was clear that he was trying to do what he could to get the expedition under way but it was also clear that some of the people he was helping did not care whether their baggage got loaded or not.

"Do you know, Mr. Daken," said Hamlin confidentially, "and I'm not saying this for the *Democrat* in Oshkosh, I think that priest and that old lady have done more for those people than the government, in a way. 'Course, they favor the Indians they call Christians, but you can't blame them for that. That's what they're in business for. He's been over here several times the last days borrowing this and that. I give him everything I can spare but my means are limited too. Still I have to admire the man."

"Is he going with them?"

"He is. Plans to start a new mission up there at a place called the Falls of the Wolf. Says he's already got a name picked for it—St. Michael Archangel, or something. He told me Mrs. Dousman would come up later to take over a school for girls which the government's going to build."

Daken watched the priest moving back and forth, joking and encouraging the people. Many of the children ran after him, pulling at his cassock, obviously asking questions he could not answer.

"I suppose he speaks Indian," Daken said.

"O yes. I don't know how well, but he certainly gets along famously. Do you know, Mr. Daken, a language is a funny thing. It can serve as a wall between two people or it can serve as a bridge. I look at these people over there and because I can't understand a word they say I can't even imagine they've got feelings.

"I know what you mean," said Daken. Suddenly he bent closer to the window pane. "Say, who is that squaw walking between those two other women, half supporting her? Looks like the one they called Nahkom."

"What do you know about Nahkom? I thought you registered from Milwaukee."

"I did, but I just happened to be in Oshkosh when the trial was on and got a chance to be there couple of sessions."

Hamlin looked over his shoulder before he spoke. "That's Nahkom, all right. I was over at Grignon's trading post fortnight ago and he told me she was grieving her heart out over that boy."

"What do you mean?"

"Sighs and moans and hardly eats I guess."

"Is that so?"

"Yes, and they say if she keeps it up she'll lose her mind. You know, I felt rather badly, Mr. Daken, when my boy was called on by the constable to help find Nahkom that time she tried to hide west of here on Pine river, but if he hadn't, you know, it would have been bad for business, and to think, those Pa'tridges skipped the country owing a lot of people. That's what I heard, and when you think all that people done for them. May God forgive me, Mr. Daken. I've tried hard to make up for it by helping Mr. Bonduel all I can even if he is, as my wife calls him, 'a mackeral snapper'."

Hamlin laughed slightly at his wife's reference to the Catholics and Daken responded with a smile. He did not wish to embarrass his host. There was a pause in the conversation as both men continued to gaze at the scene across the river.

"Mr. Hamlin," Daken said, "I heard from a hostler at Oshkosh House that the Indians got burned out. I mean someone set fire to some shanties west of here a year ago. Trying to force them to leave before the date set by treaty. Is there any truth in it?"

"No rumor, I vow. I stood right at this window one night. Colder than tarnation too, and watched some houses of the Christians go up in flames. I knew they were the frame houses because no log cabins would blaze up that high."

"Christians?"

"I mean the Menomini converts to Catholicism."

"But why them?"

Mr. Daken, I shouldn't even mention it, but you're a stranger and I can talk to you. My neighbors over here. A lot of fine people. No denying it. Hard working and church-going, but no matter how hard they pray, they don't like this priest. Some are Irishmen in his own congregation right here in Winneconne. Talk is, the Indians got burned out just to get even with him."

"For what?"

"Maybe for several reasons but mainly because he sticks up for the Indians. He did everything he could, you know, to keep them from moving to Minnesota Territory. Can you blame him? They've been living here in cabins and frame shanties, and now they'll have to leave the whole works. Cleared several hundred acres of land besides."

"Is that so. Come to think of it, I never saw a word about these fires in the papers. Didn't they try to catch the men who did it?"

"Catch who? The Indians tracked a couple of the firebugs—Irishmen—and caught them redhanded, but no white man was going to convict them. On top of that the settlers—these sturdy pioneers as some people call them—have been stealing cattle and even ponies from the Indians. And if they find an

Indian sugar camp with no one around, they smash the sap buckets and cooking kettles."

From across the river now came the thumping of a war drum, the signal for everyone to begin boarding the canoes. The family of Chief Oshkosh, his pipe bearer and aides, as well as the family of Souligny, were in the first canoe which was twenty-four feet long.

"Look at that!" said Hamlin. "Even taking the dogs along."

Daken laughed guardedly and said, "Would you leave your dog behind?"

"No, I guess you're right."

"I understand these dogs aren't just dogs," suggested Daken. "I was reading somewhere the Indian dogs have something to with totems, or beliefs about their clans like the bear and beaver and things. Maybe the dog's got a soul."

"You would think so, the way my wife pampers hers," Hamlin laughed.

"Look over there," said Daken, pointing. "Looks like that canoe is overloaded."

"Yes, and there's another. I think that's Chief Wau'kechon and his family. O Lord! How far do they think they are going to get in that beat up old boat?" said Hamlin.

There were at least two hundred canoes now strung out along the Wolf river moving northwesterly through the Winneconne marsh, all hugging the north bank to escape the wind.

"There goes Murray," said Hamlin, "the government agent and some others from the Indian Bureau. But they're not using any beat up birchbark canoe, I vow. They've got a Durham boat."

"And there goes the priest," said Daken. "Indian family up front and him in the back. I suppose that box in the middle is his books and church stuff. I wonder if that coat and thing over his head is going to be warm enough."

"I offered him my mackinaw," said Hamlin, "but he thanked me. Real reason, I imagine, is he did not want the Indians to think he had anything special to wear. Lord, I hope he makes it."

As the canoes disappeared around the first bend in the marsh, the wind began to shift, imperceptibly, to the northeast and become warmer. By the time the first canoe of Chief Oshkosh reached the open water of Lake Poygan an hour later the wind had shifted and instead of following the north shore of the lake to keep out of the wind as planned, the canoe flotilla moved straight across the lake to the mouth of the Wolf on the northwest shore.

Traveling by twos in case of accident, the canoeists shouted, back and forth, "*Po'na'nemat! Po'na'nemat!* (The wind ceases to blow.) As they continued across the lake the men discussed the lucky omen. Some of the non-Christians thought it was the power of Chief Oshkosh who had offered tobacco and smoked the holy calumet to the Thunderbird spirits that caused the phenomenon, but the Christian converts insisted that it was the power of the Black Robe who had celebrated a special mass for their safety the night before, his last in the little frame church on the Payground.

20

Dr. Francis Huebschmann, superintendent of Indian affairs for the northern district of the United States, was reading his mail in his office on Martin street in Milwaukee's 1st ward. The window at his back overlooked Court House Square with its trees and flower gardens wilting in the hot September sunshine.

Suddenly he pounded the desk with the palm of his hand and exclaimed, "*Gott mit uns!*" The letter contained information from his sub-agent in Green Bay that the bones of a child had been found in a swamp near the sugar camp once owned by Alvin Partridge. He could scarcely believe what he was reading and yet it made sense. Now he would be able to present the commissioner of Indian affairs in Washington with an overwhelming argument in favor of having the federal government intervene on behalf of the Indian mother whose boy had been stolen by the

Partridges more than two years ago.

There was a knock on the door and since his clerk was not in yet, Dr. Huebschmann got up to answer.

"Dr. Huebschmann?" enquired the stranger.

"*Ja.* Vat can I do for you?"

"My name is George Daken. I have something to tell you that might be of interest."

"*Ja, ja.* Come in den and tell me about it," he said with a strong German accent. He waved Daken to a chair and returned to his own behind the desk. "*Was ist los?*" he said, using the German expression to affect an air of informality.

"I'm a drummer for a company here in Milwaukee, the Grant Clothing people over on East Water street. Last week I was in northern Illinois on my pre-winter selling trip, and I was in a store in Woodstock. That's McHenry county, and I had my sample case out on a counter. A man and a boy walked in and my client stopped to wait on them and I sat down. Whilst sitting there the boy walked up to my sample case and looked. He was rather dark-skinned, I thought, from the side, and then he turned and looked at me, wondering I suppose if I was going to say anything if he got closer to the sample case."

"Where did you say this was, sir?"

"McHenry county, just south of the state

line in Illinois. The boy I was telling you about looked at me and when he did I knew I had seen him before. I knew it in consequence of this boy coming so close to my sample bag, and then the man who was with him says. . ."

"But what has this got to do with me, Mr. Bacon?"

"Daken sir. Well, the stranger sort of raised his voice a little and said to the boy 'don't touch anything' and the boy shook his head, although I could see he was a little hurt by this, so after the storekeeper waited on the man I told him to give me a stick of candy and he did and I said to the boy, 'Hey bub, here's something for you too.' His face lit up and he took it and after they left I asked the storekeeper who the customer was and he said Asahel Thompson."

"Asahel Thompson?"

"Yes, and I said to the storekeeper that the boy looked familiar but I could not place him and he said perhaps I had seen him somewhere else because he was a rather famous boy and I said who do you mean and he said Caspar Pa'tridge, the boy who was stolen by the Indians up in Wisconsin there somewhere."

"Is it possible that you could be mistaken, Mr. Daken?"

"Not at all sir. I attended several sessions of the trial in Oskhosh couple years ago or more and I sat less than fifteen feet from him. He's grown of course but that face I'll never forget, and whilst I never dared to express an opinion in Oshkosh. . .bad for business you know. . .I became convinced that the boy belonged to his Indian mother and I wasn't surprised to hear the court's decision, I mean if he was going to be fair about it."

"But I had no idea you were in Oshkosh at the time," said Huebschmann. "I followed the story in the newspapers but of course that was when my predecessor was in office, Mr. Murray, who said he was going to help the Indians but never did. You know, the Pa'tridges were legally in contempt of court and could be charged with kidnaping, and if I wasn't an immigrant in this country myself, I would make trouble for them, but I have my limitations too. . .bad for business did you say? *Ja!* But how does it happen that this boy is in Illinois living with. . .what did you say his name was?"

"Asahel Thompson."

"Who is he?"

"Well, I asked the storekeeper the same question and he said Thompson was a brother of Mrs. Pa'tridge."

"But why wasn't the boy living with his parents, I mean the Partridges who claimed to be his parents? They were from Trumbull county originally and whether they went back there I don't know, but any place in Ohio is a long ways by horse and buggy or even by the cars from Illinois. Did the storekeeper say how long the boy had been there?"

"Not really, but something he said or the way he said it led me to believe the boy wasn't just visiting."

"Very interesting, Mr. Bacon, very interesting. You see this letter here?" holding up the paper. "I just got this in the mail this morning from one of my agents up north. He tells me that the bones of a small child were found recently near the sugar bush once owned by Alvin Pa'tridge. I have been composing a letter in the back of my mind to ask my agent for more information. I wonder what they did with the bones. They could be the bones of the Pa'tridge boy, you understand."

"Yes sir."

"Now I have a. . .how do you say in in English? A *prima facie* case? *Ja?* I must present this matter to my superior in Washington at once and ask permission to go into Illinois and reclaim the boy. I must also inform the Menomini chiefs about it. It is a tribal matter, you understand. They will be most pleased because I remember at the annual payment, in 1853 I mean, they were presented several bills associated with the trial held in Oshkosh in 1852 and they were still so angry about the failure of the government to help restore the child to his mother, that they refused to pay any of the bills except the one to their lawyer, a Mr. Whitney as I recall. I imagine the boy's mother is still living on the reservation too. She should be pleased because I heard from people she took it very hard. Very well, Mr. Daken, you have been of great service and I want to thank you for coming here." Both men rose to shake hands and Daken said, "Glad to be of service."

21

The ice on the Wolf river was frozen over all the way from Lake Poygan north to Shawano Lake and even farther a few miles to the first falls above Keshena. No matter how many degrees below zero the weather got, this grand cascade of water seldom froze, and the vapor from the warmer air drifted along the banks where it clung to the overhanging branches and trees, immobilizing them into crystal pendants of iced filigree.

The Menomini Indians who had moved up the Wolf river in their birchbark canoes on that first week in November two years ago were now scattered over the reservation, living under the tall white pines and maples and basswoods, across the small clearings and openings, some to the northeast along the headwaters of the Oconto river, and some along the West Branch of the Wolf, and still others on both banks of the river below the falls renamed Keshena after the chief of the

Menominee river band.

Only a handful of Indians lived in the village of Keshena but it was here that the annuity payments were made although no one was calling it the "payground" any longer. It was here also that The Reverend Florimond J. Bonduel had established the mission St. Michael Archangel on November 6, 1852, a few days after the migration.

The Indians, in their dispersion, had split along religious lines, the Christian converts to Catholicism settling in certain areas and those who held to their native beliefs in other areas. The Catholic faction had gained in numbers since the migration and some of them were gradually clearing small acreages of land for corn, potatoes, squash and beans.

The majority of the non-Christians, especially the members of the Mystic Rites Lodge, were still not anxious to farm or to accept the cultural values of the white man. These people eked out a living by making sugar in spring, spearing sturgeon at the falls, picking berries and collecting wild rice. There was not much hunting for big game. The forest was too heavy for deer to thrive in and were it not for the smaller game like racoon, porcupine and muskrat, and the good fishing on the rivers and lakes nearby, the Indians would scarcely have managed to keep themselves in fresh meat.

It was a bad omen, the Indians felt, when

they reached the reservation two years ago and the river froze behind them, seemingly trapping them before they were ready to stand on their own feet. The government contractors hired to bring food in were late as usual in their deliveries and the early freeze also caught them unawares and instead of using canoes and boats for bringing in supplies, they had to hire oxen from Green Bay to haul the supplies in by sleighs. The perishable food froze and in turn became uneatable. By spring, many of the Indians were on the verge of starvation.

The second winter was little better than the first. In their weakened condition, the Indians had not been able to provide for themselves in the season between the snows. However, government-hired carpenters and blacksmiths had helped to build log cabins for the chiefs and their large families, and a frame house was built for the family of Chief Oshkosh. Nahkom and her family remained near the Catholic mission the first winter, living in a birch-bark hogan. In spring her husband and uncle, Kosko'shekau, moved the family to Elm creek, in the northeast of the reservation because Nahkom wanted to be as far away from the Long Knives as possible. She had nearly died the first winter. When the flotilla of canoes arrived on the reservation, half a foot of snow lay on the ground. It was catch-as-catch can as every family struggled for itself to build a wigwam or hogan. Kosko'shekau had brought along reed matting and skins from Poygan and with these supplies, a hogan was built as quickly as possible for the ailing Nahkom. A bed was made of the skins laid over with young cedar bows two feet deep.

While the fire was kept burning day and night, Nahkom remained in bed for nearly two months, unwilling to live any more. But the Black Robe had come to encourage her and even provide some foreign medicine which she took because she trusted him. He had urged her to accept holy baptism in the faith but she had declined. Although she no longer felt certain of her own Indian power—the power once transmitted to her when she was initiated into the Mystic Rites Lodge—she was unwilling to believe that the *Kitchimanitou* of her people had deserted her.

By spring Nahkom was again strong enough to do her own work, cook and sew. She was presently seated at her neddle doing some bead work when the Black Robe came to say goodbye. He had lost weight since he came to Keshena and Nahkom realized he had suddenly grown much older. He told her he had been transferred to a church in Milwaukee and that he was hoping soon to visit his family in Belgium. She did not know where that was but she could understand that a son would want to visit his mother, and then she had turned her face to the south and become lost in thought. The priest had left her in this attitude and walked outside the log cabin in the woods where the members of the family waited to express their appreciation. There were no handshakes, merely a lifted palm of farewell between old friends and sad memories. That evening at vespers he had celebrated his final mass in the frame chapel he had built with volunteer help from the Indians. Christians and non-Christians attended because they wanted the Black Robe to know that his mission to the Menomini was appreciated or, as Souligny said in an impromptu speech, "he would not be forgotten as long as the Falls of the Wolf defied the Thunderbirds."

Bonduel had thanked everyone and then introduced them to their new pastor, Otto Skolla. The next morning at daylight, assisted by two young Indians, he went by canoe down the Wolf to New London where he caught a river steamer for Fond du Lac and from there by stage to Milwaukee.

* * * * *

On December 25, 1854, a day of Holy Obligation, the new priest was marking his second Christmas at the mission St. Michael Archangel. He was changing his vestments preparatory to celebrating mass when he was interrupted by a knock on the door of the small frame parsonage. He opened the door and an Oneida Indian from Green Bay handed him a letter which had been forwarded to Green Bay addressed to Chief Oshkosh in care of the sub-agent. Not knowing where to find the chief, the Oneida, a Catholic convert, thought it best to bring the letter to the Black Robe. The priest opened the letter which read:

> Chief Oshkosh: Please be advised since receiving your authorization to reclaim the child of Nahkom, that I have personally recovered him in Illinois and he is now being held here pending further developments. A new hearing will be necessary, and I urge you and as many witnesses as feasible, including the mother of the boy, to come to Milwaukee at your earliest convenience. I am writing the sub-agent at Green Bay to make arrangements.—Signed/Dr. Francis Huebschmann.

The priest who had been assigned to take Bonduel's place had become familiar with the Nahkom saga. He assumed that this news would have an electric effect on his congregation and hurried over to the chapel. Chiefs Carron and LaMotte heard the news in silence. No one else spoke. It would not do to make a scene and further, it could be another trick by the Long Knives. Finally Carron motioned to two of his relatives to take the news to Nahkom, Chief Oshkosh, and the other principal men of the tribe.

Nahkom was scraping the tallow from a deer hide when the herald from Keshena approached her cabin. The herald was walking and half running on snowshoes. When he called, she recognized his voice and opened the door. "I have good news for you, Sister. The Long Knives have found your son in Illinois and the agent has brought him back to Milwaukee. He asks that you shall come there."

"*Ah-sah!*" she exclaimed, catching her breath. "*Neki'qs!* Can it be my son?" There was no answer to her question and the herald was already leaving to find the others. Big Peter, who was nearby cutting wood, had also heard the good news. He approached his niece quickly when he saw her grasp the door jamb for support, and helped her to a stool inside that stood beneath a window facing south. She looked up at her uncle, dry-eyed and asked, "Uncle, do you think it can be true?"

"I have offered tobacco and prayed with my pipe to the Great Spirit that it might be true. I can hardly believe my power has been sustained. Yes, I believe it is true. But now we must prepare to leave when our chief decides."

Chief Oshkosh, who had said nothing to Nahkom about the pending negotiations for the release of her son lest they fail and plunge her further into the valley of melancholy, was advised later in the morning of the letter from Huebschmann. He realized it would take some time to assemble the chiefs and sub-chiefs scattered over the reservation, especially now with snow on the ground. He was also wondering who was going to pay the travel expenses of his party. This too would have to be worked out with the Indian agent at Green Bay.

A week later the sub-agent from Green Bay and all the principal men of the tribe were assembled at the house of Oshkosh. The purpose of the meeting was to determine who was to be included in the Milwaukee party, what route to follow, and how much expense money would be needed. The council continued all day and into the night before it was decided who was to go. Souligny, because of his advanced age, wished to delegate his authority to younger men, but the others would not hear of it. He must come along. He had made a great speech at the trial in Oshkosh. Perhaps he would be called upon again.

Finally, it was decided that most of the witnesses who had testified at the trial in Oshkosh would go to Milwaukee. Although Chief Oshkosh had not testified, he was present, which was the same thing. The ones who would go, aside from Oshkosh and Souligny, were Nahkom, Oskehena'nieu, younger brother of Oshkosh, LaMotte,

Carron, Akine'bui, Big Peter, and Powell, the interpreter, who lived near Shawano Lake. In addition, a runner was sent the next day to request Robert Grignon of Green Bay, Archibald Caldwell and William Johnson of Neenah to accompany the party as liaison men. Eight youths were to handle the baggage and serve as canoeists on the last lap of the journey.

The delegation would travel by team and sleigh from Keshena to New London on the ice of the Wolf, and from New London over land to Oshkosh and Fond du Lac. From Fond du Lac the party would drive southeast to the headwaters of the Milwaukee river where canoes would be waiting for the descent down river to Milwaukee.

On the day appointed for departure, a snowstorm engulfed the land, and for nearly three days the Indians huddled around their small stoves and fires, waiting for the storm to let up. By noon on the third day there was no wind and no snow, and the people looked into the frozen sky, nervously wondering, for there, circling the sun, were the sun dogs!

Finally, by the second week in February trails had been broken through the snow drifts on the reservation and teamsters hired from a Green Bay livery stable came with three sleighs to pick up the Indian delegation and baggage. Nahkom was traveling with her uncle, Big Peter, leaving her second husband to care for her youngest boy. An older daughter by her second husband had died of exposure on the migration of 1852.

In Oshkosh there was a stopover for a day which allowed Nahkom time to buy a wool dress and a new red blanket. Throughout the journey, she scarcely talked to anyone except her uncle. There had been considerable drinking at the taverns where the party had stopped overnight, but she had not participated in this good fellowship because to her there was still something unreal about the entire affair. She knew she was supposed to be getting closer to her son the farther south she journeyed, but as long as she could not see him, the distance of a hundred miles was the same as one mile. She was still separated from her son, the one she loved more than any other of her children.

Canoes of birchbark provided by Agent Huebschmann were waiting at a point north of West Bend on the Milwaukee river, and the delegation arrived in Milwaukee the first week in March 1855. The canoes were beached at the steamboat landing on North Water street. To the east on the hill rose the pyramidal tower of the newly-dedicated St. John's Cathedral on Jackson street. The Christian's, Souligny, LaMotte and Carron and their aides walked slowly up the hill on Biddle street, passing St. Mary's Church, on to Court House Square and the beautiful park ground donated to the city by Solomon Juneau and Morgan L. Martin.

Bishop John Martin Henni, advised in advance of the approach of the Indian delegation, walked out from the rectory to the middle of the square and waited to greet the guests from the north. As they approached him, they bowed to their knees, as they had seen the Long Knives bow to holy persons, and waited for his benediciton. Oshkosh and the other non-Christians later shook hands with the bishop and expressed their appreciation for his gracious welcome.

Dr. Huebschmann had arranged with the bishop to house the Indians at St. John's Infirmary operated by the Sisters of Charity of St. Joseph, and after everyone had paid his respects to the bishop, the delegation was escorted to the quarters nearby.

"Where is he?" Nahkom asked, turning to Oshkosh.

"As soon as the agent of the Long Knives arrives, we will know."

"But why did they not bring him down to the river to meet me?"

"Because they must protect him."

"Protect him from what?"

"Protect him until you arrive. He has no relatives here."

"But where are the Long Knives who stole him?"

"Probably here."

"Here? Where?" she asked, fear rising. "What are they doing here?"

"I am not sure, Sister, but you remember the agent of our Great Father mentioned that another trial might be held."

"But Judge Buttrick said it was my boy," she insisted, scarcely able to control her anger.

"I know, I know, Sister," said Oshkosh, trying to assuage her. "But our people have to be patient with the Long Knives even when they are impatient with us. There will be proceedings for another trial to prove to the satisfaction of everyone that this is our son. I am sure the judge here in Milwaukee will uphold the verdict of Judge Buttrick after he hears our witnesses."

Nahkom was baffled by this reference to an appellate court.

Presently a surrey drove up to the front door of the Infirmary where Nahkom, Oshkosh, Powell and several others had paused to talk. It was Dr. Huebschmann. He stepped down carefully and came over to shake hands with the chiefs but, uncertain of his protocol, avoided shaking hands with Nahkom.

"I am glad you got here safely, Mr. Oshkosh," Huebschmann said, addressing the chief. "Did you have a good journey? You must be awfully tired all of you."

Powell translated this and Nahkom at once

spoke up, turning to Powell: "Where is my son?"

Powell translated this to Huebschmann who smiled and said, "Oh him! I suppose you are his mother? I will take you to him at once. Right now he is at the Court House across the square there, but he's not in jail. No sir! He's quite a boy and everyone has been indulging him since I brought him back from Illinois two months ago. Will you accompany us, Mr. Powell?"

Powell nodded while Huebschmann looked at his watch and said, "It is four-thirty now and she may visit the boy for one hour. That will give us time to bring you both back here in time for supper which is served promptly at six o'clock in the dining room."

After this was translated, Nahkom nodded agreement although she was not hungry for food but starving for the affection of her son.

"Well, let us go then," said Huebschmann, addressing Powell. "I'll tie up my drivers here and we will walk across the square to the Court House."

At the Court House Nahkom was taken to a reception room while Powell and one of the undersheriffs went to get the boy. Within a few minutes, Nahkom's trained ear detected the short steps of a boy approaching even though confused with the two men walking with him. But she knew it would not do to run out and greet him. She must wait for him to be brought to her. Now she could scarcely breathe. The tension of the past three years was about to be resolved and she felt like a bow-string that has been pulled too hard and is about to snap. But still the bow-string held. Presently the boy and two men appeared in the door. Nahkom looked hard and caught herself even squinting in the dim light. "My! He has grown!" she thought to herself. "Is it really my son?"

As Powell, Huebschmann and the undersheriff stood by a minute, Nahkom waited for her son to say something in Menomini and when he addressed her as "mother", she could no longer restrain herself and threw her arms around him while the tears rolled silently down her cheeks. The three men left the room. "*Neki'qs, Neki'qs,*" she finally managed to say, and then she corrected herself with a nervous laugh. "But you are no longer my little boy. You are my big boy! How you have grown! Have the people here been feeding you well?"

The boy answered her politely. In the past two months at the Court House he had been made so much of that he had actually begun to enjoy his new-found role as hero rescued from his abductors.

"Look what I have brought you," Nahkom said, digging into a small Indian basket. It was the claw of a bear on a pendant of glass beads five inches in length. He took the pendant politely, knowing that he was expected to like it.

"What will it do?" he asked shyly.

"It will bring the protector of our totem to you. Hold it up so that *Kitchimanitou* can see it, and he will give you what you need."

The boy sat down on the bench next to his mother, dangling the pendant on his finger, dazzled by the glass beads. He felt the sharpness of the claw. Now he would have something to show his friends in the sheriff's department.

"Why did you come here?" he asked.

"Our chief says that a new trial like the one in Oshkosh will be held, and for you to look good and tell the honorable judge who your mother is."

"Is that all?"

"*Neiki'qs*, you are coming home to us."

"Is it in the woods?" he asked in English, forgetting himself for an instant, quickly switching back into Menomini to repeat the same question.

"Yes, we are living far, far away on the beautiful Wolf river where there is fishing and rabbit hunting and berry picking and every spring we make sugar." She did not tell him that his half sister had died of exposure on the canoe trip to the reservation and of the many others who had died since of malnutrition. He in turn looked at her bony fingers, and felt slightly repelled by them.

Then he looked into her eyes and saw something strange he could not understand, for he was too young to know about the slow decay of the heart that sets in when life turns its disappointments into gall. She took his one hand in both of hers and began to stroke it, telling him how anxious his relatives were to see him. He tried to be sympathetic although he scarcely remembered what any of them looked like. But she talked on, her speech coming faster and faster as she sensed the time for departure approaching. As he listened to her, drinking in the gutteral tones and nuances of the Menomini language, he became deeper and deeper involved with a past he had nearly forgotten and which now seemed to be covering him like an old Indian blanket, full of pungent smells of the wigwam. Suddenly he jumped up and threw his arms around her neck. She held him to her, uttering a quiet moan, hiding the wound in her heart that was beyond sorrow. She lifted her eyes to the window and pleaded with *Kitchimanitou* to let her take the boy with her now, not tomorrow or the day after. Finally she pulled his arms away and looked at him in adoration.

At that moment Powell and the undersheriff came back and Powell told her it was time to leave.

"But why can't my boy come back with us now?"

"The judge says that the boy has to be protected until he can be sure whose boy it is."

"Don't they know that yet?"

"Sister," Powell replied, using the intimate form, "we can not do that. The honorable judge has ordered it that way."

"I see. I see. Well then, if the honorable judge had ordered it, then I must obey." She got up and suddenly felt a bit dizzy. The undersheriff caught her arm and steadied her. She pulled the hair from her eyes and straightened up. Turning to her son she said in Menomini, "I will be here as soon as the honorable judge permits me tomorrow morning."

The boy smiled and felt for his pendant with the bear claw which he had pocketed in his shirt, a brand new wool shirt which the officers of the sheriff's department had purchased for him. She thought the motion of his hand to the pocket was a secret signal and she was pleased. Her boy had the beginning of a sacred bundle. Perhaps one day he might inherit the otter skin bundle of his uncle, Kosko'shekau. The boy smiled at his mother and without another word left the room with the undersheriff.

During the period after he was brought back from Illinois in December, 1954, the boy known as Caspar Partridge was not held a prisoner, but various officers in the sheriff's department took turns watching him and getting his meals. At night he was given a cot in a corner of the main office, somewhat hidden behind a big desk. Every evening before going to bed he was allowed to walk alone down to the end of the main corridor to a lavatory.

On the evening after his mother came to see him, he had emerged from the lavatory when he heard a scratching sound on the glass at the rear door of the corridor less than ten feet away. A youth was motioning to him with a watch and fob, dangling it as if he wanted to show it to him.

"Hey Caspar!" the youth called softly, "Wanna trade?"

"Trade for what?"

"What you got?"

He thought of his jack-knife but did not want to part with that. He felt of the bear's claw and pulled the pendant out of his shirt pocket and held it up.

"Let's see it," the stranger said. "Turn the key on your side and come out here."

As the door opened the youth stepped back into the alley and disappeared. The next instant two men grabbed Nahkom's boy, one holding a hand over his mouth while the other carried him. In the struggle, the bear claw fell into a gutter.

The two men hurried to a buckboard waiting in the alley and put the boy down and one said, "Now don't you open your big mouth or "I'll knock your teeth in. Understand?"

The boy nodded.

"Put this hat and coat on and get up on that seat and stay there," the same man ordered harshly.

The driver of the team climbed into the seat beside the boy and ordered the horses forward. He started down the alley going north to Martin street and then swung east on Martin to Jackson where he turned south, galloping past St. John's Cathedral, and on to Wisconsin avenue. Not long after, he crossed the Milwaukee river drawbridge and disappeared into the country roads leading south from the city.

Four hours later the driver stopped his team under a big elm tree not far from a four-corner. "We'll be waiting here," he told the boy curtly, and climbed down from the buckboard, still holding the reins on the horses. He walked into the shadow of the tree to urinate and said, "You can stand up and piss from the seat if you want to but don't you piss on my horses, you damn Indian, or I'll beat the poop out of you. I'm not sartin what any man would want you for, but that's none of my business so long as I get paid."

The driver sat down to rest against the trunk of the elm, holding the reins and talking to himself. About half an hour later a horse and buggy approached from the south, and the stranger drove straight up to the shadow of the elm tree and stopped. Fred Partridge got down from the seat and said, "I see you made it. Any trouble?"

"None sir. The man was thar to help take him and as soon as I get paid, I'll be headin back."

"Here's the ten I promised."

"Thank you sir." He took the money and folded it into a pocketbook and asked, "Where you aimin to take him?"

"Not to McHenry county by God. Back to Ohio and no Indian agent is going to find him this time. The sheriff down there's an old friend of the family and he don't like Indians better than we do. My brothers and me must of lost ten thousand dollars to save our boy. Isn't that right, Caspar?" He turned to the boy on the seat of the buckboard. "You can get down now and we'll head for Waukegan where I've got a room at Waukegan House." The boy nodded, but the expression of bewilderment on his face was not visible in the darkness.

22

The disappearance of the boy from county jail was not noticed by anyone in the sheriff's department until midnight. One of the undersheriffs was sent at once to the residence of Dr. Huebschmann on North Third street to inform him of the abduction. Awakened in the middle of the night, he came to the front door wondering whether some drunk along the Milwaukee riverfront had come to bother him. He peeked through the curtain and saw it was an officer and went to open the door at once.

After he heard the news, he held his hand to his forehead and moaned, "*Ach*, what are we going to do next?"

"We haven't got a clue, sir," said the officer, "and about all we can do is hunt and look. We got the sheriff up and he come to the office and said we should post a hundred dollar reward for the boy's recovery."

"But who is going to tell the Indians?

Perhaps the sheriff. . ."

"The sheriff thought you should."

"Me? *Ja*, very well then. But better to wait until morning and let them have a decent night's sleep. His mother, I'm afraid, is going to take it pretty hard."

The officer tipped his hand to his cap and left, while Huebschmann went back to bed, deeply disturbed by the sudden turn of events. He awakened his wife and they talked for an hour, unable to get back to sleep. After the extended negotiations with the Indian Bureau and the Department of Interior over jurisdictional rights which followed his original request to extradict the boy from Illinois, he was afraid he might lose his job if he were to institute new proceedings. Although he suspected that the boy would not be found in McHenry county again, this close to the Wisconsin line, it would be no difficult matter to trace his whereabouts now because the story of the "lost child" had become widely known. But it might be bad for business, he told his wife, remembering something he had heard not too long ago. Why should I risk my career any further? No one not an Indian is going to care much one way or the other and I'm sure the *Milwaukee Sentinel*, which has been clamoring for justice, won't say much more about it either. Yes, Herr Sheriff, offer a reward. That will make it look good but no one is going to collect on it and he knows that as well as I in this great land of liberty and justice. *Ach!* I should be making a lot more money than I am, but just because I got an accent they don't raise my pay. *Gott straffe de Indian Bureau!* he finally exclaimed. His wife laughed quietly at his frustration.

The next morning, Huebschmann put on a new suit, frock coat and felt plug hat purchased from Steinhart's Clothing on 220 East Water street. With a clean shirt and silk cravat, he looked at himself in the mirror and decided that he should see about an appointment for a Daguerreotype Miniature with Messrs. Stamm and Upman. He ordered his chore boy to bring his drivers around to the front entrance. His wife was in the window smiling at him as he left.

Dr. Huebschmann guessed that the Indians would be up by now but he took his time reaching the Infirmary and arrived about nine o'clock. Sitting on the front steps, waiting for him, was Nahkom, her red blanket wrapped around her shoulders over the wool dress she had been wearing since she left Oshkosh. The superintendent tied the drivers to a hitching post nearby and came over to where she was sitting. Confused over his inability to communicate with her, he motioned politely for her to precede him into the building. Nahkom sensed at once that something was wrong and looked up into his face, saying half in Menomini and half in English, "*Neki'qs* good?" He made believe he did not understand and walked in to find Powell who was in a small dining room with the Indian delegation just finishing breakfast. Addressing Powell, he said, "I'm sorry to tell my friends here, very sorry indeed, and particularly this unhappy woman, that her boy was stolen last night." When Powell translated this to the others, there was a sharp shriek. Everyone turned to see Nahkom thrust both hands into the air as if she wanted to cling to an invisible vine, and then she gave a long tremelo wail. The Sister Superior and another Sister at the Infirmary rushed to her side and led her to an ante-room and closed the door, but her anguished cries could still be heard.

Chief Oshkosh asked Huebschmann what was to be done next and he replied, "I am afraid, sir, it will be difficult to pursue this case at the moment. The sheriff has offered a reward, but it is fairly certain that the people who have the boy are no longer in Wisconsin and the sheriff can't go beyond the county line."

This was translated for the chiefs and all remained silent in the face of still another *coup* counted against them by the Long Knives. But no one blamed Huebschman. Instead, the Indians felt personally ashamed and wondered what they were going to tell their people back on the reservation.

"Perhaps we can ask the editor of the *Milwaukee Sentinel* to help us," said Oshkosh. "He has written favorably on behalf of our son."

"Perhaps that would help," said Huebschmann. "I will arrange an interview for you." But the chiefs sensed a subtle change in the superintendent's attitude from the day before and knew without further probing that he was not going to press very hard for the recovery of the boy again. They wanted to thank him for all he had done to bring him back from Illinois, but now it seemed rather hopeless to thank anyone although they all realized that the superintendent had no part in the abduction, nor could he have prevented it. The Great Spirit had spoken and the Christian Earthmaker had remained silent, or was it Earthmaker who had spoken and the Great Spirit that had remained silent? The chiefs knew there was no explanation for accident or destiny and they stood around the room feeling ill at ease. Better to return to the reservation and be with one's own people. Here was not their place. But first they must go and pay their respects to the editor of the *Sentinel* who had been kind.

In the ante-room where Nahkom had been taken after the first outburst of grief, the two Sisters attending her tried to calm her but, unable to understand what she was trying to say, they looked at each other and wondered what to do. One minute the distraught mother was pacing the floor and the next minute she was on the floor, her head lowered, mumbling as if she were talking to the floor. She was also beginning to perspire and the Sisters guessed that she was running a fever. Soon her face, neck and forehead and the palms of her hands were bathed in perspiration.

"Run and get a pan of cold water and a sponge," the Sister Superior ordered. When the water was brought in she attempted to sponge Nahkom's face and wash her hands, but it did not help much. The patient was also beginning to gasp for breath.

"Run and tell His Holiness to get a doctor," Sister Superior ordered. "Hurry!"

An hour later a doctor entered the room. Nahkom, totally exhausted by now, lay on her own blanket on the floor, covered with quilts. The doctor looked into her eyes and felt of her pulse.

"I will have to give her something to bring the fever down, or she is apt to burn up," he said, nonchalantly. He went to find his medicine bag in a buggy outside, and came back with a white powder which he mixed in a glass of water. "Let's see if we can get her to drink this."

Nahkom looked at the doctor, scarcely comprehending what was taking place. When he lifted the glass to her lips she drank the liquid because she was thirsty. A few minutes later she drifted into sleep. "I don't think there is much more I can do now," said the doctor. "But I would continue with the cold applications. What caused all this, by the way?"

The Sisters explained that the Indian woman was the same whose son had been stolen the night before. "Ah, yes, what a pity," said the doctor. "I read about it in the *Sentinel* this morning. Never realized I would be having her for a patient. But that's life," he smiled. As he prepared to leave he asked, "To whom shall I send the bill?"

The Sister Superior pointed to the rectory and quickly repeated five Hail Mary's for the soul of the mercenary doctor.

Nahkom remained in a state of semi-consciousness the rest of the day, refusing to eat and taking only a sip of water now and then. The fever had abated somewhat but her eyes were burning with a dull glow of a disease impossible to diagnose.

The Sisters took turns watching her until midnight and when she finally fell asleep, the last Sister on duty closed the door and returned to her quarters.

Nahkom slept for four hours and then awoke. Finding herself alone and anxious to get to the outhouse, she got up, threw her blanket over her shoulder and left the room. Later emerging, she realized there was no one else around, and instead of returning to her room, she wandered into Court House square. She looked up at the steeple of St. John's Cathedral looming in the night sky and knew from her position that the Milwaukee river ran a short distance down the hill to the west. She walked down Biddle street and came upon the several canoes beached at the steamboat landing. A watchman had been put on the canoes but he had gone to a nearby saloon a few minutes earlier. Nahkom untied one of the canoes and pushed it easily into the river, picked up a paddle and instinctively began to use it as a rudder. The current took her down stream, under the drawbridge, and toward the city harbor which was still covered with a sheet of ice along the shore line. Out further, a hundred yards or more, the lake was open.

Nahkom sat in the canoe, lost in confusion, peering intently into the eastern sky as the first sign of dawn began to break. A voice called to her from across the lake. "Mother, are you coming for me?"

"Yes my son, I am coming. You must never leave me like this again. Where are you now?"

"I am here, mother, to the east where the sun begins to warm up the dawn. Our enemies have taken me captive."

The strange vibrations increased in intensity and, unable to resist them any longer, she beached the canoe and ran out on the thin ice. "I am coming, my son, I am coming," she called, rushing toward the rising sun. Then the ice broke beneath her and she disappeared forever.

When the Indian delegation began looking for Nahkom, Kosko'shekau took two of the young men and went down to the Milwaukee river and finding one canoe missing, quickly guessed that she had taken it and drifted down stream to the harbor on Lake Michigan. The three men jumped into a canoe and paddled swiftly down stream to the harbor mouth where they found the missing canoe beached against a sheet of ice along the north shore. Tracks of moccasin feet led east across the ice and then one of the young men, whose eyes were sharper than the others, pointed at an object lying about fifty yards out.

"It looks like the color of Nahkom's blanket," Kosko'shekau said. Testing the ice ahead of him with the handle of his paddle, he reached the spot and carefully picked up the blanket. He felt of its soft texture, tenderly caressing the wool and smelling the sweet odor of Nahkom's hair. With tears running down his cheeks, he held the blanket up at arms length to the rising sun and said, "O Great Spirit, make easy the path of our brave sister on her journey to the western regions."

Further out the subdued waves of Lake Michigan lapped, indifferently, against the ice.

EPILOGUE

The boy known as Nigabianong to his Indian mother was raised by the Partridges who settled on a farm near Orland, Indiana. His name was changed to "Joseph W." and in an early history of Steuben county, Indiana, he is included as one of the children of Alvin and Lucia Partridge. The name of Caspar is not mentioned.

"Joseph" attended Hillsdale College, Michigan in the fall of 1864 but left on or before February 11, 1865 to join the 152nd Regiment, Indiana Volunteers. He served as a bugler in the Civil War and after mustering out on August 30, 1865, he spent the rest of his life in a tangled web of marital arrangements with several women while waging a constant struggle against alcoholism. He died in 1916 in the village of Camp Douglas, Wisconsin, seventy-five miles from the "Payground" where he was born. The final irony of his confused career seems reflected in the headstone that marks his presumed grave at Camp Douglas cemetery: it bears the name "Joseph P. Parker." His bugle and other memorabilia have recently been donated by his grandchildren to the State Historical Society.

Alvin and Lucia Partridge and two daughters, one adopted, and the Wakeman Partridges, and Fred Partridge, are all buried at Orland, Indiana. The oblesque which dominates the family plot has the family names on three sides and on the fourth side the epitaph "Asleep in Jesus' Blessed Sleep.'

A DICTIONARY OF CORRECT ENGLISH

PUBLISHED BY PITMAN

BUSINESS LETTERS IN ENGLISH

By W. J. Weston, M.A., B.Sc. (Lond.). Part I is devoted to the English material of business letters, and deals with discrimination and correct use of words, while Part II treats of the structure, style, and purpose of the letter itself.

In crown 8vo, cloth, 231 pp. **4s.**

ENGLISH GRAMMAR AND COMPOSITION

By the same Author. A manual of grammar taught through composition.

Crown 8vo, cloth, 320 pp. **3s. 6d.**

PITMAN'S BOOK OF SYNONYMS AND ANTONYMS

Containing a selected list of words with those of similar and opposite meanings, this book will greatly help the speaker, or the writer, and enable him to select the words which will the most felicitously express his mind.

In crown 8vo, cloth, 140 pp. **2s. 6d.** net.

MANUAL OF COMMERCIAL ENGLISH
Including Composition and Précis Writing

By Walter Shawcross, B.A. A handbook covering all the requirements of students of English for commercial purposes.

In crown 8vo, cloth gilt. Without Answers, 240 pp. With Answers, 280 pp. Each **3s. 6d.**

A DICTIONARY OF CORRECT ENGLISH

A MANUAL OF INFORMATION AND ADVICE CONCERNING GRAMMAR, IDIOM, USE OF WORDS, POINTS OF STYLE, PUNCTUATION, PRONUNCIATION, AND OTHER PRACTICAL MATTERS

BY

M. ALDERTON PINK, M.A.

LONDON
SIR ISAAC PITMAN & SONS, LTD.

SIR ISAAC PITMAN & SONS, Ltd.
PITMAN HOUSE, PARKER STREET, KINGSWAY, LONDON, W.C.2
THE PITMAN PRESS, BATH
PITMAN HOUSE, LITTLE COLLINS STREET, MELBOURNE
UNITEERS BUILDING, RIVER VALLEY ROAD, SINGAPORE
27 BECKETTS BUILDINGS, PRESIDENT STREET, JOHANNESBURG
ASSOCIATED COMPANIES
PITMAN PUBLISHING CORPORATION
2 WEST 45TH STREET, NEW YORK
205 WEST MONROE STREET, CHICAGO
SIR ISAAC PITMAN & SONS (CANADA), Ltd.
(INCORPORATING THE COMMERCIAL TEXT BOOK COMPANY)
PITMAN HOUSE, 381–383 CHURCH STREET, TORONTO

MADE IN GREAT BRITAIN AT THE PITMAN PRESS, BATH
D2—(B.6143)

PREFACE

THE purpose of this volume is to bring together in a convenient form all the miscellaneous information and advice that is of practical importance to the writer of everyday English. In selecting the material I have been guided by the results of extensive experience in preparing adult students for the various professional examinations. I have tried to deal only with those difficulties which I find do actually confront the inexperienced writer, and with those errors into which he is really liable to fall.

I have not assumed that the reader possesses any special knowledge of the technical terms of the art of writing, and I have therefore endeavoured to make every article completely intelligible either by itself or when read in conjunction with the other articles to which cross-references are given. In the explanation of grammatical errors, the misuse of words, etc., it is impossible to avoid using a certain number of technical terms and referring to the basic principles of grammar. These terms and principles are all explained as simply as possible in separate articles. I have not included any grammatical material that does not bear directly on the articles concerned with the practice of writing.

In illustrating faults in grammar and composition I have drawn as far as possible on examples collected from the newspapers, especially from the correspondence columns and the reports of company meetings.

Since the first publication of this book a number of additional articles have been included. I am indebted to several correspondents who have kindly suggested points on which notes would be useful.

A good deal of new material has been added on pronunciation. This matter has received considerable public attention since the Advisory Committee appointed by the B.B.C. began to issue lists of recommendations to Announcers concerning words of doubtful pronunciation. Where it is of interest, I have quoted the B.B.C. recommendation.

M. A. P.

CLASSIFIED LIST OF THE CHIEF ARTICLES

(*NOTE: Articles on particular words are not mentioned in the following List unless they have special importance or illustrate some general principle.*)

COMPOSITION: EXPRESSION, IDIOM, USE OF WORDS, POINTS OF STYLE

EXPLANATION OF GRAMMATICAL TERMS

EXPLANATION OF GRAMMATICAL ERRORS

PUNCTUATION

SPELLING

LETTER-WRITING

PRONUNCIATION

Accessory, acoustic, acumen, admirable, adult, aerated, alias, alibi, ally, allies, amateur, anaesthetist, applicable, archives, artiste, aspirant, assignee, ate, bas-relief, bedizen, calumny, capitalist, Celtic, centenary, centrifugal, chagrin, chicanery, chimera, chimerical, chiropodist, cinema, clandestine, clientele, comment, communal, commune, comparable, condolence, conjugal, conjure, consols, consummate, contemplative, contrary, controversy, conversant, coup, courtesy, culinary, decade, decadence, decadent, decorous, decorum, deficit, demoniacal, despicable, desultory, deteriorate, diphtheria, diphthong, dishabille, dishevelled, doctrinal, economics, elixir, England, English, ennui, envelope, environs, ephemeral, equitable, evolution, exigency, exigent, exquisite, extempore, Fascism, Fascist, fauteuil, fetish, flaccid, flagrant, forehead, formidable, fracas, frequent, frontier, gala, garage, gesticulate, gesture, gibberish, gibbet, heinous, hospitable, hotel, humour, idyll, illustrative, impious, inchoate, indict, indictment, inexorable, inveigle, inventory, irrefutable, irreparable, irrevocable, Koran, laboratory, lamentable, lichen, longevity, machination, medieval, mediocre, memoir, metallurgy, migratory, mischievous, nadir, naïve, naphtha, nonchalant, obligatory, orgy, pariah, patent, patriot, patron, patronage, peremptory, pharmaceutical, phthisis, pianoforte, plebiscite, posthumous, precedence, precedent, premier, profile, quandary, recondite, remonstrate, replica, reputable, reredos, respite, residuary, retail(er), romance, salutary, satire, satyr, seraglio, sheik, sinecure, soviet, stabilize, status, suave, subsidence, sycophant, syncope, trait, tryst, untoward, vagary, vagrant, valet, *vice versa*, viking, viola, visa, vitamin, wrath.

MISCELLANEOUS

IMPORTANT NOTES

1. ANY discussion of what is correct or incorrect in grammar, style, or (especially) pronunciation necessarily involves the question: Who decides what is right or wrong? On this matter the reader should turn to the article: *Correct English: How is the Standard of Correctness Fixed?* (pp. 41–5).

2. Although the grammatical material included has been selected for its bearing on the practical matters dealt with in the other articles and is intended chiefly for reference, it is sufficiently comprehensive to give the reader a good working knowledge of grammatical principles. For the understanding of these principles the following articles are of the utmost importance: they should be read in the order here given—

Sentence; Subject and Predicate; Parts of Speech; Articles on separate Parts of Speech; Phrase; Clauses; Object (Direct and Indirect); Predicative Words; Adjective-phrases and Adjective-clauses; Adverb-phrases and Adverb-clauses; Noun-clauses; Simple Sentence; Complex Sentence; Double Sentence; Multiple Sentence; Case; Rules of Agreement.

KEY TO PRONUNCIATION

In order to indicate correct pronunciation the following symbols are used where necessary. Usually no attempt is made to give a complete phonetic rendering of a word; that is to say, no mark is put over a vowel unless there is likelihood of mispronunciation—

ā	pronounced	as in	bate
âr	,,	,,	bare
ă	,,	,,	bat
ah	,,	,,	bah
ē	,,	,,	be
ĕ	,,	,,	bet
er	,,	,,	berth
ī	,,	,,	bite
ĭ	,,	,,	bit
ō	,,	,,	both
ōr	,,	,,	bore
ŏ	,,	,,	body
oo	,,	,,	boot
ū	,,	,,	bugle
ch	,,	,,	chat
th	,,	,,	thing

A syllable bearing the accent is shown by the mark (′) placed after it; thus—en′ter, prefer′, content′ment.

Note: The references to particular pronunciations adopted by the B.B.C. Announcers are based on the official lists of recommendations to Announcers regarding certain words of doubtful pronunciation. These lists are published from time to time by the British Broadcasting Corporation.

A DICTIONARY OF CORRECT ENGLISH

A, AN.

THE general rule is that *an* is used instead of *a* before a vowel-sound or a silent *h*—an office, an honest man. Textbooks commonly state that *an* should also be used when the following word begins with an aspirated *h* in an unaccented syllable; thus—an historical novel, an habitual smoker. This rule is by no means generally observed to-day, and it is doubtful whether it should be insisted on. It used to be the practice to use *an* before words like *European, universal, one*—an European reputation, an universal system, such an one. But these words really begin with a consonantal sound, although they have an initial vowel letter, and *a* is now regularly employed in such cases. (See also ARTICLES.)

ABBREVIATIONS.

The following is a list of abbreviations in common use in business—

a/c, acct.	Account
ad lib.	(Lat.: *ad libitum*) At pleasure
ad val.	(Lat.: *ad valorem*) According to value
a/o	Account of
a/or	And, or
A/D	After date
A/s	Account Sales
A/S	After sight
B/E	Bill of Exchange
B/L	Bill of Lading
B/P	Bill payable
B/R	Bill receivable
B/S	Balance sheet
C/B	Cash Book
cf., cp.	Compare
c.f.	Cost and freight
c.i.f.	Cost, insurance, and freight
C.H.	Custom House

C/N . . Credit Note
c/o . . Care of
C.O.D.. . Cash on Delivery
c/s . . . Cases
C/P . . Carriage paid
cum div. . With dividend
C.W.O. . Cash with Order
D/A . . Documents against acceptance
D/D . . Days after date
deld., dd. . Delivered
Dft. . . Draft
D/N . . Debit Note
D/O . . Delivery Order
D/P . . Documents against payment
D/S . . Days after sight
d/y, dely. . Delivery
e.g. . . For example
Enclo(s) . Enclosure(s)
exd. . . Examined
ex div. / e.d. / x. div. } Exclusive of dividend
et seq.. . And that which follows
et sqq.. . And the things following
f.a.s. . . Free alongside ship
fcp., fcap. . Foolscap
f.o.b. . . Free on board
f.o.c. . . Free of charge
f.o.r. . . Free on rail
f.o.s. . . Free on steamer
f.o.t. . . Free on truck
fo., fol. . Folio
f'wd. . . Forward
G.M.Q. . Good Merchantable Quality
H.M.C. . His Majesty's Customs
Ibid. . . (Latin: *ibidem*) The same
i.e. . . (Latin: *id est*) That is
inst. . . Instant (that is, the present month)
Int. . . Interest
Inv. . . Invoice
I O U . . I owe you
M. . . . Monsieur (French)
M/D . . Months after date
Mem. / Memo. } Memorandum
Mlle . . Mademoiselle (French)
Mme . . Madame (French)
Messrs. . Gentlemen; Sirs (Fr.: messieurs)
mo. . . Month
M/S . . Months after sight
MS(S) . . Manuscript(s)
n/a . . No account (Banking)
N.B. . . North Britain (that is, Scotland) Take Notice (Lat.: *nota bene*)
n/s . . Not sufficient (Banking)
o/d . . On demand
On a/c . On account
o/p . . Out of print
O.R. . . Owner's Risk
O/S . . On sale; out of stock
per ann. / p.a. } (Lat.: *per annum*) By the year
per pro. / p. pro. / p.p. } . (Lat.: *per procurationem*) On behalf of
pkg., pkge. Package
P. & L. . Profit and Loss
P.O.D. . Pay on Delivery
P.P. . . Parcel Post
pro. tem. . (Lat.: *pro tempore*) For the time being
prox. . . (Lat.: *proximo*) Next month
P.S. . . Postscript
P.T.O. . Please turn over
q.v. . . (Lat.: *quod vide*) Which see
r/d . . Refer to drawer (Banking)
R.P. . . Reply Paid

R.S.V.P. .	(Fr.: *Répondez s'il vous plaît*) Please reply	U.K. . .	United Kingdom
Ster., Stg..	Sterling	ult., ulto. .	(Lat.: *ultimo*) Last month
Tr. . .	Trustee	viz. . .	(Lat.: *videlicet*) Namely

ABSOLUTE PHRASES.

An Absolute Phrase is a group of words containing a noun or pronoun together with a participle, and having no grammatical connection with the rest of the sentence. (See PARTICIPLES.) Thus, in the sentence, "This being your decision, I have no more to say," the pronoun *this* is not the subject or the object of the verb *have*, nor does the participle *being* qualify any word outside its own phrase. *This being your decision* is therefore said to be "absolute," i.e. "set free." Other examples—

The shares having risen unexpectedly, many people are buying.

The business having been completed, the meeting adjourned.

For the punctuation of Absolute Phrases, see COMMA.

ACCEPTANCE—ACCEPTATION.

These words are now quite distinct in use. The *acceptation* of a word or phrase is its particular sense, its generally accepted meaning; e.g. The translator does not appear to use the term "genius" in its common *acceptation*.

Acceptance is a noun formed from the verb *accept* used in its ordinary sense; e.g. I beg your *acceptance* of this little gift. It is doubtful whether these views will ever find general *acceptance*. The company refused *acceptance* of the bill.

ACCESSORY.

The best dictionaries prefer the accent on the first syllable. The B.B.C. recommends: access'ory.

ACCOMMODATE.

Nine people out of ten spell this word wrongly.

ACCUSATIVE CASE.

(See CASE.)

ACOUSTIC.

The usual pronunciation is: acows'tic The less common alternative is: acoos'tic.

ACQUIESCE.

Followed by *in*. The committee *acquiesced in* the chairman's proposal.

ACTIVE VOICE.

(See VOICE.)

ACUMEN.

Pronounced: acū'men.

ADEQUATE.

When a preposition is required after *adequate*, the correct one is *to*.

The resources of the company are *adequate to* provide the necessary capital for the new enterprise.

The bridges over the Thames are not *adequate to* the requirements of London's traffic.

ADJECTIVE.

An adjective is a word used to qualify, i.e. limit the meaning of, a noun or pronoun. Adjectives are used: (1) to describe: a *fine* day; a *heavy* bag; (2) to point out: *this* house; *that* book; (3) to ask questions: *What* time will suit you? (4) to indicate number: *two* men; *ten* ships; (5) to indicate order: the *first* post; (6) to express an indefinite number or amount: *few* people came ; *other* men thought differently ; *much* cry, *little* wool ; (7) to show possession : *my* partner ; *their* business.

ADJECTIVE-PHRASES AND ADJECTIVE-CLAUSES.

An *adjective-phrase* is a group of words which does not contain a subject and predicate, and which does the work of an adjective. Thus, in the sentence, "The cover of the book is torn," the group of words *of the book* is equivalent to an adjective qualifying *cover*. Other examples—

A bird *in the hand* is worth two *in the bush.*
I found Jones *sitting by the fire.*

An *adjective-clause* is a part of a complete sentence ; it contains a subject and predicate of its own, and acts as an adjective qualifying a noun. Thus, in the sentence, "The house which you mentioned is sold," the group of words *which you mentioned* contains a subject (*you*) and a predicate (*mentioned which*), and it is equivalent to an adjective limiting the meaning of *house*. Other examples—

We dislike people *whose opinions differ from our own.*
This happened in the days *when I was young.*

(See CLAUSES ; PHRASE ; SUBJECT AND PREDICATE.)

ADMIRABLE.

Pronounced with the accent on the first syllable.

ADMIT.

May be followed by *of*. Such conduct does not *admit of* excuse.

ADULT.

In the usual pronunciation the accent is on the second syllable. The B.B.C. Announcers stress the first syllable.

ADVERB.

Adverbs are words used to qualify, i.e. limit the meaning of, verbs, adjectives, or other adverbs. They may sometimes qualify prepositions and conjunctions. Many adverbs are formed from adjectives by adding *-ly*. *Happy* (adj.), *happily* (adv.). Examples—

He works *hard* (*hard* qualifies the verb *works*).

It is a *very* difficult task (*very* qualifies the adjective *difficult*).

She acts *extremely* well (*extremely* qualifies the adverb *well*).

Simple adverbs denote time (Come *now*) ; place (Stay *there*) ; manner (He plays *badly*) ; reason (*Therefore* I cannot agree) ; degree (He was *completely* overcome) ; order (*Secondly*, I wish to ask . . .). Adverbs are also used to ask questions (*Why* are you late ?), and to connect clauses (Is that the house *where* he lives ?).

ADVERB-PHRASES AND ADVERB-CLAUSES.

An *adverb-phrase* is a group of words which does not contain a subject and predicate, and which does the work of an adverb. Thus, in the sentence, " The letter was written in a hurry," the group of words *in a hurry* is equivalent to an adverb of manner qualifying the verb *was written*. Other examples—

He walked *through the office*. I will come *in a minute*.

An *adverb-clause* is a group of words containing a subject and predicate of its own, and performing the function of an adverb. Thus, in the sentence, " I will go because you ask me," the group of words *because you ask me* contains a subject (*you*) and a predicate (*ask me because*), and it is equivalent to an adverb of cause qualifying the verb *will go*. Adverb-clauses belong to various kinds. They may express: (1) time (He went *when he had finished*); (2) place (Stay *where you are*); (3) cause (*As he was not there*, I went home); (4) purpose (He argues *in order that he may convince you*); (5) result (He argues so much *that he wearies you*); (6) condition (*If he calls*, I shall not see him); (7) concession (*Although he works hard*, he takes an interest in sport); (8) comparison (He behaved *as he always does*; You are older *than I am*). (See CLAUSES; PHRASE; SUBJECT AND PREDICATE.)

ADVERBS: THEIR POSITION IN A SENTENCE.

Care should be exercised in placing adverbs or adverb-equivalents in a sentence, for wrong placing either ruins the sense or violates idiom. It is clear that the sentence, "He *almost* resigned all his appointments," means something different from "He resigned *almost* all his appointments." The first says that he did not resign, and the second that he did: the change is due to the position of *almost*. Consider also the following sentence: "He did *not* carry out the work because it was necessary, but because he wished to gratify his vanity." Here *not* is placed so that it qualifies the verb *carry out*; but the sense intended is that he did in fact carry out the work, though for a personal reason. *Not* should come before *because*.

When an adverb is used with a compound verb-form, i.e. one containing an auxiliary verb (has done, shall be coming, etc.), it should be placed immediately after the auxiliary (e.g. He has *often* done it). The following sentences are unidiomatic: If this *indeed* has happened, you must act. We *earnestly* have desired to remedy the evil. (Write: has indeed happened; have earnestly desired.)

Again, in a sentence containing a transitive verb and an object, the adverb or adverb-phrase should not come between the verb and the object. The following sentences are faulty: After a few days he mastered *completely* the situation. (Write: completely mastered.) This is a question that affects *seriously* the whole staff. (Write: seriously affects.) Similarly the adverb-phrase is wrongly placed in—Applicants must possess *in a high degree* ability in salesmanship. (Move the phrase to the end.)

For the misplacing of *only*, see ONLY.

For the placing of adverbs used with infinitives, see SPLIT INFINITIVE.

AERATED.

Pronounced with four syllables—ā′-er-āt′-ed.

AEROPLANE—AIRPLANE.

In certain quarters the attempt is being made to substitute the form *airplane* for the older-established *aeroplane*. No doubt *airplane* is simpler and more English in appearance, but it seems rather late in the day to make the change. At present, the position is that there are two words in use for the same thing.

AFFECT—EFFECT.

Affect is a verb, and has two distinct uses—

(1) It means *to assume*; *to pretend to have, to feel,* or *to do*: He *affected* a cultured manner of speech. In spite of his annoyance he *affected* a haughty indifference. I *affected* to approve of the plan although I disliked it.

(2) It means *to attack*; *to touch the emotions*; *to produce an effect on*. Rheumatism *affects* people living in damp localities. I was deeply *affected* by her tale of misery. Thousands of people are *affected* by the floods.

Effect is both a noun and a verb. As a verb it means *to bring about; to achieve*. At length he *effected* his purpose. The fugitive *effected* his escape. The firm has *effected* a new insurance.

AGGRAVATE.

Aggravate is used colloquially to mean *annoy, exasperate.* Its true meaning is *make worse* or *more serious*: The bad climate *aggravated* his disease. The sudden reduction of our staff *aggravates* the difficulty of our situation. The word should be used only in this sense when it is employed in writing.

AGREEMENT.

(See RULES OF AGREEMENT.)

AIM.

Aim should be followed by *at*: We are *aiming at* exceeding last year's figures. It is incorrect English to say "aiming to exceed," though this is the recognized American usage.

ALIAS.

Pronounced: ā'lĭăs.

ALIBI.

Pronounced: ă'lĭbī.

ALLY, ALLIES.

Pronounced: ăllī', ăllīz'.

ALRIGHT.

This word is not to be found in English dictionaries. The colloquial expression "all right" (He seems all right after his holiday) should be so spelt when used, but it should be avoided in serious writing.

ALSO.

Also is an adverb and not a conjunction; accordingly it should not be used alone after a comma instead of *and*, or *and also*, or *as well as*. Such sentences as the following are slovenly: We wish to give our customers full information about our activities, *also* every facility for examining our goods. In investigating the depression in the cotton industry we note the high prices of the raw material, *also* the changes in fashion. (Write : *and also*, or *as well as*, in both cases.)

It is inelegant to begin a sentence with *also*, although this is very commonly done. It is better to put this word in the middle of the sentence, or to replace it by connectives like *moreover, again*.

ALTERNATIVE.

The following notes (based on the *Oxford English Dictionary*) may serve to elucidate the idiomatic uses of the noun *alternative*—

1. In its original and strict sense *alternative* means a permission to choose between two things ; e.g. the garrison had the alternative of surrender or starvation.

2. In modern English either of the two things to be chosen may be called an alternative, and we may thus speak of the *two alternatives* ; e.g. the garrison was faced with the two alternatives, surrender and starvation ; the garrison decided on surrender, for the alternative was starvation ; the garrison had either to surrender or starve ; there was no other alternative.

3. *No alternative* may mean practically *no choice* ; e.g. the garrison had no alternative but to surrender.

4. *Alternative* may also be applied to any one of *several* things that may be chosen. Thus Gladstone wrote : " My decided preference is for the fourth and last of these alternatives." (This usage used to be condemned by the older textbooks ; but it is now firmly established.)

AMATEUR.

It is a pity that the B.B.C. has given its sanction to the half-French pronunciation of this word (the last syllable rhyming with *fur*). The fully anglicized pronunciation "amatūre" is well established and is recommended by the best authorities.

AMBIGUITY.

(See OBSCURITY.)

AMENABLE.

Followed by *to*. He was dismissed because he was not *amenable to* discipline. Pronounced: amē'nable.

ANAESTHETIST.

Pronounced: anē'sthetist.

AND WHICH, AND WHO.

Sentences like the following should be avoided—

He is a man highly respected in the City, *and who* can be relied on to carry out his engagements.

What is the function of the conjunction *and* here? As is explained in the article on Relative Pronouns, *who* is itself a conjunction as well as a pronoun, and therefore no other connective is needed to introduce the second clause. The *and* would be required if the sentence were put in this form—

He is a man *who is* highly respected in the City, *and who* can be relied on. . .

Here the function of *and* is to connect two relative clauses referring to the same antecedent. The correct type of sentence-structure in such cases is:

Antecedent (relative clause) *and* (relative clause).

Another example of the error—

A Rembrandt, reported to be a very fine example of the master's work, *and which* has until lately been in the collection of a wealthy connoisseur, is now for sale. (Write: which is reported.)

A worse instance of the fault is the following—

A new road has been under construction for some months, *and which* will most probably be opened in the autumn.

Here it is not possible to introduce another relative clause referring to *road*. Replace *which* by *it*.

Similar mistakes are made in the use of *but who, but which.*

ANTITHESIS.

(See EMPHASIS.)

ANYBODY, ANYONE.

These words stand for single persons and should not, therefore, be followed by plural words referring to them. The following are incorrect: Would *anybody* in *their* senses say such a thing? *Anyone* can now make *their* choice. (Substitute *his* in both cases.)

APOSTROPHE.

The apostrophe is used to mark the omission of a letter (It's raining), or to indicate the genitive (possessive) case. (See CASE.)

The genitive case of a noun is formed in the singular by adding *'s* to the nominative: *clerk, clerk's.*

In the plural it is formed—

(*a*) By adding an apostrophe only to the nominative plural, when that form ends in *-s* or *-es*: *the directors, the directors' fees; the horses, the horses' food.*

(*b*) By adding *'s* to the nominative plural, when that form does not end in *-s*: *the men, the men's wages.*

For difficulties in the use of *'s*, see GENITIVE PROBLEMS.

APPALLING.

Appalling means *terrifying, dismaying.* It is correctly used in such a sentence as: The attacking troops were met by heavy fire, and they sustained *appalling* losses. In talk we employ the word with no thought of its real signification (What an *appalling* day! His manners are perfectly *appalling*). The careful writer has few occasions for the use of this word.

APPLICABLE.

The stress is on the first syllable. It is very commonly put on the second syllable, but this accentuation is against dictionary authority.

APPOSITION.

When two nouns name the same person or thing, and one limits the meaning of the other, they are said to be *in apposition*. Thus, in "I met Mr. Smith, the foreman," *the foreman* is in apposition to *Mr. Smith*. Besides nouns, any noun-equivalents can be in apposition.

APPRECIABLE—APPRECIATIVE.

Appreciable means *capable of being appreciated* or *estimated*: There is no *appreciable* difference between the two colours. The rainfall was so small as to be hardly *appreciable*.

Appreciative means *showing appreciation; estimating aright*: Actors are stimulated by *appreciative* audiences. He is always *appreciative of* kindness.

ARCHAISMS.

Why does the correspondent in the local newspaper delight to "comment on the remarks of Mr. So-and-So *anent* such-and-such a subject"? Is he merely trying to avoid the obvious "with regard to," "with reference to," or simply "on"; or does he imagine he is exhibiting one of the graces of style? The inexperienced writer may be warned not to yield to the temptation to sprinkle his pages with obsolete expressions such as: *albeit, ere, erstwhile, oft, perchance, proven, thereof, thereto, well-nigh, withal.* Their effect on the reader is apt to be merely irritating. In the course of centuries many words have decayed and died. Sometimes they are wakened to new life by a poet, but it is not decent for the writer of workaday prose to drag them from their graves.

The use of archaic expressions, generally together with circumlocution, is a common trick of writers who aim at humorous description. The effect is usually feeble. The following example is, perhaps, less objectionable than most—

> By the middle of December, as Selina stuck her nose cautiously out of the covers into the midnight blackness of early morning, you might have observed, if it had been at all light, that the tip of that elegant and *erstwhile* alabaster feature had been encarmined during the night by a mischievous brush wielded by that same *wight* who had been busy painting fronds and lacy ferns and gorgeous blossoms of silver all over the bedroom window.

ARCHIVES.

Pronounced : ar'kīves.

ARRANGEMENT OF WORDS.

As several other articles deal with particular problems concerning the arrangement of words in sentences, it is not necessary to do more here than to insist that few matters require more care than the ordering of the parts of a sentence. The writer who aims at clearness and vigour must so build up his sentence that every part has its definite place in the plan, and every word makes its contribution to the general effect. Misplacement of words or groups of words leads to obscurity, false emphasis, and faulty rhythm. Full discussion of these matters will be found under Adverbs : Their Position in a Sentence; Emphasis; Rule of Proximity; Rhythm.

ARTICLES (*A, AN, THE*).

A (*an*) is called the Indefinite Article, and *the* the Definite Article. For the uses of *an* see A, AN.

Note that, if two separate persons or things are meant, the article must be repeated before the second. " Not the same qualifications are required for a works manager and foreman " is incorrect if two people are referred to. Write: a works manager and *a* foreman.

ARTISAN.

The accent is on the last syllable.

ARTIST, ARTISTE.

An *artist* is one who practises one of the fine arts; an *artiste* (pronounced: artēst') is a professional singer, dancer, etc. (male or female).

AS.

Mistakes are frequently made, especially in conversation, in the use of pronouns following *as*; e.g. My brother is as rich as *him*. The correction becomes obvious if the understood verb is supplied: My brother is as rich as *he* (is). The pronoun should be in the nominative (not accusative) case, because it is subject of (*is*). It should be observed that *as* is a conjunction and not a preposition. (See CASE.)

AS GOOD (AS) OR BETTER THAN.

(See OMISSION OF NECESSARY WORDS.)

AS IF, AS THOUGH.

The following sentences are incorrect—

I feel as if I am going to faint.
It seems as if he means to be unpleasant about it.
He acts as though he is a madman.

The correct forms are—

I feel as if I *were* going to faint. (If expanded, this sentence would read: I feel as I should feel if I *were* going to faint.)

It seems as if he *meant* to be unpleasant about it.

He acts as though he *were* a madman.

AS MUCH (AS) IF NOT MORE THAN.

(See OMISSION OF NECESSARY WORDS.)

ASPIRANT.

Pronounced either: ă′spĭrant, or aspīr′ant.

ASSET.

Asset is a word that receives very bad treatment nowadays at the hands of journalists and others. *Assets* (with the *-s*) is a technical term, meaning property which balances or should balance liabilities. Careless writers however, use *asset* constantly for any sort of possession or advantage, or for an idea vaguely connected with advantage; e.g. In spite of the lightness of this machine, its great *asset* is its strength. (Substitute: advantage, merit.) Mr. Smith is a great *asset* to the local Labour Party. (Substitute: pillar of.) In proposing a vote of thanks to Mr. Justice Sankey at a public meeting of the Discharged Prisoners' Aid Society, Sir Henry Jackson expressed the view that it was a tremendous *asset* to have a man with great qualities of head and heart presiding. (Substitute: advantage.)

ASSIGNEE.

Pronounced: assĭnē′.

AS TO.

Writers nowadays constantly make use of *as to* either quite unnecessarily or in place of some other preposition.

In the following examples *as to* is superfluous and should be omitted—I am doubtful *as to* whether I ought to go. I am wondering *as to* how long it will take. The committee will consider the question *as to* whether the grant can be made.

In the following sentences the preposition given in brackets should be substituted: He seems to have no notion *as to* (*of*) the powers he possesses. No information can be given *as to* (*about*) the prospects of the firm.

ATE.

Ate, the past form of the verb *eat* (I ate nothing yesterday), should be pronounced: ĕt.

ATTORNEY.

Pronounced: atter′ney.

AUGUR.

The following sentences exemplify the idioms in which this verb may be used: I do not *augur much good to* the firm from the new policy. From the first he had *augured ill of* the scheme. The reports of recent sales *augur well for* the future prosperity of the firm.

AUXILIARY VERB.

An auxiliary verb is one that is used with another verb in a compound form. Thus, certain forms of the verb "to write" contain the auxiliary verb "to have"—I have written, I had written, etc.; other forms contain the auxiliary verb "to be"—I am writing, it is written, etc. The auxiliary verbs are—*be, have, do, may, might, shall, will, should, would.*

AVERSE.

According to modern usage either *from* or *to* may follow *averse* and *aversion*. The manager seems *averse to* the proposal. The directors are not *averse from* giving him full powers.

BAS-RELIEF.

The *s* of *bas-* is pronounced.

BECAUSE.

(See Reason Why . . . Because.)

BEDIZEN.

Pronounced either: bedĭz′en, or bedī′zen.

BETWEEN.

Notice that we must say "*between* one thing *and* (not *or*) another." The following is incorrect: He was forced to choose between resigning his post immediately *or* receiving dismissal (*and*).

BLAME.

It is a vulgarism to say, "He tried to blame it on to me." The correct idioms are: He tried to put the blame on me; He said I was to blame; He tried to blame me.

"BUSINESS ENGLISH."

On the matter of the meaningless jargon generally known as "Business English" or "Commercial English," there are some interesting and important comments in the report on "The Teaching of English in England" (1921), issued by the Departmental Committee appointed by the Board of Education. We may first quote the samples of the dialect as they are there given: *prox.* (next month); *ult.* (last month); *inst.* (this month); *of even date* (of to-day); *beg to* or *hereby beg to* (a meaningless prefix found before verbs of all kinds, e.g. "I beg to inform you," "hereby beg to say," etc.). *Your favour, your esteemed favour, yours* (your letter); *I am in receipt of your favour, your favour duly to hand*, or more familiarly, *yours to hand* (your letter has reached me); *per* (by); *as per* (in accordance with); *same* (it, e.g. "Yours to hand and we beg to say we shall give all attention to same"); *make* or *quote you* (make an offer, e.g. "We can make you a discount of 6 per cent," "My traveller had the pleasure of quoting you for the order"), *the favour of your immediate reply will oblige* (I shall be glad to hear from you at once).

After having received the evidence of representative business men, the Committee reports "that 'Commercial English' is not only objectionable to all those who have the purity of the language at heart but also contrary to the true interests of commercial life, sapping its vitality and encouraging the use of dry, meaningless, formulae just where vigorous and arresting English is the chief requisite." Fortunately, the use of this special jargon is already on the wane. The chief business houses are taking the lead in showing that the ordinary resources of the English language are quite adequate to the needs of commerce; and it is to be hoped that before long "Business English" will be dead.

BUT.

When *but* means *except* it is a preposition, and should be followed by an accusative case. Nobody met him but *me*; I met nobody but *him*. (See CASE.)

When *but that* is used to introduce a noun-clause a following negative is not required. Who knows *but that* when the business has been re-organized increased profits may *not* be made? (Omit *not*.)

When *but* is used as a conjunction, it should not be followed by *however*. He seemed almost powerless; *but* one course, *however*, still lay open to him. (*However* is superfluous.)

BUT WHICH, BUT WHO.

(See AND WHICH, AND WHO.)

CALUMNY.

The stress is on the first syllable.

CANNOT HELP BUT.

To say "I *cannot help but* think you are wrong" is to employ a meaningless phrase which is the result of confusing two idioms—(1) I cannot but think you are wrong; (2) I cannot help thinking you are wrong.

CANVAS—CANVASS.

Canvas is the name of the material; *canvass* means *to solicit votes or orders.*

CAPITALIST.

The stress is on the first syllable.

CASE.

So many errors in English are due to wrong use of cases that it is most important to grasp what is meant by "case." The essential principles are quite simple, but they must be thoroughly understood before they can be applied. In the notes here given only such points are explained as have a practical value for the ordinary writer of English.

A noun or a noun-equivalent (e.g. a pronoun) is said to be in a certain "case" according to its relationship to other words in the sentence. If we consider the sentence, "I posted the letter for my brother," we see that *I* is the subject, *letter* is the object, and *brother* is governed by the preposition *for*. *I* is therefore said to be in the Nominative Case, and *letter* and *brother* in the Accusative Case. (Before proceeding further, the reader should make certain that he understands the matters dealt with in the articles on SUBJECT AND PREDICATE; OBJECT; PREDICATIVE WORDS; PREPOSITION.)

There are five cases in English—

1. THE NOMINATIVE. This is the case of—

(*a*) The subject of a sentence or clause—

The day is fine. Has the *man* explained where *he* went?

(*b*) A predicative noun or pronoun referring to the subject—

His brother is a *printer*. She became a *typist*. It is *I*.

2. THE VOCATIVE. This is the case of a person or thing addressed—

I think, *sir*, that this is wrong.

3. THE ACCUSATIVE (or OBJECTIVE). The most important uses are for—

(*a*) The object of a sentence or clause—

He brought the *message*. I want to know *what* he said. I met *him*. *Whom* did you see?

(*b*) A noun or noun-equivalent governed by a preposition—

The boy has called for the *parcel*. Will you give it to *me*? To *whom* did you give it? (*For* and *to* are prepositions.)

4. THE GENITIVE (or POSSESSIVE). This is used to denote that one thing belongs to, or is connected with another thing or person—

The *manager's* house. This *morning's* letters. *Whose* book is that?

The genitive case of nouns is always marked by the apostrophe. (See APOSTROPHE.)

5. THE DATIVE. This is the case of the Indirect Object. (See OBJECT, DIRECT AND INDIRECT.)

I sent *her* the flowers.

CASE-PHRASES. Instead of a genitive case we often use a phrase equivalent to it. He is manager *of the works.* Similarly we may have a phrase equivalent to a dative. I sent the flowers *to her.* He tied up the parcel *for me.* In these examples *works, her,* and *me,* are in the accusative case because they are governed by the prepositions *of, to,* and *for.*

English nouns do not change their form according to case, except for the genitive; differences of case are therefore most readily observable in the pronouns, which have many different forms. (See PERSONAL PRONOUNS.)

(See also ERRORS IN CASE.)

CAVIL.

Followed by *at.* It is unreasonable to *cavil at* an error of a few pence in an account of some thousands of pounds.

CELTIC.

A good many people pronounce the initial consonant *k*, but the *s* pronunciation has the best dictionary authority, and is used by the B.B.C. The spelling with the *c* is the established one.

CENSOR—CENSURE.

A *censor* is an official who licenses or suppresses books, plays, etc., or who exercises control over military intelligence. *Censor* is also used as a verb (to censor a film).

A *censure* is an adverse judgment, an expression of disapproval (The committee passed a vote of censure; The review of the book contained censures which I considered unfair). As a verb, *to censure* means to criticize unfavourably, to blame (The officer was censured by the court-martial).

CENTENARY.

The usual pronunciation is: sentē'nary, though sen'tĕnary is allowable.

CENTRIFUGAL.

The accent is on the second syllable.

CHAGRIN.

According to the best dictionary authority the pronunciation is: shăgrēn'. The B.B.C. Announcers, however, say: shă'grin for the noun, and shăgrēn' for the verb.

CHICANERY.

Pronounced: shicā'nery.

CHIMERA, CHIMERICAL.

Pronounced: kĭmēr'a, kĭmĕr'ical.

CHIROPODIST.

Pronounced: kīrŏp'odist, or kĭrŏp'odist.

CINEMA.

Pronounced: sĭ'nema. An initial *k* in the spelling and the pronunciation has been advocated on the ground that the Greek root-word contains a *k;* but if this argument were to be followed we should have to say "kykle" for "cycle" (Greek: *kuklos.*) Moreover, *cinema* was borrowed from the French *cinématographe* (*c* pronounced *s*), and not direct from the Greek.

CIRCUMLOCUTION (PERIPHRASIS).

Circumlocution, or Periphrasis (pronounced: perĭf'-răsis)—saying things in a roundabout way—is a favourite device of the feeble writer who wishes to avoid the obvious even when the obvious is inevitable. There is really no virtue in writing: "With the British Isles situated on the western flank of a large Continental anticyclone, *the prospects of considerable periods of genial holiday weather are by no means negligible.*" All that is meant is that considerable periods of fine weather are likely. Nor did the writer of the following passage (in the correspondence column of the *Daily Telegraph*) achieve an admirable distinction of style: "Many people ask why plover's eggs should be consigned to the exigencies of egg-destroying weather; to the *furtive ravages of the thieving corvine tribe and of sundry rodents of ill repute*; and to the requirements of farmers in the matter of rolling their arable lands." It is annoying to the reader to have to paraphrase "the furtive ravages of the thieving corvine tribe" into "the ravages of crows," and then to be left wondering whether the "sundry rodents of ill repute" are rats and rabbits.

Financial journalists deserve sympathy in their unenviable task of giving the appearance of novelty to facts which must be the same from day to day; but, from the point of view of style, there is nothing to be said for "Business remains conspicuous by its absence," and "Business in the share market has approached the irreducible minimum" as variants of "There is little or no business."

It is a sound rule never to use several words when one will do. To substitute "in the event of" for "if" (In the event of your agreeing to our proposal . . .), and "in view of the fact that" for "as" (In view of the fact that our arrangements are not yet complete . . .), and so on, produces inflation, but not dignity of style.

CLANDESTINE.

Pronounced: clandes'tĭn.

CLAUSES.

Some sentences consist of two or more groups of words, each containing its own subject and predicate.

(See SUBJECT AND PREDICATE.) Such word-groups are called clauses. The following sentence contains four clauses ; they are separated by vertical lines—

> When the boy returns, | I will send him to inquire | whether the secretary has received the letter | that he is expecting.

The clause which states the main fact is : I will send him to inquire. This is called the *main clause*. The other groups of words, though each having a subject and a verb, depend for their meaning on the main clause : they are therefore called *subordinate clauses*. A subordinate clause is equivalent to either a noun, an adjective, or an adverb. Thus, in the above example, " whether . . . letter " acts as a noun used as the object of the infinitive " to inquire " ; " that . . . expecting " acts as an adjective qualifying " letter " ; " When . . . returns " acts as an adverb of time qualifying " will send." Subordinate clauses are introduced by conjunctions like *that, when, where, because, if, since, whether*, or by relative pronouns (*who, which, that, what*).

(See ADJECTIVE-PHRASES AND ADJECTIVE-CLAUSES ; ADVERB-PHRASES AND ADVERB-CLAUSES ; NOUN-CLAUSES ; COMPLEX SENTENCE ; DOUBLE SENTENCE, MULTIPLE SENTENCE.)

CLICHÉS.

(See HACKNEYED PHRASES.)

CLIENTELE.

This word is often given the French pronunciation, as well as the French spelling (*clientèle*). The *Oxford English Dictionary* gives the pronunciation : klīĕntēl′, and it is to be hoped that this will become universal. The word is now thoroughly English.

CLUMSY CONSTRUCTIONS.

In this article are collected a number of typical sentences which, while not necessarily grammatically inaccurate, annoy the reader through some clumsiness of construction.

1. The chief obstacle to trade recovery *was* trade barriers which impeded the free flow of labour, capital, and goods.

Here the reader at first sight probably says, "Should not *was* be *were*?" Actually *was* is correct, for it should agree with its subject *obstacle*. But this feeling of awkwardness and incorrectness will always be produced in a sentence containing a singular subject (*obstacle*) and a plural predicative noun (*barriers*), or *vice versa*. (See PREDICATIVE WORDS.) It is well, therefore, to avoid such a sentence-form, if possible.

2. The portion of the locomotive *which* requires the greatest degree of accuracy in its production is the valve-gear, *which*, as its name denotes, is the mechanism *which* actuates the movement of the valves *which* control the admission and exhaust of the steam to and from the cylinders.

The succession of relative pronouns referring to different antecedents is unpleasant to the ear.

3. Constructions like the following have a great vogue nowadays—

> Owing to his (him) being unable to be present, the meeting was postponed.
>
> In the event of his (him) being unable to be present, the meeting will be postponed.
>
> His action resulted in the meeting being postponed.

More often than not, sentences like the first two are made grammatically wrong by the use of *him* for *his*. The third sentence contains a similar error. (See CONFUSION OF PARTICIPLE AND GERUND.) But, in any case, these examples surely exhibit extremely awkward variants of the simple expressions: As he was unable to be present . . .; If he is unable to be present . . .; His action caused the meeting to be postponed.

COGNIZANT.

Followed by *of*. When I made the remark quoted by the last speaker, I was not *cognizant of* all the facts.

COLLECTIVE NOUN.

A collective noun is the name of a group of persons or things, e.g. *crowd, government, flock.* For difficulties in the agreement of collective nouns, see ERRORS IN AGREEMENT.

COLLOQUIALISMS.

One of the first lessons that inexperienced writers have to learn is that the written language is by no means identical with the spoken language. Literary English is an artificial product free from the undesirable features of conversational language. This is not to say that there is a complete divorce between written and spoken English; many great writers (e.g. Hazlitt) have aimed at imitating the ease of good conversation. Ordinary talk, however, is unfit to be reproduced in writing because it naturally tends to be slipshod in grammar and the use of words. Besides containing slang (an extreme form of colloquialism), it is generally full of expressions like the following, all of which have special colloquial senses: What *beastly* weather! That is a *sweet* hat. He won by a *fluke.* He was *badly let down* at the interview. *Lots of people* were there. He is *out to* get more customers.

It is this careless use of words which is apt to intrude itself into writing, especially in these days when colloquialisms abound in the articles of popular newspapers. Guard against using the colloquial "different *to*" instead of "different *from,*" and "a lot of" in place of "much" or "many." Do not use "thing" as a substitute for a noun which you cannot think of without some trouble, and do not make "nice" similarly do duty for some more precise adjective. "Idea" is a word badly misused in conversation: it is worth while to refer to the dictionary for its true meanings. The colloquial "you" (meaning "anybody," "people in general") should generally be avoided in serious writing, although its use is becoming common in journalism.

Not only are words misused, but mistakes in grammar are commonly made in conversation. Some of these errors are vulgar, but others are heard even in educated speech. "Like" is wrongly used as a conjunction (I wish I could sing *like* (as well as) he can); "than" is used as a preposition although it is really a conjunction (He is older than *me* (I)); the relative pronoun "which" is employed without a clear antecedent (He told me that I was careless, *which* was most unfair); "nobody," "everybody," etc., are incorrectly treated as plural (Everybody has a right to *their* opinion). We may whisper that Jane Austen constantly treated "everybody" as plural, that Thackeray often wrote "different to," and that Thomas Hardy regularly split his infinitives. It may be that these and other colloquial uses will eventually become so well established in the speech of the educated classes that the rules of grammar will be modified to meet such cases. In the meantime, however, writers who are in no danger of becoming standard authors should eschew expressions which contravene grammatical rules.

COLON.

The colon (:) marks a longer pause than any other stop except the full stop. It is used—

1. To separate the two parts of a double sentence when the second part explains or amplifies the statement

made in the first. (See DOUBLE SENTENCE, MULTIPLE SENTENCE.) E.g.—

He is very well suited for the appointment : he has wide technical knowledge, and he has had experience in handling men.

The sound of wheels or the din of machinery was hardly known in the island : all went barefoot about the house, and scarcely in the world could there have been found a deeper silence than in Stevenson's house in the forest.

Great difficulty is likely to be encountered during the passage of the bill : vested interests of various kinds are doing their best to mobilize the opposition.

Notice that the conjunctions *and, but, for* are not used after a colon.

2. Before a list of items—

The library is rich in several branches of literature: biography, poetry, travel, and drama.

3. Sometimes before a quotation—

Just then Smith's voice was heard above the general talk : "You can't get rid of the man like that!"

(See PUNCTUATION : GENERAL HINTS.)

COLOSSAL.

Colossal means *gigantic* ; *of enormous size.* It is often carelessly used, especially in talk. It is such a strong word that in its true sense it does not fit many contexts.

COMMA.

The comma (,) marks a short pause. It is used—

1. To separate words or phrases forming a series—

His desk was covered with books, papers, and letters.

He is a careless, lazy, untidy person.

Slowly, quietly, but effectively, he put forward all his strongest arguments.

He acts as secretary of the cricket club, chairman of the debating society, and producer for the dramatic club.

Nowadays we may travel by rail, by car, or by aeroplane.

NOTES

(1) In sentences like the first example given above, the comma is sometimes omitted before *and*. This practice is undesirable: a pause is made after *papers* as well as after *books*.

(2) When two adjectives precede a noun, a comma is sometimes required between them, and sometimes not. We should write: *a pretty little girl* (where *little* is so closely connected with *girl* that the two words suggest a single idea), but, *a shy, reserved girl* (where the adjectives have equal value in relation to the noun). Similarly *a rich old man*, but, *a rich, influential man.*

2. To mark off words and phrases like *in fact, of course, no doubt, therefore, for instance*—

His remarks, in fact, were most annoying.

He thought, of course, that I should be afraid to reply.

3. To mark off (*a*) words used in address, (*b*) words in apposition (see APPOSITION), (*c*) phrases containing participles and requiring a pause in the reading—

(*a*) I will explain, my lord, as well as I can.

(*b*) Thomas Hardy, the greatest English writer of modern times, died in 1928.

(*c*) Having received your explanation, I am satisfied.

The necessary preparations having been completed, the expedition is about to set out.

At last the garrison, finding further resistance hopeless, determined to surrender.

4. In complex sentences, to separate clauses *when a pause would naturally be made in the reading*. (See COMPLEX SENTENCE)—

Although I thought you would come, I did not expect you so soon.

Many imagined that labour troubles were over for a time, and that trade would recover.

I gave the letter to the office-boy, who posted it.

5. In double sentences, to separate the two parts when the subject of the second clause is expressed. (See DOUBLE SENTENCE, MULTIPLE SENTENCE)—

At first he seemed to be nervous, but he soon gained sufficient confidence to acquit himself well.

(See COMMA MISUSED and PUNCTUATION: GENERAL HINTS.)

COMMA MISUSED.

The comma is such an important stop that, besides giving the rules for its use, we may usefully collect some typical examples in which it is misplaced—

1. "The distinction between the two types, is a sure guide to the relative superiority of each system." A comma should not be used, as here, to separate the subject of the sentence from its verb.

2. "His professional duties require that he should report only, what the statesman said and what his audience thought of him." A comma is not used before a noun-clause. The regular practice would be to omit the comma after *only*, and to insert one before *and* to mark off the second noun-clause from the first.

3. "I will have no more dealings with a man, who treats his clients in such a fashion."

"The proper treatment of war news is the most serious problem, which a newspaper has to face."

Omit the comma in both cases. Relative clauses should be preceded by a comma only when *who* or *which* can be replaced by *and he, and it, and they,* etc. (I gave the letter to the office-boy, who (and he) posted it; I have just received your reply, which (and it) I must confess is rather disappointing.)

4. "He will try to treat it exhaustively and not

return to the office, until he has his story complete." It is customary to use a comma between an adverb-clause and a main clause only when the adverb-clause *precedes* the main statement. Here the adverb-clause follows.

5. "The candidate, having concluded his speech, his chief supporter moved a vote of thanks." Omit the first comma. This sentence contains an absolute phrase (see ABSOLUTE PHRASES) which should be treated as a whole and separated from the rest by a comma.

It will be observed that in none of the places where a comma has been wrongly inserted in the above examples would a pause be made in the reading.

COMMENT.

The accent is on the first syllable in the noun and the verb.

COMMUNAL.

The accent may be on either the first or the second syllable. It is, perhaps, more common to accent the first.

COMMUNE.

The noun (meaning *territorial division*, etc.), has the accent on the first syllable. In the case of the verb (meaning *converse*) the accent is allowed on either syllable. It is probably more common to hear the first syllable stressed.

COMPARABLE.

The stress is on the first syllable.

COMPARATIVE DEGREE.

(See DEGREES OF COMPARISON.)

COMPARE TO, WITH.

Should we use *to* or *with* after *compare*? Sometimes either preposition is correct. But if by *compare* we mean *suggest a likeness*, we should use *to*; e.g. Portia compared mercy *to* the gentle rain from heaven. If, on the other hand, our comparison is an extended process setting forth the details of similarity, we must use *with*; e.g. The English chemist compared his results *with* those of the Frenchman, who had been working under similar conditions.

A similar distinction exists between *comparable to* and *comparable with.*

COMPARISONS FAULTILY EXPRESSED.

The statement of a comparison often causes difficulty. The important point to remember is that only things of the same kind can be compared. Sometimes essential words are omitted (especially after *than*), so that unlike things appear to be compared. The fault is clear in such cases as: "The value of the coal exported is greater than any other product." (Insert *that of* before *any*; otherwise value is compared with product.) "The lecturer said that the Public School system was anomalous as contrasted with France and Germany, where rich and poor were educated side by side." (A system is contrasted with two countries.)

The following sentences contain similar but less obvious errors—

> As regards current trading, the increase of sales, both in the furniture and timber sections of the business, as compared with the corresponding period of the previous year, is particularly gratifying to your directors.

(Increase of sales is compared with a period. Say: the

increased sales . . . as compared with those of . . . are particularly . . .)

> I was recently paying a visit to two countries where tobacco is ridiculously cheap as compared with its enormous prices here.

(Write: where the prices of tobacco are ridiculously low as compared with those in England.)

COMPATIBLE.

Followed by *with*. His extreme Labour views are hardly *compatible with* his position as shareholder in a rubber company.

COMPLEMENT.

(See PREDICATIVE WORDS.)

COMPLEX SENTENCE.

A complex sentence consists of *one* main clause together with one or more subordinate clauses. (See CLAUSES.) E.g.—

> When the manager returns, I will ask him whether the books which you ordered have arrived from the publishers.

This includes a main clause (I will ask him), an adverb-clause (when the manager returns), a noun-clause (whether the books have arrived from the publishers), and an adjective-clause (which you ordered).

COMPOUND SENTENCE.

(See DOUBLE SENTENCE, MULTIPLE SENTENCE.)

COMPRISE.

Comprised should not be followed by *of*. We may say that a house *consists of* three reception rooms, five bedrooms, etc., or that it *comprises* those rooms, but not that it *is comprised of* the rooms. Other examples of correct use—

The new committee *comprised* men of widely differing views.

The properties *comprised in* the sale are three cottages, a larger residence, and a shop.

The wrong use of *comprised* is very common.

CONCUR.

We concur *with* a person *in* an opinion. This word is most commonly used in a construction containing *in*. The other directors did not *concur in* his proposal to extend the works. Mr. Jones and Mr. Robinson *concurred in* opposing the policy of the board.

CONDOLENCE.

The stress is on the second syllable.

CONFUSION OF EXPRESSION.

Errors frequently arise through the confusion of two constructions in one sentence. The writer starts with one mode of expression in his mind, and when he is half way through the sentence he changes to another mode. A few typical examples will make clear what is meant—

1. "The committee suggests the holding of a competition for the best design, and that the judging should take place before the end of the year." The verb *suggests* has two objects; one is a noun (*the holding*), and the other is a clause beginning with *that*. Both objects should have the same form. Re-write thus: The committee suggests *that a competition should be held* . . . and that . . .

2. "Hardly (or Scarcely) had the manager left the shop than the goods arrived." *Than* must be used after

a comparative. We may say: *No sooner* had the manager left the shop *than* . . .; but if we begin with *hardly* or *scarcely* we must follow with: *when* the goods arrived.

3. "With the possible exception of Mexico, the rapidity of development of oil production in Venezuela has not been equalled in the history of the industry." Here the two constructions that have been mixed are: (*a*) With the possible exception of Mexico, *no other country* has equalled Venezuela . . . (*b*) The rapidity . . . in Venezuela has not been equalled anywhere *except possibly in Mexico* . . .

4. "All these works are equipped with modern plant and situated in strategical centres, placing the company not only in a position second to none *for dealing* with obsolete tonnage and other dismantling operations to the best advantage, but *to command* supplies of materials in all districts." *For commanding* is needed as a parallel to *for dealing*. Change the position of *not only*, and write: in a position second to none *not only for dealing* with obsolete tonnage . . . *but for commanding* supplies . . .

5. "Our advertising agents are confident that it will then be with Triplex as it has been with pneumatic tyres, electric lighting, self-starters, four-wheel brakes, and other items *that* the public now expect to be included in the equipment of any motor-car, *but which* for a long time there was an extra charge." Two parallel clauses containing *which* should be used; and *for* is needed before the second *which* to complete the sense. Write: items *which* the public . . ., but *for which* for a long time . . .

6. "The real *reason why* British cars are not designed to meet general conditions in the export markets of the world is not *in the hope* that roads will eventually accommodate themselves to British cars, but *because* our manufacturers are hampered by the present method

of taxation." There is a complete muddle here. Having started with *the reason why*, the writer changes to another form of expression in *in the hope that*, and later reverts to the first form with *because*, but thus introduces the error of redundancy. (See REASON WHY . . . BECAUSE.) Write: The real reason why . . . is not *that* our manufacturers hope . . . but *that* they are hampered . . . Or better—British cars are designed without regard to the general conditions in the export markets of the world *not because* it is hoped that . . . *but because* our manufacturers . . .

CONFUSION OF PARTICIPLE AND GERUND.

The confusion of the participle and the gerund that has become so common among present-day writers is condemned by H. W. Fowler in *Modern English Usage* as a serious offence against grammar. In order to appreciate properly the point at issue it is necessary to understand the subject-matter of the articles on GERUND and PARTICIPLES, though the simplest cases of the difficulty can be made clear at once. Considerations of logic demand that "I dislike *him* coming late," should be changed to "I dislike *his* coming late." The first sentence says that I dislike him; but I may like him personally very much. What I dislike is his *action* of coming late. Using grammatical terms, we may say that in the first case *him* is the object of the verb, and it is qualified by the participle *coming*; the object required, however, is *coming*, which should therefore be a gerund preceded by the possessive *his*. Similarly, in "I object to him going early," *him* should be *his* because the preposition *to* ought to govern *going*.

In the examples just given the verb-form ending in *-ing* is preceded by a pronoun that can easily be converted into a possessive form. No such simple change is possible, however, in such cases as the following: "We still have faith in this disease *being* curable, if it is taken in time"; "Protests were made in the House of Lords against so many bills *being introduced* late in the session." (The difficulty can be avoided, of course, by writing "that this disease is curable," "against the introduction of.")

Professor Jespersen (in Tract No. XXV, Society for Pure English) defends the confused gerund-participle as an idiom long employed by writers and now well-established. In, for instance, "There is no danger of this happening again," he treats the preposition *of* as governing the whole phrase "this-happening-again."

The *Oxford English Dictionary* (under -ING[1] (2)) supports Jespersen's view.

CONJUGAL.

The stress is on the first syllable.

CONJUNCTION.

A conjunction is a word used to connect words or groups of words: He *and* I will go. Give it to John *or* me. He came, *but* I was not in. Many conjunctions are used to introduce subordinate clauses (see CLAUSES), e.g. *as, after, since, though, if, unless, because, when, how.*

CONJURE.

When this word means *to beseech* (I conjure you not to do this great wrong) it is pronounced: conjūr'.

In its other senses (To perform conjuring tricks; His is a name to conjure with; He did his best to conjure up a picture of the scene; The witches conjured spirits to appear before Macbeth) it is pronounced: cun'jer.

CONNIVE.

Followed by *at.* The warder *connived at* the prisoner's escape.

CONSEQUENT.

Followed by *upon.* There was severe trade depression *consequent upon* a number of serious strikes.

CONSIDER—REGARD.

Regard should be followed by *as,* but *consider* should not. The correct forms are: I *regard* him *as* unfitted for the post; I *consider* him unfitted for the post.

CONSIST OF, CONSIST IN.

Consist has different meanings according to whether it is followed by *of* or *in.* To *consist of* is to be composed of; e.g. The property consists of a large house and seven acres of grounds. The meaning of *consist in* is exemplified in the following sentences. The chief merit of the novel *consists in* the skilful delineation of character. The difficulty of his task *consists in* securing harmony between the management and the workpeople.

CONSOLS.

The accent is on the second syllable.

CONSUMMATE.

The adjective has the accent on the second syllable. The verb is pronounced: con′summāt.

CONTEMPLATIVE.

Pronounced with the stress on the first syllable.

The pronunciation which gives the stress to the second syllable is often heard, but it does not seem to be allowed by the latest dictionaries.

CONTEMPTIBLE—CONTEMPTUOUS.

Contemptible means *worthy of contempt; contemptuous* means *showing contempt.* Such a *contemptible* action is beneath my notice. His pride and egoism led him to speak of his opponents in most *contemptuous* terms. He showed himself *contemptuous of* public opinion.

CONTINGENT.

Followed by *on* (*upon*). His promotion was made *contingent on* his securing sufficient new business to justify the creation of an additional department.

CONTINUAL—CONTINUOUS.

The distinction between these two words is rather subtle. Something is *continual* when it is always going on and is not thought of as coming to an end. *Continual* can be replaced by *constant, perpetual.* He suffered from *continual* thirst. There were *continual* delays. There is a *continual* coming and going of visitors.

When we use *continuous* we have in mind the beginning and the end; *constant* and *perpetual* would not be appropriate. The records of the period are not *continuous* as documents, for the years 1610–1612, are missing. The canals form a *continuous* waterway for 300 miles. The new aeroplane is capable of three days' *continuous* flight.

CONTRARY.

The accent is on the first syllable. The word is pronounced: contrăr′y, however, when it is used colloquially to mean perverse, self-willed.

CONTROVERSY.

The first syllable should be accented.

CONVERSANT.

The accent is on the first syllable. The word should be followed by *with.* I made no remarks as I was not *conversant with* the subject.

CORRECT ENGLISH: HOW IS THE STANDARD OF CORRECTNESS FIXED?

It will not be out of place in a book which seeks to discriminate between what is correct and what is incorrect in the use of English to give some explanation of how we arrive at our standard of judgment in these matters. This is the more necessary since there are few subjects on which so much nonsense is talked and written. As we all use the English language and most educated people have some knowledge of the tongues from which much of our vocabulary is derived, it is, perhaps, not surprising that everybody should think himself competent to give his views about a point in pronunciation or usage. Yet the letters which fill the correspondence columns of the newspapers as soon as a hare of this sort is started show that the writers usually have hardly begun to understand the problems involved.

How is a Disputed Point in Pronunciation to be Settled? A clergyman recently wrote to *The Times* protesting against the B.B.C.'s ruling that its Announcers should pronounce *electricity* with the first *e* short (ĕlectricity); he thought it unquestionable that the initial *e* should be long because the first syllable of the original Greek word is long. Now, the fact of the matter is, as very little consideration will show, that the length of vowels in Latin or Greek is of no value in determining the pronunciation of the derived word. Thus, if we followed the ancient tongues, we should have to discard present usage and say ălien, dĕcent, ĭdĕa, mīlitary, ŏdour, sōlitary, varĭety, to mention only a few cases.

Another illustration of the pitfalls in the path of those who discuss the canons of English speech was provided not long ago by a leader-writer in *The Times* who called in question Mr. Fowler's recommendation (in *Modern English Usage*) that the *th* should not be pronounced in the plural *clothes*. Most people, no doubt, consider it vulgar to say *close*. Mr. Kenneth Sisam, however, took the opportunity of pointing out that the pronunciation without *th* is at least five centuries old. Moreover, *close* was the ordinary pronunciation of the educated Englishman of the eighteenth century: the chief poets rhymed the word with *foes*, *woes*, etc., and Dr. Johnson went out of his way in his Dictionary to say " pronounced *clo's*." The modern pronunciation is a reconstruction from the spelling.

If even the man of literary training is incompetent to settle many of the disputed points, who is to decide the matter? The ultimate ruling comes from the usage found amongst the majority of educated speakers. If we want to know how to pronounce *pejorative*, the question to ask is not, " How ought it to be pronounced according to its derivation? " but, " How do most educated people pronounce it? " It may seem that we are applying a vague and unscientific standard; but there is, in fact, no other standard.

It has been suggested that we should accept as final all the rulings given in the *Oxford English Dictionary*. This invaluable and monumental work is no doubt as near as we are likely to get to a final authority, but it must be remembered that the first volumes were published a generation ago and pronunciation of some words has changed since then. It is arguable that the *Oxford Dictionary* should be made to set the standard and thus be erected into a final authority, but it cannot be maintained that the Dictionary is at present an absolutely faithful record of present-day speech. To obtain such a record it would be necessary for a body of men to carry out a wide investigation into the speech of numbers of people in various grades of society throughout the English-speaking community.

We may observe, in passing, that the rulings on pronunciation given by the B.B.C. for the benefit of

Announcers are not intended to be infallible, nor do they represent an attempt to standardize the spoken language. The prime object of the B.B.C.'s Advisory Committee is to secure uniformity in official wireless speech. When they recommend that a particular word should be pronounced in a particular way, they do not say that other pronunciations are wrong. After consulting the best authorities they make their choice out of a number of variants. The task is often very difficult, and their choice would not always command general acceptance by competent judges.

What is "Good" Spoken English? The problem of finding a standard applies not only to individual words but to the spoken language as a whole. We say that a certain person's speech or "accent" is "good." What do we mean by "good," and who decides whether it is "good" or not? As we look into the matter we become aware that there are many varieties of spoken English. We at once think of the dialects to be found in different parts of the country; and then it will occur to us that even in one town there is no uniformity of speech. In London, for instance, the parson or the barrister speaks differently from the average small shop-keeper, and again, the small shop-keeper speaks differently from the coster; in other words, speech varies according to social class.

Standard Spoken English. In spite of the differences just noted we feel that there must be some form of speech that we could call "Standard English"—the English that we should teach a foreigner. If we are prepared to allow for individual peculiarities and to use the term in a wide sense, there is indeed something that we can describe as Standard English. There is a form of speech which is common to almost all educated people, whether they come from London, Exeter, York, or Worcester. It marks them as a class, and people who wish to enter that class find it necessary to imitate this mode of speech as nearly as possible. We all recognize Standard English when we hear it, but we should find it hard to define it with any precision. An authority on the subject has described it as "that form of carefully spoken English which will appear to the majority of educated people as entirely free from unusual features." And this definition is deliberately loose.

It must be emphasized that Standard English is essentially a class-dialect. From an historical point of view it has no more claim to be called "right" than has the dialect of Manchester or Somerset. It was itself originally the dialect of London and the Court. It has reached its supremacy over other forms of the language through the social prestige attaching to it. Hence, when we state that this, that, or the other is "right" in speech, all that we mean is that most people of a certain class say it thus.

Language is Always Changing. We must not be led by the term "Standard English" to suppose that there is one form of the language that has remained, and will remain fixed and immutable. Language is always in the process of change, and the effects of the process are observable even in a generation. A striking example is to be seen in the words like *cloth, cross, off, froth.* Two pronunciations exist, one with the vowel sound heard in *on* and one with the vowel sound in *broad.* Within the writer's memory the first of these was fashionable; now the second has come into vogue. Certain changes are also occurring in the diphthongal sounds, so that *are, ire, our,* are almost identical in the speech of many people.

Literary English. The written language is not, of course, the same as the spoken language. It is an artificial form of expression created by the great writers, and it is thus the product of a long tradition. Many forms (e.g. the Subjunctive Mood) are preserved in the literary language though they are almost or entirely disused in talk. How do we arrive at what is good literary English? Again the standard of correctness is settled by a majority vote: but this time the voters are the writers of recognized ability. On many points the writers of the past may be consulted, but on others those of the present age are alone entitled to a hearing; for in the literary as in the spoken language change is always in progress. Words alter their use and idioms vary: thus—to take one or two examples at random—Addison wrote "When we *were* arrived," where we should write "When we *had* arrived"; Macaulay often used *frugal* to mean *sparing in the use of money*, whereas to-day the word is generally restricted in its application to meals or diet; and the older writers used the phrase "the same *with*" instead of the modern "the same *as*." Again, the slang expressions of one generation may win a recognized place in the literary language of the next generation. A few years ago "*to turn down* a scheme" would have been regarded as slang; but it has such good authority nowadays that it would be pedantic to object to it.

Let us apply these considerations to a particular problem. Should we write *different from* or *different to*? It is first to be noted that *different to* is firmly established in the colloquial language. But may we admit it in writing? On theoretical grounds it is argued that *from* is the correct preposition, but the soundness of the argument has been questioned. Turning to the practice of the great writers of the past, we find that *different to* is fairly frequently used, though *different from* is normal. What of the present day writers? No doubt the use of *to* is becoming increasingly common, but the weight of authority is still on the side of *from*. Therefore, those, at least, who are conservatives in these matters will prefer *from*.

CORRELATIVE CONJUNCTIONS.

Correlative Conjunctions are connecting words used in pairs; e.g. *both . . . and*, *either . . . or*, *not only . . . but also*, *rather . . . than*. On the correct placing of these words see RULE OF PROXIMITY.

COUNCIL—COUNSEL.

Council is always a noun, and means *an assembly; a deliberative body*. *Counsel* as a noun means *advice* (e.g. to give good *counsel*). It is also used in the idiom *to keep one's own counsel*, and in the legal term *King's Counsel*. *Counsel* may also be a verb (to give advice).

COUP.

Pronounced: coo.

COURTESY.

Pronounced: kertesy.

CREDIBLE—CREDULOUS—CREDITABLE.

Credible means *worthy of belief*. It is generally applied to statements; e.g. He gave so many convincing details that his story was perfectly *credible*. It may also be applied to persons; e.g. Many *credible* witnesses have affirmed this. (Cp. the use of the adverb: I am *credibly* informed that . . .) *Credulous* is applied to persons, and means *too ready to believe*; e.g. There are still to be found some *credulous* people who believe in witches. *Creditable* is sometimes confused with *credible*. It really means *bringing credit or honour*; e.g. His achievement in finding the criminal was most *creditable*.

CRITERION.

This word is often used loosely by people who have only a vague idea of its signification. A criterion is a principle or standard by which we can judge something.

Americans are said to regard the amount of money a man makes as a *criterion* of his ability. A man's speech and manners are usually taken as a *criterion* of his social position.

The plural is *criteria.*

CULINARY.

Pronounced: kū'linary.

CULMINATE.

Followed by *in.* For several years he suffered a series of misfortunes which *culminated in* the death of his wife.

DASH.

The mark of punctuation called the Dash (—) is frequently over-worked by careless writers. It is made to do duty for almost any other stop. The dash has certain definite uses, and it should be reserved for these—

1. It is used before and after a parenthetical remark—

We are not at the moment proposing to pay more than 8 per cent, but later on—I cannot say when—we shall no doubt issue additional amounts of Debenture stock.

2. It marks a sudden change of thought—

I now come to the latest plan proposed—but perhaps I had better leave this until another occasion.

3. It is inserted before a repeated word in sentences like the following—

Before we can proceed with the scheme we have many preparations to make—preparations which I think will occupy several months, and will fully tax our resources.

4. It may be used with, or instead of a comma, in order to give special emphasis to a remark—

The Prime Minister gave a pledge at the last election that this evil would be remedied,—but we all know the value of election pledges.

DATIVE CASE.

(See CASE.)

DECADE.

Pronounced: dĕ'kad.

DECADENCE, DECADENT.

Pronounced: dĕ'kadence, dĕ'kadent.

The B.B.C. Announcers were at one time instructed to say: dekā'dence, dekā'dent, but they are now required to conform to the common accentuation.

DECOROUS—DECORUM.

Decorum has the accent on the second syllable.

According to the dictionaries *decorous* should also have the accent on the second syllable; but the pronunciation in which the first syllable is stressed is very common.

DEFECTIVE—DEFICIENT.

While both these words have the synonym "incomplete," *defective* tends to be definitely restricted to uses connected with *defect*, so that it means *faulty*. *Deficient*, however, is connected with *deficit*, and means *insufficient in quantity, etc.* Examples of the two words—

The aeroplane had to descend through a *defective* engine. His drawing is *defective*. The article is cheaper because it is slightly *defective*.

Through the bad weather the harvest is sadly

deficient. A home for the mentally *deficient.* He is by no means *deficient in* courage.

Sometimes either word is appropriate; e.g. As a statesman he was *defective* (*deficient*), for he lacked imagination.

DEFICIT.

This word should not be accented on the second syllable. The pronunciation should be either: dĕ'fĭsĭt or dē'fĭsĭt.

DEFINITE—DEFINITIVE.

These two adjectives are not synonymous: the one is not merely a longer form of the other, as some writers seem to think. *Definite* means *clear, precise, not vague. Definitive* (pronounced: defĭn'ĭtive) means *conclusive, unconditional, final.* A definite answer or treaty is one that is stated in precise terms; it is definitive if it finally settles the matter at issue. A definitive edition of a novelist's works is one which gives them in their best and final form, and which is not likely, therefore, to be superseded. If a firm makes a definitive offer, that offer must be accepted or rejected without haggling.

DEGREES OF COMPARISON.

Many adjectives have three forms: (1) the Positive (the simple form), e.g. *rich, beautiful*; (2) the Comparative, used when two persons or things are compared, e.g. *richer, more beautiful*; (3) the Superlative, used when more than two persons or things are compared, e.g. *richest, most beautiful.*

Many adverbs are similarly compared: *fast, faster, fastest; quickly, more quickly, most quickly.*

DEMONIACAL.

Pronounced: dēmonī'acal.

DEMUR.

Followed by *to*. He maintains that the profits have shown a continuous increase during the past five years; but I *demur to* the truth of this statement. He was inclined to *demur to* the demand that he should take the responsibility.

DEPRECATE—DEPRECIATE.

Deprecate means *plead against*; *express disapproval of*. He assumed a humble attitude as if to *deprecate* her anger. No matter what our situation is, hasty action is to be *deprecated*.

Depreciate means *diminish in value*; *lower the price of*; *disparage*. The shares are *depreciating* daily. He is so envious of others that he always *depreciates* the work of his rivals.

DEROGATE.

Followed by *from*. A few minor faults and inaccuracies can never *derogate from* the solid merits of this writer's work.

DEROGATORY.

Followed by *to*. The manager considered it *derogatory to* his position to accept the terms of the trade union leaders.

DESPICABLE.

Pronounced with the stress on the first syllable.

DESULTORY.

Pronounced: dĕss'ultory.

DETER.

Followed by *from* and either a noun or a verb-form ending in *-ing*. One of the aims of imprisonment is to *deter* men *from* crime. He said that he hoped he would never be *deterred from* doing his duty by threats.

DETERIORATE.

Notice that this word has five syllables. A common mistake in speaking and writing is to leave out the fourth syllable.

Deteriorate means *to grow worse*; e.g. Many savage tribes have *deteriorated* through contact with white civilization. The dictionaries give also the meaning *to make worse.* Although occasional examples of this transitive use are to be found in good authors, it is best avoided. In present-day English we do not normally say, "Damp will *deteriorate* these goods," but, "Damp will *cause* these goods *to deteriorate.*"

DEVASTATING.

The only meaning of *to devastate* is *to ravage, lay waste.* It has become fashionable to use the word *devastating* with little or no regard to its signification. The following are some examples—

> Finally he told his friend his views with devastating candour.
>
> The most recent figures show a devastating increase in unemployment.
>
> Mr. Shaw has written a play which is devastatingly dull at times.
>
> No one can fail to be impressed by Lady Simon's quiet, but devastating account of slavery in this year of grace.
>
> It would be a devastating world if all the good people took charge of it.

In one or two of these cases it might perhaps be argued that the word is given a legitimate metaphorical sense, but it is to be doubted whether in any of the examples the writers did more than thoughtlessly make use of a popular cliché.

DEVOLVE.

Followed by *on* (*upon*). The task of trying to arrange a compromise *devolved on* the managing director.

DIFFER—VARY.

Differ should be followed by *from* when a preposition is needed. Your opinion *differs from* mine. I *differ from* you in opinion. We are so unlike that we shall always *differ*. But this verb should not be followed by *according to*. It is wrong to say : One's view of life tends to *differ according to* one's state of health. Here *vary* should be substituted.

DIFFERENT.

The textbooks have always told us that we should write *different from*, although *different to* is very common colloquially. (The reason given is that one thing differs *from*, not *to*, another.) It is true that *different to* has been used frequently by standard authors, and no less an authority than Mr. H. W. Fowler has recently defended it. But humble writers who are not animated by reforming zeal may be counselled to keep to *different from*. They will thus escape the criticism of the many who have heard that this is the correct expression, and who are prepared to be supercilious towards poor creatures who know no better than to say *different to*.

Whatever defence there may be for using *to* with *different*, there can be no excuse for using *than*. The following exemplifies a common error—Several volumes have been published on this subject, but they were intended for *different* purposes *than* the present book. (Write : for *different* purposes *from* that of . . . ; or, for *other* purposes *than* that of . . .)

DIPHTHERIA—DIPHTHONG.

Pronounced: difthēr'ia; dif'thong.

The pronunciations: dipthēr'ia; dip'thong, are vulgarisms.

DISHABILLE.

Pronounced: dis'abēl, or disabēl'.

DISHEVELLED.

Pronounced: dish-ĕv'elled.

DISSENT.

Followed by *from*. I *dissent from* you on this matter.

DOCTRINAL.

Pronounced: doctrī'nal.

DOUBLE SENTENCE, MULTIPLE SENTENCE.

A Double Sentence contains two clauses of equal importance, i.e. clauses which will make sense taken separately. A Multiple Sentence contains more than two such clauses. (See CLAUSES.) Examples—

> I opened the door, and after some hesitation I entered the shop. (Double.)
>
> I opened the door, and after some hesitation I entered the shop, but there was no one inside. (Multiple.)

Sentences of this type used to be called "Compound."

Double and Multiple Sentences may contain subordinate clauses dependent on the main clauses

DUE TO.

One of the latest fashions in writing is to misuse *due to* for *owing to,* as in the following sentence: "The houses were almost uninhabitable, *due to* the bad materials employed." *Due* is really an adjective (The rent is *due* ; You should have your *due* proportion ; The accident was *due* to carelessness), and it should therefore qualify a noun, but it has no such grammatical relationship in this sentence. In place of *due to* we need the compound preposition *owing to* to govern *materials.* Other examples : The Post Office has for some time been financially successful, undoubtedly *due to* the extortionate charges inflicted on telephone subscribers. (The Post Office is not due ; and there is no other word to which *due* can refer. Write : *owing to.*) *Due to* the Central Electricity Board's activities, and to the developments undertaken by the more progressive municipalities and power companies to meet the growing demand, the most highly developed plant is now being called for. (*Owing to.*)

EACH.

Each, whether used as an adjective or a pronoun, refers to persons or things taken singly. Any other words that relate to it must therefore be singular. The following are incorrect : Each person who considers the matter must make up *their* own mind. (Write : his own mind.) Each of them *have* brought *their* own contribution to the fund. (Write : has brought his own.)

EACH OTHER—ONE ANOTHER.

It is frequently said that *each other* should be used in reference to two, and *one another* in reference to more than two. Many writers, however, do not observe this distinction, and it seems hardly worth while to insist on it.

ECONOMICS.

The first syllable should be pronounced : ē.

EFFECT.

(See Affect—Effect.)

EFFECTIVE—EFFECTUAL—EFFICACIOUS—EFFICIENT.

All these words mean *producing an effect*, but they are not completely synonymous although some of them have certain uses in common. *Efficacious* is distinguished from the rest nowadays by being applied almost exclusively to medicines and remedies. The following notes on the remaining three may serve to bring out their chief divergencies in meaning—

1. *Effective* often means *having a striking effect*: He made an *effective* speech. He is an *effective* speaker. We talk of the *effective* membership (actual membership) of a trade union; and we say that an Act of Parliament becomes *effective* on a certain date.

2. To take *effectual* steps is to take steps which answer the purpose. A remedy may be *effectual* (or *efficacious*).

3. *Efficient* is often applied to persons, and means *capable, competent* (An *efficient* workman). It is similarly used with reference to things which successfully achieve the desired purpose: The business succeeded because of the *efficient* management, or its *efficient* methods.

EITHER.

Either should be used in reference to two only: Has *either* of the two men arrived? But: Has *any one* of the four arrived?

Either is singular and should not be followed by a plural verb. Incorrect: Do you think that either of the books *are* useful? (*is*).

EITHER . . . OR.

(See Rules of Agreement. Errors in Agreement, Rule of Proximity.)

ELIXIR.

Pronounced: ĕlĭx'er

EMPHASIS.

Writers of business letters, reports, and memoranda, and all who wish to cultivate a forceful style should study the various devices that may be employed to give added point to sentences. It is obvious that an idea may generally be stated—and quite correctly and clearly stated—in more than one way. But if just the necessary emphasis is to be given to a particular aspect of the idea only one form of statement is the right one.

1. The most important principle to be grasped concerns the *arrangement of words.* There is a certain natural order of words to which any sentence will conform unless there is a special reason to the contrary. Thus, we should normally say "The fire spread with incredible rapidity through room after room." But if we wished to give a different emphasis, we might say either, "With incredible rapidity the fire spread through room after room," or "Through room after room the fire spread with incredible rapidity." By taking a word or group of words out of its normal place we call the reader's attention to it, and so give it special emphasis. Some other examples may be given—

Great as was his reputation, it did not outlive this reverse.

Feeble and ineffectual were his efforts to improve the conditions.

The only man who proved to be at all useful in this emergency was *Jones.*

To her grandchildren she could be, when occasion demanded it, *severe.*

2. An idea may often be given striking expression by embodying it in a sentence built up according to a

clearly marked pattern. The sentence may contain a series of parallel phrases or clauses formed alike ; e.g.—

> The effect of monopoly generally is to make articles scarce, to make them dear, and to make them bad.
>
> Just as the absurd acts which prohibited the sale of game were virtually repealed by the poacher, just as many absurd revenue acts have been virtually repealed by the smuggler, so will this law be virtually repealed by piratical booksellers.

Or the sentence may exhibit a balanced structure—

> He is but a short-sighted friend of the common people who is eager to bestow on them a franchise which would make them all-powerful, and yet would withhold from them that instruction without which their power must be a curse to themselves and to the State.

(An outline of this sentence makes clear the balance of the parts : He is short-sighted . . . *who* is eager to *bestow* something *which* . . ., and (*who*) yet would *withhold* something *without which* . . .)

When parts of a sentence are balanced in such a way as to produce a striking contrast of words and ideas we obtain what is known as *antithesis.* This is a valuable means of securing emphasis ; e.g.—

> There may be a change of *men* ; but there will be no change of *measures.*
>
> You will find that, in attempting to impose unreasonable restraints on reprinting the works of the *dead*, you have, to a great extent, annulled those restraints which now prevent men from pillaging and defrauding the *living.*

3. The judicious *use of correlative conjunctions* (see CORRELATIVE CONJUNCTIONS) is another helpful device. Thus, the sentence " He was an actor and a dramatist "

can be made more effective by altering it to: "*Not only* was he an actor, *but also* a dramatist." Other examples—

I long ago espoused the cause of religious liberty, *not* because the cause was popular, *but* because it was just.

My purpose is *rather* to clear away difficulties *than* to initiate a new scheme.

4. In the hands of a skilful writer *repetition* can be made an excellent means of securing emphasis. Of course, the novice admits the same word or phrase two or three times in a sentence through sheer inadvertence; and the result is disastrous. But deliberate repetition for emphasis is a legitimate weapon of the writer no less than of the orator. The following passage (by Macaulay) illustrates its use—

English law transplanted to that country has all the *vices from which we suffer* here; it has them in a far higher degree; and it has other *vices*, compared with which the worst *vices from which we suffer* are trifles. *Dilatory* here, *it is far more dilatory* in a land where the help of an interpreter is needed *by every* judge and *by every* advocate. *Costly* here, *it is far more costly* in a land where the legal practitioners must be imported from an immense distance.

ENAMOURED.

This word should be followed by *of* and not *with*.

In his youth he was *enamoured of* romantic poetry.

ENGLAND, ENGLISH.

Certain people who have not reflected sufficiently on the discrepancies between the spelling and the pronunciation of our language insist on saying: ĕngland, ĕnglish. The standard pronunciation of these words is: ĭngland, ĭnglish.

ENNUI.

This word retains a half-French pronunciation: on′wē.

ENVIRONS.

Pronunciation: envīr′ons, or en′vĭrons.
The B.B.C. Announcers adopt the former.

EPHEMERAL.

Pronounced: ephĕm′eral.

ENVELOPE.

This word has been so long established in our language that the perpetuation of a pseudo-French pronunciation (ŏn′velōp) is pointless. The pronunciation ĕn′velōp has dictionary authority, and should be generally adopted.

EQUALLY AS WELL AS.

This redundant phrase is frequently met with in statements like—

I can do the work *equally as well as* he can.

We may correctly say either (*a*) I can do the work *equally* well, or (*b*) I can do the work *as well as* he can. The phrase *equally as well as* states the same idea twice.

EQUITABLE.

Pronounced with the stress on the first syllable.

ERRORS IN AGREEMENT.

See RULES OF AGREEMENT for the rules which apply to the errors noted below. In the sections which follow, a number of typical examples of mistakes are given, together with explanations of the corrections necessary.

1. **Agreement of Subject and Verb.**

(*a*) A chain of huge lakes extending for hundreds

of miles *form* the boundary between Canada and the United States.

Write : *forms.* The subject is *chain,* and the verb has been attracted to the wrong number because of the intervening plural words *lakes* and *miles.*

Sir Mark would also like to see added to the balance sheet a series of notes explaining the basis on which the value of certain assets *have* been ascertained.

Write : *has.* The subject is *value.*

(*b*) The general with the whole of his staff *were* present at the function (*was*).

He says that he as well as his secretary *are* thinking of resigning (*is*).

When a singular subject (*general, he*) is followed by a phrase beginning with *with* or *as well as,* the verb must be singular.

(*c*) Beyond the pasture lands of the plain, *rise* to the west a wall of mountains reaching 6,000 feet in height (*rises*).

There *was* in that period a prolonged agitation for reform and even an attempted revolution (*were*).

In these cases the fault has arisen because the subject follows the verb, and has not been recognized as such. In the first example, *wall* (not *mountains*) is the subject, and is singular. The second sentence has a double subject, viz., *agitation* and *revolution.* A plural verb is therefore required.

(*d*) Neither he nor his secretary *were* in the office (*was*).

Two singular subjects connected by *either . . . or, neither . . . nor* require a singular verb.

(*e*) I do not think that either he or you *is* fitted for the post (*are*).

He requires *is*, but *you* requires *are*. When two subjects of different person are connected by *either . . . or*, *neither . . . nor*, the verb should agree with the nearer.

(*f*) COLLECTIVE NOUNS. A collective noun is the name of a group of persons or things. Grammatically, a word like *committee* is singular (for we can have the plural *committees*); but we frequently find that it is followed by a plural verb and plural pronouns and adjectives referring to it.

> The committee *were* divided on the matter, and *they were* long in coming to *their* decision.

This use is to be justified on the ground that we are here regarding the committee, not as a single body, but as a number of separate individuals having different views. While we should use the singular in—

> The whole staff *is* offended by the chief's action,

we should use the plural in—

> All the staff *have* signed a letter of protest.

Care must be taken, however, not to treat a collective noun as singular in one part of the sentence and as plural in another.

The following are examples of a fairly common error—

> The Cambridge crew *has* made remarkable progress, and it is possible to say that *they are* at this stage much better than any Oxford crew of recent years.

(Change either *has* to *have*, or *they are* to *it is*.)

> Now that the Central Electricity Board *is* at work, the demand for heavy plant is bound to improve, but time must be allowed for this body to launch *their* schemes and bring them into being.

(*g*) *Each, Every, Everybody, Anybody, Either, Neither, No-one, Nobody, None,* are frequently followed by plural words when singulars are required. See the articles on each of these words.

2. **Adjective and Noun.** A very common error is seen in the expressions " these kind of things," " those sort of people." *These* and *those* are plural, yet they refer to the singular nouns *kind, sort.* We should say " things of this kind," " people of that sort."

3. **Relative Pronoun and Antecedent.** Sometimes the verb in a relative clause is put into the wrong number because the true antecedent of the relative pronoun is not recognized.

> This is one of the most exciting plays that *has* been produced this season (*have*).

The antecedent of *that* is *plays,* not *one. That* is therefore plural and its verb should be plural.

ERRORS IN CASE.

See CASE for the rules which apply. English nouns do not show any difference of form between the nominative and the accusative, but the pronouns do, and it is in their use that mistakes are often made.

> (1) *He* who makes most progress, the firm will certainly promote (*him*).
>
> *Who* did you meet at the concert ? (*whom*).

He and *who* are respectively the objects of *will promote* and *meet,* and they must be in the accusative case. The forms *he* and *who* are used only for the nominative case.

> (2) Between you and *I,* there is going to be trouble (*me*).
>
> *Who* did you give the money to? (*whom*).

In both cases the pronouns are governed by prepositions (*between, to*), and should be in the accusative.

One or two words which are really conjunctions are sometimes treated as though they were prepositions, and are wrongly followed by an accusative. (See As and THAN. See also BUT.)

(3) I must introduce you to the new manager *whom* we all think is going to be a great success (*who*).

The relative pronoun *whom* is the subject of *is going*, and should therefore be in the nominative. It has been erroneously regarded as the object of *think*. The words *we all think* are really in parenthesis.

(4) If you wish to know the culprit, it is *me* (*I*).
If I were *him*, I should go (*he*).

Me and *him* are predicative pronouns, not objects. They should therefore be in the nominative, and not the accusative, case. (See PREDICATIVE WORDS.)

EVENTUALITY—EVENTUATE.

These words are beloved of journalists—

In view of the likelihood of a general strike, the Government must be ready for any *eventuality*.

A scheme for new roads costing several hundred thousand pounds was proposed, but it did not *eventuate*.

There seems small need to employ these pretentious words. The ordinary English for *eventuality* is *event*, *emergency*, etc.; and for *eventuate* a simpler equivalent can always be found to suit the context.

EVERY.

When *every* is used before a noun, it must not be followed by plurals (*they*, *their*, etc.). An example of the error—

The Daily Telegraph has, I believe, contrived that the play should continue, for, although *every* paper gave it an excellent review, *they* did not make one realize how wonderful and how important it is.

(*Every paper* implies that single papers are taken separately, and we ought to have a singular pronoun in place of *they*. But the natural correction here would be to say *all the papers*, and retain *they*.)

EVERYBODY—EVERYONE.

These pronouns are grammatically singular; hence pronouns and possessives that refer to them should be singular. Frequently in colloquial language, however, and sometimes even in serious writing, they are treated as plural. Examples of this use may be considered in two categories—

(1) *Everybody* (*everyone*) must make up *their* own mind in the matter.

Here there is no justification for the plural *their*. We are definitely taking people separately. *His* (serving as both masculine and feminine) should be used.

(2) When the fire alarm was given, *everyone* lost *their* heads.

Here we are thinking rather of all the people at once than of each person singly. Thus the plural *idea* is so strong that it would seem unnatural to substitute *his* for *their*. In such a case (especially in conversation), there can be no reasonable objection to the plural; but anyone who is fastidious might, in writing, replace *everyone* by *all the people*.

Colloquially, in questions containing a pronoun referring to *everybody* (*everyone*), the plural is always used (even following a singular verb); e.g. Everybody has gone, haven't *they*?

EVOLUTION.

The first syllable may be pronounced either ē or ĕ. The B.B.C. adopts ē.

EXCEPT—EXCEPTING.

Except is a preposition ; *excepting* is also occasionally a preposition. But the two are not interchangeable. *Excepting* should be used only after a negative.

All the staff, *not excepting* the heads of departments, have agreed to a reduction of salaries (*or*—the heads of departments *not excepted*).

But—

All the staff *except* the heads of departments have agreed . . . (*excepting* would be incorrect).

Except was formerly used as a conjunction (*Except* the Lord build the house, their labour is but lost that build it). In modern English *unless* must be used instead.

EXIGENCY—EXIGENT.

Pronounced : ex'ĭjency, ex'ĭjent.

EXOTIC.

This word is not infrequently used in a way which shows that its signification is not properly understood. It means "introduced from abroad," and is applied to plants, fashions, words, etc.

EXQUISITE.

The stress is on the first syllable.

EXTEMPORE.

Pronounced with four syllables : extemp'or-ē.

FACILITATE.

The misuse of this word is to be guarded against. *Facilitate* should not have the name of a person as subject. (*He* was facilitated in his task by . . .) Examples of correct use—

His task of gathering the required information was

greatly *facilitated* by the help received from numerous correspondents.

All buildings in the line of fire were removed to *facilitate* the defence of the city.

FACTOR.

Factor has a great vogue nowadays; and it is sadly maltreated in consequence. People use it either as a mere variant of *fact*, or as a beast of burden made to carry all sorts of meanings vaguely connected with the true one. A *factor* is a *circumstance, fact, or influence contributing to a result.* It is essential that the notion of "contributing to a result" should be present if the word *factor* is to be properly used. Examples of correct use—

The increase of wages in the industry is the chief *factor* in the rise in prices.

The vigorous sympathy of England was one of the decisive *factors* in the final achievement of Italian unity.

EXAMPLES OF WRONG OR SLIPSHOD USES.

Venezuelan crude oil has become an important *factor* in the operation of Mexican refineries (*important source of supply for*).

Probably the chief *factor* in the autumn situation will be the weight of the new production which will have materialized by that time (*element, fact*).

One of the main *factors* involved when the Public Health (Destruction of Vermin) Bill comes before the House of Lords on Tuesday is that vague and most cherished article of the Englishman's faith—liberty (*facts, considerations*).

So superbly has Compston played throughout the match, that Hagen regards him as a dangerous *factor* not only for the British, but the American, championship (*competitor*).

FASCISM, FASCIST.

In the corresponding Italian words the *sc* is pronounced like *sh.* Some English speakers retain this sound. It seems better, however, to anglicize the words by giving the *sc* the sound of *s*.

FAUTEUIL.

How is this awkward French word to be pronounced? The French pronunciation is inappropriate on most occasions. The B.B.C. has anglicized the word to: fō′til, and this seems the best way out of the difficulty. It is a mystery why we ever troubled to borrow the word, for the English terms "armchair," "stall" are quite adequate.

FETISH.

Pronunciation: fē′tish or fĕ′tish. The B.B.C. adopts the former.

FEWER.

Fewer should not be used to refer to the word *number*. It is wrong to say—

> The *number* of orders received last year was *fewer* than might have been expected.

Substitute *smaller*.

FLACCID.

Pronounced: flak′sid.

FLAGRANT.

Pronounced: flā′grant.

FOREHEAD.

Some people try to say this word according to the spelling. The true pronunciation is: fŏr′ĕd.

FOREIGN WORDS AND PHRASES: A LIST WITH MEANINGS.

The following list gives the meanings of the commonest foreign terms in general or technical use. (F. = French, L. = Latin, G. = Greek.)

ab initio (L.), from the beginning
ab ovo (L.), from the egg (beginning)
à compte (F.), on account, in part payment
ad finem (L.), to the end
ad infinitum (L.), to infinity
ad libitum (L.), at pleasure
ad nauseam (L.), to the point of disgust
ad valorem (L.), according to value
a fortiori (L.), with stronger reason
alter ego (L.), another self
amour-propre (F.), self-love; vanity
anglice (L.), in English.
a posteriori (L.), (argument) from effect to cause
a priori (L.), (argument) from cause to effect
argent comptant (F.), ready money
arrière pensée (F.), mental reservation; ulterior motive
au fait (F.), well acquainted with
bête noire (F.), bugbear; one's abomination
bêtise (F.), stupid remark or action
bona fide (L.), in good faith; genuine(ly).
bonhomie (F.), good-natured simplicity
bon vivant (F.), gourmand
carte blanche (F.), full discretionary power
casus belli (L.), act justifying war
ceteris paribus (L.), other things being equal
chef d'œuvre (F.), masterpiece
ci-devant (F.), former(ly)
comme il faut (F.), well-bred
compte rendu (F.), account rendered
coup d'état (F.), violent or illegal change in government
coup de grace (F.), finishing stroke
coup de main (F.), sudden violent attack
cui bono? (L.), for whose benefit is it?
cul de sac (F.), blind alley
cum grano salis (L.), with a grain of salt; i.e. with some allowance
de facto (L.), in fact; really
dégagé (F.), easy, unrestrained
de jure (L.), by (legal) right
de novo (L.), anew
de trop (F.), not wanted; in the way
dies non (L.), day on which no legal business is done
double entendre (pseudo-F.), phrase capable of two meanings
entre nous (F.), between ourselves
esprit de corps (F.), regard for the interest or honour of a body to which one belongs
ex officio (L.), by virtue of one's office
ex parte (L.), on (in the interest of) one side only
fait accompli (F.), thing already done
faux pas (F.), false step; mistake

flagrante delicto (L.), in the very act
hic jacet (L.), here lies
hinc illae lacrimae (L.), hence proceed these tears
hoi polloi (G.), the many; the rabble
in esse (L.), in being
in extenso (L.), at full length
in extremis (L.), at the point of death
in forma pauperis (L.), as a poor man
in loco parentis (L.), in the place of a parent
in medias res (L.), into the midst of things
in posse (L.), potentially
in propria persona (L.), in person
in re (L.), in the matter of
in situ (L.), in its original position
in statu quo (L.), in the same place (as formerly)
inter alia (L.), among other things
in toto (L.), completely
ipse dixit (L.), dogmatic statement
ipso facto (L.), by that very fact
jeu d'esprit (F.), witticism
laissez faire (F.), absence of restraint
lapsus linguae (L.), slip of the tongue
Lares et Penates (L.), the home
le beau monde (F.), the fashionable world
lettre de change (F.), bill of exchange
lettre de créance (F.), letter of credit
locum tenens (L.), a deputy
locus standi (L.), recognized position; right to appear in court, etc.
magnum opus (L.), great work
mal-à-propos (F.), ill-timed
mauvaise honte (F.), false modesty
mauvais sujet (F.), a worthless fellow
mise-en-scène (F.), scenery and properties of an acted play
modus operandi (L.), way a person goes to work; way a thing operates
modus vivendi (L.), arrangement between disputants pending the result of a controversy
ne plus ultra (L.), farthest point attainable; culmination
noblesse oblige (F.), rank imposes obligations
nom de plume (pseudo-F.), pen-name
non sequitur (L.), it does not follow
nous verrons (F.), we shall see
obiit (L.), he (she) died
on dit (F.), they say; piece of hearsay
pace (L.), by leave of
pari passu (L.), with equal pace; together
passim (L.), in every part
per (L.), by; by means of
per capita (L.), by the head
per diem, per mensem (L.), (so much) by day, by month
per saltum (L.), by a leap or jump
per se (L.), by or in itself; intrinsically
pis aller (F.), last resource
poste restante (F.), to be left till called for
pot pourri (F.), medley or mixture
prima facie (L.), (based) on first consideration
pro forma (L.), as a matter of form
pro rata (L.), at the same rate; proportionally

pro tempore (L.), for the time being
quid pro quo (L.), one thing for another
raison d'être (F.), reason for a thing's existence
rara avis (L.), rare bird ; prodigy
re (L.), in the matter of
réchauffé (F.), warmed-up dish ; rehash
recherché (F.), rare, exquisite
reductio ad absurdum (L.), reducing a position to an absurdity
rentes (F.), stocks
sang-froid (F.), composure ; coolness
sans frais (F.), without expense
savant (F.), learned man
savoir-faire (F.), tact
savoir-vivre (F.), good-breeding
sine die (L.), without naming a day
sine qua non (L.), an indispensable condition
soi-disant (F.), self-styled ; pretended
stet (L.), let what was deleted stand (in proof-correcting)
sub judice (L.), under judicial consideration
sub rosa (L.), privately
sui generis (L.), not belonging to a class ; unique
tant mieux (F.), so much the better
tant pis (F.), so much the worse
tempus fugit (L.), time flies
tête-à-tête (F.), confidential ; private conversation
tour de force (F.), feat of strength or skill
tout ensemble (F.), thing viewed as a whole ; general effect
ultra vires (L.), beyond legal powers
vade mecum (L.), something (e.g. a handbook) constantly carried about
verbum sat sapienti (abbreviation : *verb. sap.*) (L.), a word is enough to the wise
via media (L.), a middle course
viva voce (L.), oral(ly)
vox populi, vox dei (L.), the voice of the people is the voice of God

FOREIGN WORDS AND PHRASES : UNNECESSARY USE.

A large number of foreign words and phrases (chiefly French) are in more or less common use among English people. Writers would be well advised, however, never to use a foreign expression unless there is a special reason for doing so. Of course, French terms such as *aide-de-camp, chauffeur, chassis, garage, ballet, bouquet, communiqué, hors d'œuvre* are ordinary English for the things named, and no one would suggest that we should abandon them. Again, it is sometimes convenient to employ words like *blasé, naïf* (generally spelt *naïve*), *bizarre, savoir-faire, habitué* because there is no English equivalent, and they obviate the use of a roundabout phrase. But there are other expressions, e.g. *abattoir* (slaughter-house), *bêtise* (stupid remark or action), *bon mot* (witticism), *entre nous* (between ourselves), for which we have perfectly good English equivalents. People who use such foreign terms in writing generally do so either to satisfy a desire for novelty or to exhibit to others their superior learning.

FORMIDABLE.

The accent is on the first syllable.

FRACAS.

This word is pronounced without the *s*, as in French (fră'cah).

FREQUENT.

The stress is on the first syllable when this word is an adjective (He makes frequent visits here); it is on the second syllable in the case of the verb (Only wealthy people can frequent such places).

FRONTIER.

Pronounced: frunt'ier, or frŏnt'ier. The B.B.C. prefers the former.

FULL STOP.

The full stop (.) is used—

1. At the end of all sentences except questions and exclamations.

2. To mark abbreviations, e.g.—

A. Browning, Esq., M.A.; i.e.; T. G. Smith & Co. With regard to abbreviations which include the first and the last letters of the word, the practice varies. Some people write *Mr. Jones, Messrs. Jones & Co., Ltd., Dr. Jones;* while others omit the full stop and write

Mr Jones; Messrs Jones & Co., Ltd; Dr Jones. The second method seems preferable, for it makes a useful distinction between abbreviations like *Dr* which contain the last letter of the word, and those like *Capt.* which do not contain the final letter. In print, however, it is customary to mark all abbreviations with a full stop.

(See PUNCTUATION: GENERAL HINTS.)

GALA.

Pronounced: gā'la, or gah'la.

GARAGE.

Among the classes who speak French this word is generally pronounced: gar'ahge (the second *g* like *s* in measure). This is the pronunciation adopted by the B.B.C. Many people who do not speak French make the word rhyme with *carriage.* This pronunciation now has dictionary authority, and may in time oust the other.

GENITIVE (POSSESSIVE) CASE.

(See CASE.)

GENITIVE PROBLEMS.

The rules for the use of the apostrophe in marking the genitive case are given under APOSTROPHE. Special points of difficulty arise in connection with proper nouns ending in *s*. Should we write "H. G. Wells's novels" or "H. G. Wells' novels"? Both forms are met with in print, but the form "H. G. Wells's" is tending to become normal. In using the *'s* in such cases, we are not only adhering to the ordinary rule, but we are representing the pronunciation. We say the genitive case of the name with two syllables; we should therefore write the extra syllable. Pronunciation is, in fact, the best guide in the matter. Nobody who tries to record what he says will write "St. James' Square," "The Prince of Wales' tour," "Collins' Odes"; he will give the correct forms—"St. James's Square," "The Prince of Wales's tour," "Collins's Odes."

Further likelihood of confusion occurs when we come to plurals of proper nouns ending in *s*. *Jones* has the plural *Joneses* (We saw the Joneses yesterday). The genitive singular is *Jones's* (Is that Jones's hat?); the genitive plural is *Joneses'* (Is that the Joneses' house?).

It is not easy to bring the test of pronunciation to bear in the case of foreign names ending in *s*. There is a strong temptation to keep to the older practice of writing—"Aristophanes' comedies," "Theocritus' idylls," "Moses' law," since most people jib at pronouncing a genitive ending to such words. But even here the modern tendency (except in verse) is to use the *'s*.

GERUND.

The part of a verb which ends in *-ing* and is used as a noun is called a *gerund*. Examples—(1) *Seeing* is *believing*; (2) I like *driving* a car; (3) On *returning* home I found the letter. In (1) *seeing* is used as a noun, subject of *is*, and *believing* acts as a predicative noun. In (2) *driving* is used as a noun, object of *like*. In (3) *returning* is used as a noun, governed by the preposition *on* (We might say: On my *return*).

Another form of the gerund is made up with the auxiliary verb *to have*; e.g. having returned, having driven, etc. (After *having returned* home, I found the letter.)

(See GERUND MISUSED and CONFUSION OF PARTICIPLE AND GERUND.)

GERUND MISUSED.

(*a*) On *entering* the shop, the till was found to have been broken open.

(*b*) After *passing* the castle-gates, the next building of interest to the visitor is the old posting-inn.

These two sentences exemplify a common mistake. Both contain gerunds governed by prepositions (*on*, *after*). (See GERUND.) In (*a*), who entered the shop ? Obviously some persons. But the subject of the sentence is *till*. Similarly, in (*b*), who passes the castle-gates ? The visitor. But the subject of the sentence is *building*. The implied subject of the gerund must not differ from the subject of the complete sentence.

Sentence (*a*) can be corrected thus—On *their* entering . . . , or, When they entered . . .

In (*b*) the gerund should be eliminated—

When the visitor has passed the castle-gates, the next building of interest is the old posting-inn.

In the following example a ludicrous result is produced by the error just explained—

If we had accepted even the engines from the Continent, instead of having a British make of semi-Diesel put in, we could, on those alone, have saved over £1,000 ; but in addition to *being* patriotic, the British article is, I believe, worth while.

(Apparently the article is patriotic.)

GESTICULATE.

Pronounced : jĕstĭc'ulate.

GESTURE.

Pronounced : jĕst'ure.

GET.

In talk, everybody is constantly using the verb *get*—

often as a substitute for another verb. Here are some examples—

Have you got a pen ?
I have got to go at once.
I shall be glad when we get there.
They have recently got married.
The boat sank and he got drowned.
Will he get promoted ?

Some of these expressions are good colloquial English ; some are vulgar. All should be changed in literary English, thus—

Have you a pen ?
I have to go (or, I must go) at once.
I shall be glad when we arrive.
They have recently (been) married.
The boat sank and he was drowned.
Will he be promoted ?

GIBBERISH.

The initial consonant is pronounced hard (as in *gate*).

GIBBET.

Pronounced : jibb'et.

HACKNEYED PHRASES.

Many expressions that were once strikingly novel have appeared in print so very often that they have become merely tiresome. When we are told that something is *conspicuous by its absence*, that something else gives us *food for thought*, that a certain innovation has *come to stay*, that we are *at the parting of the ways*, or that So-and-so dined *not wisely but too well*, we no longer respond as the writer intended we should. The edge of novelty has worn off. Nothing more clearly marks the feeble writer than a fondness for such hackneyed phrases.

He who after writing *slowly* cannot refrain from adding *but surely*, or to *last* must append *but not least*, is either unpractised in the use of the pen, or insensible to the monotony of repetition.

The great purveyor of these stereotyped phrases is the journalist. He, in fact, creates fashions in them. Thus it is to his example that we owe it that nobody nowadays seems to be able to say that a business or a movement has made great progress: we must all use the stale metaphor—"it has made great strides." This expression apparently comes to mind with such mechanical patness that a newspaper can actually give us such a sentence as—"Empire raisins, stimulated by preferential tariffs, *have made enormous strides* during the past few years."

The writer of a recent newspaper article on "The Next 'Best Seller'" managed to get a surprising number of clichés into about thirty lines. He told us that the composition of the next "best seller" *defied analysis*, that there would be in it some theme that *strikes a responsive chord in the hearts* of thousands of readers. He referred to Mr. Hutchinson's "If Winter Comes" as having a success *not likely to be eclipsed* in our generation; this book, he said, came at *the psychological moment*, and it *captured the imagination* of an enormous public.

The journalist no doubt has his excuse for writing this sort of stuff. In the stress of hasty composition he is glad to make use of any ready-made phrase that is to hand. But the writer who aims at excellence in his craft will eschew such makeshifts.

HANGED—HUNG.

When the reference is to hanging a person, we use the form *hanged*—

They *hanged* the prisoner; the prisoner was *hanged*.

In other cases the form is *hung*—

I *hung* the picture on the wall.

HARDLY . . . THAN.

(See CONFUSION OF EXPRESSION.)

HECTIC.

This word is properly applied to the fever or the flush of the cheeks associated with consumption and similar diseases. It has recently become a fashionable colloquial adjective meaning *exciting, wild, extremely hurried*— "We were moving last week, and we had a *hectic* time for a few days." This misuse of the word often finds its way into print, e.g.—

His *hectic* piece of dramatic declamation about the alleged perils of ethyl had little effect on the audience.

HEINOUS.

Pronounced: hā'nous.

HOSPITABLE.

The first syllable should be stressed.

HOTEL.

Pronounced with or without the *h*. The B.B.C. Announcers sound the *h*.

HUMOUR.

Some old-fashioned speakers drop the *h*; the present-day custom is to sound it.

IDEA.

In philosophical and general literary use, *idea* has several shades of meaning, for the explanation of which a good dictionary should be consulted. In colloquial language the word is very loosely used—

The *idea* of such a thing!

Do you think it is a good *idea* (plan)?

What is the *idea* (principle of working) of this machine?

My *idea* (plan, object) is to convert the premises into three flats.

In writing, the slipshod substitution of *idea* for *plan, scheme, purpose,* etc., should be avoided.

IDIOM.

An idiom is a mode of expression peculiar to a language. It is natural for an Englishman to say, for example—

He will *come of age* next week; they *came to blows* over the matter; he *set his face against* the proposal; this *goes against the grain.*

But these phrases would be meaningless to a foreigner if they were literally translated into his language. Idiomatic expressions do not always square with the accepted rules of grammar; but they are not to be rejected on that account. Language is a living thing, and is not always amenable to logical restrictions. Thus, when we say, "This play *acts* well," we are using the verb *acts* in a way which it is difficult to account for grammatically (the expression means—The play goes well when it *is acted*); but we are using a perfectly good idiom. On the other hand, a sentence may be grammatical and yet unidiomatic. "The music sounds *harshly*" is open to no objection on the score of grammar; yet the recognized idiom is, "The music sounds *harsh.*"

The idiomatic use of prepositions is a matter that causes trouble. Certain words are regularly followed by particular prepositions: e.g. I agree *to* a proposal; I agree *with* a person; I concur *in* his judgment; I acquiesce *in* his decision; he is immune *from* infection. The use of wrong prepositions in cases like this is a bad error. (Words with which mistakes are most frequently made are dealt with in separate articles.)

It is important to realize that an idiom may not be varied at the whim of an individual writer. The maltreatment of idiom is a common fault in writing. It arises either from the desire for novelty in expression or from the confusion of two similar phrases. Examples:

He nearly died *with* laughter. (The proper idiom is *died of*.)

The Buddhists, with a view to *get* the help of the Catholics, and to *implicate* them in the rebellion, maliciously spread false rumours. (With a view to *getting*; or, in order to *get*.)

After three hours' search they gave him up *as* lost (*for* lost; but we may give up a *task as hopeless*).

As regards production of business, we have another record to register, and we can claim still another direction in which we have *set the lead to* a new development likely to be of service to the insuring public (*given* a lead in; or, *set* the pace in).

Your company is keeping *abreast with* the latest improvements in plant and machinery (keeping abreast *of*; or, keeping pace *with*).

We recently had the pleasure *to send* you a sample of our well known speciality (*of sending*).

Are these considerations to give way *for* the odd fear we have of shocking some people? (give way *to*. We *make* way *for*).

IDYLL.

The pronunciation is either ī'dil, or ĭ'dil. The B.B.C. Announcers adopt the former.

IF AND WHEN.

If and when is a meaningless tag much favoured by writers who think that their utterances can be made more impressive by a spurious legal precision in phraseology. Why is not either *if* or *when* alone sufficient in the following examples ?—

If and when production overtakes consumption, the industry will have another difficult period to face.

With reference to the opening lines of your recent leader, I am afraid that *if and when* the Deposited Book passes through its troubled journey, there will be many other surprises disclosed.

ILLEGIBLE—INELIGIBLE.

Illegible means *unreadable.*

His writing is so bad as to be almost *illegible.*

Ineligible means *not fit to be chosen ; not suitable.*

He is *ineligible* for the post because he is above the age-limit.

ILLUSTRATIVE.

The second syllable is stressed.

IMMUNE.

This word is followed by *from, against,* or *to.*

Inoculation makes people *immune from* (*against, to*) certain diseases.

IMPERVIOUS.

Followed by *to.*

The rock is *impervious to* water.

He is *impervious to* criticism.

IMPIOUS.

Pronounced: im'pious.

IMPLY—INFER.

These words are often confused. *Infer* means *deduce, conclude.*

In a particular statement a man may *imply* more than he actually says. If I see his drift I *infer* what he leaves unexpressed.

In the following cases, *imply* is the right word—

His letter of yesterday seems to *infer* that he will not be in London during the coming week.

Dear Sir,—A headline in your issue of even date proclaims "£500,000 Contract for the Clyde," *inferring,* no doubt, some fresh work for Scotland.

INCHOATE.

This is pronounced: in'kŏate, and means *just begun; undeveloped.*

INCIDENT.

Followed by *to.*

Measles is a disease *incident to* childhood.

INCREDIBLE—INCREDULOUS.

Incredible means *not worthy of belief.*

His story was so full of unlikely details that it was *incredible.*

Incredulous means *not readily believing* (applied to persons).

In spite of my efforts to convince him, he remained *incredulous.*

For some time the public was *incredulous of* the stories of wealth obtained from the new goldfields.

INCULCATE.

Mistakes are often made in the preposition following this word. We inculcate a principle or an idea *upon* or *in* someone. The following sentences contain errors—

The Chancellor of the Exchequer must *inculcate* his

colleagues in the Government *with* the principles of economy to which he professes to adhere. (Inculcate *upon* his colleagues the principles . . .)

Not only must there be shown an increasing desire to give better rewards for better work, but employers must practise the efficiency they desire through their management to *inculcate into* their workmen. (Inculcate *in*, or, instil *into*, their workmen.)

(Cp. INFUSE and INSTIL.)

INDICT, INDICTMENT.

Pronounced: indīt′, indīt′ment.

INDIRECT SPEECH.

(See REPORTED SPEECH.)

INDIVIDUAL.

Individual is used by the ignorant as if it meant nothing more than *person*. Inferior (especially comic) writers love to talk of "a seedy-looking individual," "an individual of unprepossessing appearance," and so on. *An individual* is really a *single* person, as opposed to a group or class. Thus we may say that a staff achieves its highest efficiency when every *individual* in it does his best work; or—a state is prosperous when the majority of the *individuals* composing it are prosperous. In both these cases the idea of contrast between a single person and a collection of people is present. Unless such a contrast is intended the word *individual* should not be used.

INDULGE IN.

To indulge in something is to take pleasure freely in it. It is obvious, therefoɹe, that what we indulge in must be something pleasurable. Yet this expression is often wrongly used instead of *take part in, engage in,* with reference to things which are distinctly unpleasant, e.g.—

Those who do not wish to *indulge in* a long and arduous course of study can acquire the necessary information by our special system.

INEXORABLE.

The second syllable bears the stress.

INFINITIVE.

The part of a verb known as the infinitive is generally easily recognizable because it is preceded by *to.* The simple present infinitive of the verb *see* is *to see.* (I hope *to see* the match. *To see* him now is impossible. I went *to see* him yesterday.) The continuous form is *to be seeing.* The perfect infinitive is *to have seen* (continuous form : *to have been seeing*).

(See SPLIT INFINITIVE.)

INFRINGE.

Infringe is not followed by *on,* although *encroach* is.

The company was brought into court for *infringing* the patent rights of a rival firm.

But—

The manager thought his assistant was *encroaching on* functions that did not belong to him.

INFUSE.

This word must be followed by *into.* We infuse an emotion *into* somebody ; we do not infuse somebody *with* an emotion.

He *infused* such a spirit of enthusiasm *into* his men that his department soon became the most efficient in the store.

(Cp. INCULCATE, INSPIRE, and INSTIL.)

INIMICAL.

Followed by *to.*

We shall find our lack of capital *inimical to* further progress.

IN ORDER THAT.

In order that is normally followed by *may or might.*

I am writing to-day *in order that* he *may* receive the letter to-morrow.

I wrote yesterday *in order that* he *might* receive the letter to-day.

Occasionally *shall* or *should* may be used in the second clause, but *can* or *could* and *will* or *would* are always wrong. Examples of the error—

Firms change their posters frequently in order that the public *shall* not become indifferent to their advertisements (*may*).

The firm is granting additional holidays now in order that the men *can* work longer hours next month (*may*).

They hurried the work as much as possible in order that the building *would* be ready for occupation in April (*might*).

In these cases, *shall, can,* and *would* might be retained if *so that* were used instead of *in order that.*

INSPIRE.

We can inspire an emotion *in* a man, or we can inspire him *with* an emotion.

During the period in which we worked together, he *inspired* me *with* a great admiration for his powers.

During a war a leader is required who will *inspire in* his countrymen a faith in their ability to win.

(Cp. INFUSE and INSTIL.)

INSTIL.

This word must be followed by *into*, and not *with*.

I tried to *instil into* him a proper sense of his position (*not*—instil him with . . .).

(Cp. INCULCATE, INFUSE, and INSPIRE.)

INTENSE—INTENSIVE.

Intensive is being wrongly used nowadays as if it had the same meaning as *intense*. *Intensive* is really a technical word, and it is usually known to the ordinary person only in the phrase *intensive cultivation*.

By *intensive* methods the farmer increases the production of a given area of land through the use of fertilizers.

In the following examples, *intensive* is clearly wrong—

They were doing, and would continue to do, all they could to meet the increasing and *intensive* competition (*intense*).

America is not the originator of the system of payment by weekly or monthly instalments, but the plan, by reason of *intensive* advertising and "super-salesmanship" methods, has become more generally adopted in America than in any other country.

(If *intensive* were correctly used in connection with advertising, it would mean that a firm, instead of scattering its advertisements throughout the country, limited its publicity campaign to a particular area so as to obtain the maximum return in that area.)

The voting of a new 10,000-ton armoured ship by the Reichstag is a tribute to the *intensive* propaganda which the naval interests in Germany have been conducting for the past few years (*vigorous*).

INTERJECTION.

An interjection is a word expressing sudden emotion, e.g. Oh ! Alas !

INTERROGATIVE PRONOUN.

Who (*whom, whose*), *which, what,* are called Interrogative Pronouns when they are used in place of a noun in asking questions; e.g. *Who* has come? *Whom* did you see? *Which* did you take? *What* did he say?

An Interrogative Pronoun may be used with a preposition; e.g. *To whom* did you give it? Sometimes, especially in colloquial language, the preposition comes at the end of the sentence; e.g. *Whom* were you laughing *at*? But note that *at* still governs *whom.* (See ERRORS IN CASE.)

IN THE CIRCUMSTANCES.

(See UNDER THE CIRCUMSTANCES.)

IN THE NEIGHBOURHOOD (REGION) OF.

Why do financial journalists and others delight in the four-word phrase *in the neighbourhood* (or *region*) *of* as a substitute for the simple *about,* as in the following examples ?—

> The total benefit which the Union has received from price movements during the past year seems to be *in the neighbourhood of* £5,000,000.
>
> A music-hall share, which at best must be classed as speculative—quoted *in the region of* par not so long ago, has by this deal been made a sound investment.

It is not obvious what special attraction this phrase has to justify the breach of the sound rule that several words should not be used when a single one will suffice.

INTRANSITIVE VERB.

(See TRANSITIVE VERB.)

INVEIGLE.

The *Oxford English Dictionary* gives the pronunciation: invē'gle; but invā'gle is very common, and is adopted by the B.B.C.

INVENTORY.

Pronounced: in'ventory.

INVERTED COMMAS.

Inverted commas (" ") are used to mark off directly reported speech (i.e. the actual words used by a speaker), or words quoted from written matter. The following examples illustrate not only the use of inverted commas, but the use of the comma and the capital letter in conjunction with them—

"That is very unlikely," he said at once.

I felt bound to ask, "Do you think so?"

"Now you must agree," he continued, "that very little has so far been done in the matter."

IRREFUTABLE, IRREPARABLE, IRREVOCABLE.

The second syllable is stressed in all three words.

IT'S ME.

As will be seen from the article on CASE, it is grammatically wrong to say "It's me," because *me* is a predicative pronoun, and therefore should be in the nominative case (*I*). But the expression is so well established in the colloquial language, even of the educated classes, that it is pedantic to object to it.

-IZE or -ISE?

Should we use the spelling *-ize* or *-ise* in verbs like *criticize, organize, italicize*? Which of the two spellings is strictly correct depends on the history of the particular word. The great majority of such verbs should have *-ize*, if we consider their derivation, but in a number of quite common words *-ise* is correct. How is the ordinary person with a limited knowledge of etymology to know when he should write *-ize* and when *-ise*? Many people cut the Gordian knot by spelling all such words with *-ise*, and English printers very commonly adopt the same practice. The printers of this book, however, follow the recommendation of *The Authors' and Printers' Dictionary* and use *-ize*; and this spelling is preferred by such important publications as *The Times* and *The Encyclopaedia Britannica.* In the absence of general agreement on the matter, the reader may please himself. But if he elects to write *-ize* he should be careful to remember those words which must always have *-ise* (advertise, comprise, despise, devise, disguise, enterprise, exercise, supervise, surprise, etc.).

JOB.

This word has many colloquial uses which are not admissible in the literary language—

> It's a good job he does not know; He has a job worth a thousand a year; They will have a hard job to finish in time; It's no use coming to me about it: it's not my job; etc.

In writing, use *task, post, appointment, business,* etc., and not *job,* according to the sense required.

JUDGEMENT—JUDGMENT.

Either spelling is allowable in modern usage.

JUDICIAL—JUDICIOUS.

Both words contain the root idea of judgment; but the application of *judicial* is limited to law courts and legal matters, whereas *judicious* means showing judgment, discernment, prudence in the ordinary concerns of life. A court of law transacts *judicial* business ; a court-martial is a *judicial* assembly convened to inquire into the conduct of someone ; a man with the mental qualities of a judge possesses a *judicial* mind and may decide a matter with *judicial* impartiality. But we make a *judicious* selection out of a variety of articles ; writers are gratified by the praise of *judicious* readers ; and in awkward circumstances we maintain a *judicious* silence.

KORAN.

Pronunciation: kōr′an, or korahn′. The B.B.C. adopts the latter.

LABORATORY.

The Oxford English Dictionary puts the accent on the first syllable, but accentuation on the second syllable is often heard and is adopted by the B.B.C.

LAMENTABLE.

The first syllable is stressed.

LATTER.

The slipshod writer betrays himself most easily perhaps by his fondness for the use of *the latter.* In his inability to control his pronouns, he takes refuge in *the latter*, hoping that his readers will see what previous noun he intends to refer to. But often he bungles even in using this device, and his *the latter* becomes not only awkward, but meaningless. Some examples with comments will make clear what is meant—

(1) No financial assistance of any kind is given by the Canadian Government to immigrants from foreign countries, and the fact that so many of *the latter* are willing to adventure in new lands . . .

Here three nouns (Government, immigrants, countries) precede *the latter*, but *the latter* means the second of two only. Moreover, it is not even the last of the three nouns that the writer intends to refer to, as the reader would naturally expect.

> (2) The increase in the rates is the result of an outcry by farmers that, owing to a lack of proper protection, French agriculture is suffering from a severe crisis, and it is very unfair that *the latter* should not benefit by duties proportional to those enjoyed by industry.

Again several nouns are mentioned, and of these it is natural to take *crisis* as the one to which *the latter* relates. The sentence has to be re-read before it becomes clear that *the latter* stands for *agriculture.*

> (3) It will be readily understood how inconvenient it is to small boarding-house proprietors or tradesmen to have to send for their letters on Saturday, or else wait till Monday. Competition is keen, and it may mean the loss of pounds in the *latter* event.

Here the *latter* does relate to the second of two things, it is true ; but the connection is so vague that the passage has to be read twice before the meaning is grasped.

The latter serves a good purpose in conjunction with *the former,* but writers would generally do well to avoid using it by itself. It can frequently be replaced by an ordinary personal pronoun (*he, it, they,* etc.), perhaps with some readjustment of the sentence ; otherwise, in order to avoid clumsiness and obscurity, the antecedent noun should be repeated.

LAY—LIE.

These two verbs are often confused. *To lay* is transitive, i.e. it is followed by an object (to lay a book on the table, to lay a foundation-stone, etc.) ; whereas *to lie* is intransitive (to lie down, to be lying in the road) The principal parts of the two verbs are—

	Present Tense	*Past Tense*	*Perfect Tense*
(1)	I lay	I laid	I have laid
	I am laying	I was laying	I have been laying
(2)	I lie	I lay	I have lain
	I am lying	I was lying	I have been lying

LESS.

Less should be used only in connection with quantity (less material, less ability); when number is expressed, *fewer* is the correct word. The following sentence contains an error—

On the omnibuses the best day is Saturday, with an average of 5,338,970 passengers carried; Wednesday comes second with roundly 600,000 *less* passengers (*fewer*).

LETTERS: CORRECT FORM, PUNCTUATION, etc.

This article is concerned only with business letters. Many formalities necessary in business communications are omitted in familiar correspondence between friends.

Business letters are constructed on a stereotyped plan: they contain the following parts—(*a*) Heading; (*b*) Name and Address of Recipient; (*c*) Salutation; (*d*) Body of the Letter; (*e*) Subscription and Signature. Notes on each of these parts are given below.

(*a*) **Heading**. The note-paper of business firms usually has a printed heading (giving name of firm, name of partners, address, telephone number, etc.). If the address of the firm has to be written or typed, it will appear (followed by the date of dispatch) thus—

39–41, Parker Street,
Kingsway,
London, W.C.2.
2nd March, 19...

19, Queen's Sq.,
Manchester.
15th Jan., 19...

Note the use of the comma and of the full stop. Sometimes a comma is not inserted after the number of the house or premises. In writing dates, the order *15th Jan.,* is preferable to *Jan. 15th.* The use of numbers only (*15.1.41*) is not recommended. The following are the recognized abbreviations for the months—*Jan., Feb., Aug., Sept., Oct., Nov., Dec.* There are no abbreviations for *May, June, July. March* and *April* may be either written in full or shortened to *Mar., Apr.*

(*b*) **Name and Address of Recipient.** The name and full address of the person to whom the letter is sent must always appear. Sometimes it is put at the foot of the letter, but generally it is written or typed at the left-hand side below the address and date, and before the salutation (Dear Sir, etc.); thus—

H. J. Barker, Esq.,
48, Mount Road,
Folkestone.

Mr. James Hardwick,
4, Landon Crescent,
Bath.

Messrs. Haig & Co., Ltd.,
Timber Merchants,
56, Condor St.,
Gravesend.

NOTES.

1. A full stop is not always used for abbreviations like *Mr., Messrs.* On this point, see FULL STOP.

2. On the use of *Mr.* and *Esq.*, see MR. OR ESQ.

3. *Messrs.* (Fr. *Messieurs*) is applied to partnerships and limited companies. It should not be used when the firm has an impersonal name, e.g. *The London Passenger Transport Board.*

4. In letters sent to limited companies and large corporate bodies, it is usual to address the General Manager, the Secretary, or other responsible official.

5. For special forms of address and salutation for persons of rank or high office, see TITLES: SPECIAL FORMS OF ADDRESS AND SALUTATION.

(*c*) **Salutation.** The salutation (*Sir, Dear Sir, Dear Sirs, Gentlemen, Dear Mr. ...., Madam, Dear Madam, Mesdames*) is put immediately below the name and address of the recipient.

Sir is very formal, and is not now often used in business correspondence, though it is regularly employed by Government departments.

Dear Sir is the regular salutation to-day in all cases where nothing more than a business relationship exists between the correspondents.

Dear Mr. . . . is used when the writer has personal acquaintance with the recipient, and when he wishes to adopt a more familiar tone than is suggested by *Dear Sir.*

Dear Sirs is the usual salutation in the case of letters addressed to *Messrs. . . . . .* (Obviously *Dear Sir* would be incorrect.)

Gentlemen is falling out of use except for letters addressed to boards of directors, committees, or public bodies.

(*d*) **Body of Letter.** In drafting the body of the letter it is essential to observe rules of paragraphing—

1. The opening paragraph must briefly introduce the subject-matter. If the letter is a reply, reference will be made to previous correspondence, thus—

I have received (or, *am in receipt of*) *your letter of*

the 5th inst., . . . We have pleasure in acknowledging the receipt of your letter of yesterday, . . In reply (or, *with reference*) *to your letter RP/J of the 3rd May . . .*

This opening paragraph may, and frequently does, consist of only one sentence. Sometimes a title is inserted just below the salutation in order to give the reader immediate indication of the contents, e.g.—

Re Sale of 79, Fall's Road, Coventry.

Appointment of Secretary to Hill Farm Golf Club.

2. In a letter about a single topic, all the facts and explanatory details will be given in the second paragraph. If, however, several matters have to be dealt with, a separate paragraph must be devoted to each. The first line of each paragraph should be indented.

3. In many letters the final paragraph (like the first) contains only one sentence, or even a short conventional phrase, such as—

Awaiting the favour of your commands; Assuring you of our best attention at all times; Thanking you in anticipation.

If such participle-phrases are used, the subscription must contain a pronoun (*I* am, *We* remain, etc.); otherwise a grammatical fault is committed. (See UNRELATED PARTICIPLE.)

When a letter sets out opinions or states a case, the final paragraph will, of course, be very important, for it will contain the conclusion to which the arguments lead. It may be of some length.

(*e*) **Subscription and Signature.** The subscription must agree in wording with the salutation. *Yours faithfully* is the commonest form for business letters. *Yours truly* may be used in the same circumstances. Both these forms accompany *Dear Sir* as salutation. *Yours very truly* is appropriate for a slightly more intimate letter, when *Dear Mr. . . . .* appears as salutation. *Yours sincerely* and *Yours very sincerely* occur in business letters only when the writer is addressing a personal friend with whom he can properly drop formalities. In such cases, the salutation is *Dear Mr. . . . .*, or the still more intimate *Dear So-and-so.* *Yours respectfully, Yours obediently,* and *Your obedient Servant* are not often used to-day in business. *Your obedient Servant* is retained to some extent in official correspondence.

Except when the letter closes with a participle-phrase (see above), the use of *I am, I remain, We beg to remain,* etc., in the subscription is optional.

The following examples illustrate correct punctuation and use of capital letters—

I am,
Yours faithfully,
J. R. Townly.

We are, dear Sir,
Yours faithfully,
Robertson & Sons, Ltd.
H. Roper,
Manager.

In the signature the name of the firm is often typed or imprinted with a rubber stamp. The responsible official signs his name beneath and adds the description of his position (as in the second example above). Unimportant letters and post cards are frequently signed by a clerk, thus—

The Metropolitan Cement Co., Ltd.,
per (or *p.*) *F. Marchant ;*

or; *For The Metropolitan Cement Co., Ltd.,*
F. M.

If an official of a firm has been granted legal power of attorney to sign on behalf of the principal, *per pro.* or *p.p.* (abbreviation of the Latin *per procurationem*) is prefixed to the signature, thus—

per pro. (or *p.p.*) *Philp, Stanford & Co.,*

C. Manton.

LETTERS IN THE THIRD PERSON.

Short letters of a very formal character are sometimes written in the third person. The address of the writer and the date are put at the end. The name and address of the recipient are not given at the head. There is no signature. The following is a specimen—

Mr. H. W. Barton very much regrets that owing to a previous engagement he cannot be present at the concert on 6th April in aid of the Cottage Hospital. He hopes the evening will be a success, and he has much pleasure in enclosing a cheque for £5 as a subscription to the fund.

The Willows,

Cheshunt.

4th April, 19...

In such letters the third person must be maintained throughout, i.e. after beginning with *he*, the writer must not lapse into *I*.

LICENCE, LICENSE.

The noun is always spelt *licence* (marriage-licence, public-house licence, poetic licence, licence (i.e. excessive freedom) of speech or behaviour).

The verb is spelt either *licence* or *license.* It seems better to keep the *s*-spelling for the verb, on the analogy of *practice* (n.)—*practise* (v.), *advice* (n.)—*advise* (v.), etc.

(The premises are *licensed* for dancing; to *license* the publication of a book, or the performance of a play; a *licensed* victualler.)

LICHEN.

Pronounced: līk′en.

LIKE.

As an adjective, *like* is peculiar in being able to govern a noun or pronoun in the accusative case: it thus resembles a preposition—

He is like his brother. He is like me.

(*Like* governs *brother* and *me* in these sentences.)

But there is another use of *like* in vulgar language, and this is to be avoided. Examples are—

I cannot type rapidly *like* you do.
I wish you had painted it *like* you said you would.

Here the word introduces a subordinate clause of comparison, i.e. it is followed by a verb (*can, said*). But *like* is not a conjunction, and should not therefore be used in this way. *As* should be used in both cases.

LITERAL(LY).

Many people who use *literal* and *literally* do not understand what the words mean, and consequently they perpetrate absurd errors. *Literally* means the opposite of *figuratively* or *metaphorically*; a *literal* statement has to be interpreted according to the letter. If we say that an artist *starved* for some time before achieving success, we generally mean that he made very little money and could barely live. If we said he *literally starved*, we should mean that he actually did not have sufficient food to support life. It is wrong to say that you were *literally stunned* by the news if you did not fall down unconscious. Here are some examples of the misuse of the word—

> I have struggled hard at golf: I have *literally* removed mountains.

(The writer of this remark meant to be funny: he was funnier than he knew.)

> One of the main features of markets last week was the extraordinary rush to buy shares on Monday for "new time." Dealers in the industrial markets, especially those interested in the more popular shares, were *literally* mobbed by brokers who had buying orders.

(No doubt *literally* is intended to mean *almost.*)

> I cannot too strongly emphasize that the British industrialist, who fears no ordinary competition, is terribly hampered by increasing rates and taxation, higher railway rates, and so on, until the burden is *literally* too heavy to be borne.

(Why *literally*? The word *burden* is obviously to be taken metaphorically. The required adverb seems to be *really.*)

> Sir,—I have long been convinced that there is a lack of method in the way jurors are summoned. For 40 years I have been *literally* "peppered" with summonses to appear at one court or another.

(After inserting *literally*, the writer uses inverted commas to show that *peppered* is not to be taken literally. This is sinning against the light.)

LONGEVITY.

Pronounced: lŏnjĕ′vity.

LONG WORDS INSTEAD OF SHORT.

There is no special virtue in the long word. You do not make your writing more effective by discarding the short, plain word for a longer and more pretentious substitute. Yet the pointless use of polysyllabic variants is very common, e.g.—

The Prince was present at the *initial* performance (first).

He was most *meticulous* in carrying out the duties assigned to him (careful, exact).

The scheme did not *materialize* (was not carried out).

The Government *evidenced* no desire to meet this *eventuality* with firmness (showed ; situation).

The *meteorological* conditions did not favour a good day's sport (weather).

He occupied a house *in close proximity* to the Town Hall (near, close to).

They gained notoriety as the *protagonists* of the Women's Suffrage Movement (leaders).

Nobody last week *visualized* the situation which has now arisen (expected, foresaw, imagined).

The excessive use of long words generally leads to clumsiness and pomposity in style, and not infrequently it produces obscurity.

MACHINATION.

Pronounced: makinā'tion.

MAJORITY.

When *majority* means *superiority in numbers,* it must be treated as singular.

The Government's majority *is* so small that a General Election is imminent.

When it means a group of people superior in number to another group, it may be regarded as singular or plural according to whether the group or the individuals composing it are uppermost in the mind. (See the section on Collective Nouns in ERRORS IN AGREEMENT.)

The Government majority *was* hard pressed during the passage of the Bill.

The Conservative majority *were* elated at *their* victory.

When it means merely *most men, people*, etc., it is plural.

The majority of the audience *were* disappointed by the lecture.

Of those who take the examination, the majority *fail* in the foreign language.

MEDIEVAL.

Also spelt *mediaeval.* Pronounced: mĕdiē'val

MEDIOCRE.

Pronounced: mē'diōker.

MEMOIR.

Pronounced: mĕm'war.

METALLURGY.

Pronounced: mĕt'alurjy, or mĕtal'urjy.

METAPHOR.

Metaphor consists in the substitution of one name or term for another in such a way as to imply a comparison; e.g.—

The proposal produced a *storm* of protest.

(The word *storm* is not to be taken literally: the protests were so violent as to be *like* a storm.) Metaphor is a valuable means of giving vividness to a statement; thus it is arresting to be told that "Palmerston was very bold; and nothing gave him more exhilaration than to steer the ship of state in a high wind, on a rough sea, with every stitch of canvas on her that she could carry." But in using figurative language of this sort there are pitfalls for the unwary. When a metaphor has once been adopted it must be continued throughout the sentence. Ludicrous results are often produced by the sudden dropping of a metaphor, or the introduction in the same sentence of another metaphor inconsistent with the first. A collection of examples taken from the daily Press and from current literature will make clear how easy it is to come to grief in this matter—

(1) The recommendations of the Standing Committee appointed under the Merchandise Marks Act that all currants, sultanas, and raisins shall be marked with the country of origin has caused a slight flutter of protest in the grocery world; while Free Traders, *scenting the thin*, safeguarding *edge* of a Protectionist *wedge*, are *sniffing* inquiringly and hostilely round the Committee's report.

(The two totally different metaphors of (*a*) an animal scenting an enemy and (*b*) the thin end of a wedge, have been mixed.)

(2) "Let us take steps to *purge* the Republican Party of the *stigma* of oil money given to the Republican National Committee for campaign funds," urges Senator Borah.

(A stigma is a branded mark, a stain: it cannot be purged.)

(3) Mr. Nye declares to-day that there is reason to believe that the investigation has *scratched* only the *surface* in discovering the grand total of the money *poured* into the Republican campaign funds, as well as the *sources* of this cash.

(Mr. Nye has jumbled together the notions of prospecting for mineral wealth and of exploring the sources of a river.)

(4) A large number of governing men are always better than the bad laws they administer or the brutal

commands they receive. This, coupled with the certainty that oppression carried beyond a certain point will make men rebel, has *tempered* the most cutting *blades* of despotism, has made bearable systems which, on paper, seem destructive of all freedom, elasticity, and joy.

(This passage from a well-known writer contains a curious error. From the context it is clear that in using the word *tempered* he was thinking of the metaphor of tempering the wind to the shorn lamb. But, unfortunately, he introduced the second metaphor of the sword. To temper a sword is to make its edge more sharp. He has thus said the opposite to what he intended.)

MIGRATORY.

Pronounced: mī′gratory.

MR. or ESQ.

The title *Esq.* ought strictly to be confined to graduates of universities, Members of the House of Commons, private gentlemen, and the members of certain professions. For this reason it used to be customary in business correspondence to address tradesmen as *Mr.* Although this practice is still observed to some extent, the tendency nowadays is to use *Esq.* irrespective of the status of the person addressed.

MILITATE.

Followed by *against.*

His bad manners will *militate against* his success in business.

MINIMIZE.

This is one of the words that have become fashionable and are therefore carelessly used. *To minimize* is *to reduce to a minimum* (i.e. *the smallest possible amount*).

It should not be used to mean *reduce* or *underestimate* as in the following examples—

Before long there will be attempts to organize air-routes that will *minimize* the time taken to travel from one part of the Empire to another (reduce, or greatly reduce).

While I do not wish to *minimize* the strides made by wireless telegraphy during the past year, I maintain that there is room for both the beam and the cable systems (underestimate).

MINUTES OF MEETINGS.

This is not the place in which to deal with the technical details of minuting, but as minutes of meetings follow a more or less stereotyped form, it will be useful to give a specimen set of minutes for the guidance of secretaries of committees.

MINUTES OF MEETING OF THE GENERAL COMMITTEE OF THE BLANKTOWN RATEPAYERS' ASSOCIATION HELD AT 8 P.M. ON THE 6TH JAN., 19..

The following members were present—

Mrs. S. Jameson, Miss Philpots, Messrs. H. J. Taylor, R. F. Lloyd, E. Smith, S. Raynor, R. P. Tozer, B. R. Horsley.

1. The minutes of the last meeting were read and confirmed.

Business arising from the minutes—

The Chairman read a letter received from the Borough Council in reply to the Committee's communication of the 11th Nov., regarding the Swimming Baths.

2. *Correspondence.* The Secretary read—

(*a*) Letter from Mr. H. J. Barlow resigning his

membership of the Publicity Sub-committee on the grounds of ill-health.

The Secretary was instructed to send a suitable reply.

It was agreed to ask Mr. H. Antrim to serve in place of Mr. Barlow.

(*b*) Letter from the Manager of the Blanktown Assembly Rooms informing the committee that the Rooms would not be available for the General Meeting of the Association on 10th Feb.

The Secretary was instructed to make inquiries regarding another suitable hall.

3. *Reports.*

(*a*) The Treasurer's Report was read and adopted.

(*b*) The Report of the Publicity Sub-committee was read and adopted.

4. *Site of the New Recreation Ground.*

The Secretary read a letter from the Borough Council stating that they would be willing to receive a deputation to put forward the views of the Association regarding the site of the proposed new Recreation Ground.

It was resolved that the Council's offer should be accepted, and that a deputation of three should be appointed.

The following members were elected to serve—

Miss Philpots, Messrs. S. Raynor and B. R. Horsley.

5. *Resolution.*

It was proposed by Mr. H. J. Taylor, seconded by Mr. R. F. Lloyd, and resolved that the next Annual General Meeting should be asked to sanction the alteration of Rule X by the addition of the words "and three additional members to be co-opted by the General Committee."

There being no other business, the meeting adjourned at 9.30 p.m.

NOTES

(1) Minutes are intended to give a concise record of the decisions arrived at and the business transacted. Details of speeches are, therefore, not given except in special circumstances.

(2) In the case of important resolutions, the names of the proposer and the seconder, and a record of the voting, may be included. Generally, however, these details are omitted.

MISCHIEVOUS.

Pronounced: mis'chĭvous.

MOOD.

The tenses of a verb are grouped into three " moods ": the *indicative*, the *imperative*, and the *subjunctive.*

1. The Indicative Mood is used in statements and questions—

He *came* yesterday. *Did* you *see* him?

2. The Imperative Mood is used in commands and entreaties. The subject is always in the second person (*you*)—

Open the door.

3. The Subjunctive Mood is used when we are not stating a fact (as we are when we use the indicative), but are asserting something as being *thought of* as desirable or possible.

I wish he *were* here.

The subjunctive has different forms from those of the indicative, as is shown by the following lists—

PRESENT TENSE (" to be ")

Indic. I am, thou art, he is; we are, you are, they are.
Subj. I be, thou be, he be; we be, you be, they be.

PAST TENSE

Indic. I was, thou wast, he was; we, you, they were.
Subj. I were, thou wert, he were; we, you, they were.

PRESENT TENSE ("to see")

Indic. I see, thou seest, he sees; we, you, they see.
Subj. I see, thou see, he see; we, you, they see.

In the past tense of "to see," the forms of the indicative and the subjunctive are the same.

(See SUBJUNCTIVE MOOD: MODERN USAGE.)

MULTIPLE SENTENCE.

(See DOUBLE SENTENCE, MULTIPLE SENTENCE.)

MUTUAL.

The use of *mutual* is fraught with danger. It is necessary to be clear about its meaning. If we say that Jones and Smith entertain *mutual* suspicion, we mean that Jones is suspicious of Smith, and Smith is suspicious of Jones; that is, there is a reciprocal feeling between them. It is not possible, therefore, to speak correctly of Robinson as a *mutual friend* of Jones and Smith. Here we mean that Robinson is the friend of Jones and of Smith; we are not thinking of any reciprocal relationship between Jones and Smith. Robinson is the *common* friend of the two.

Again, since *mutual* implies the notion of *each other*, these two words should not appear in the same sentence with *mutual*. Incorrect—

> The two friends had a *mutual* influence *on each other* that was all to the good.

(Omit *on each other.*)

MYTH.

A *myth* is "a purely fictitious narrative usually involving supernatural persons, etc., and embodying popular ideas on natural phenomena, etc." Since the word has this definite technical signification, it seems a pity to degrade it and treat it as though it meant merely a fiction, as in the following—

He died in exile, having lost his distinguished status in the German diplomatic service because he had the courage to oppose the *myths* on which Germany's appetite for war was fed (lies, fictions).

NADIR.

Pronounced: nā'der, or nā'dẽr.

NAÏF, NAÏVE.

Although the original French form is *naïf*, the word is generally spelt *naïve* in English. It is commonly pronounced : nah-ēv ; few people seem to have the courage to anglicize it completely to : nāv.

NAPHTHA.

Pronounced : naftha.

NEAR-BY.

There is growing up a practice of using " near-by " as an adjective, e.g.—

Motor excursions can be made to all the *near-by* places of interest.

This is an Americanism. If we wish to follow the true English idiom, we may use the two separate adverbs *near by* (. . . to all the places of interest near by), or we may substitute *neighbouring* (. . . to all the neighbouring places of interest).

NEITHER.

Neither refers to two only.

Neither of the two books is to be found.

When more than two are referred to, *none* should be used.

Neither is singular, and should not therefore be followed by a plural verb. Incorrect—

He advances two arguments, neither of which *are* sound (*is*).

NEITHER . . . NOR.

(See Rules of Agreement, Errors in Agreement, Rule of Proximity.)

NICE.

In colloquial language, *nice* is used vaguely to describe anything agreeable or pleasant. Many people never employ this adjective in any other way. Yet in literary use it has several important senses, some of which may be illustrated—

The careless writer does not distinguish *nice* (delicate, subtle) shades of meaning.

Whether he did right is a *nice* (delicate) question.

The experiment requires the *nicest* (most precise) attention.

He is determined to make money, and will not be too *nice* (fastidious) about the means he employs.

NOBODY, NO-ONE.

These words are singular and (except in colloquial language) should not be followed by plural words referring to them. Incorrect—

No-one blessed with eyesight should withhold *their* assistance, as the blind workers of London are largely dependent on the amount collected on Geranium Day (his ; or, all those blessed . . . should give their . . .).

Colloquially, in questions containing a pronoun referring to *nobody* (*no-one*), the plural is always used.

even after a singular verb, e.g. *Nobody* believes it, do *they*?

NOMINATIVE CASE.

(See CASE.)

NONCHALANT.

Pronounced: non'shalant.

NONE.

This pronoun may be treated as singular or plural according to the sense. When it means *not a single one*, it must obviously be followed by singular words.

> Of all the arguments that have been brought, *none* (not one) *is* sufficiently strong to convince me.

But when it means *not any*, it may be followed by a plural verb—

> *None* of the characters in this scene *display* any sign of feeling, although a man has just been murdered in the room.

NON-EXISTENCE, NON-SUCCESS, etc.

The unnecessary use of these compounds with *non-* has become fashionable.

> Owing to the *non-appearance* of the principal speaker, the meeting did not begin at the advertised time.
>
> The *non-success* of the company in coming to terms has not deterred them from continuing their efforts.
>
> Fifty years ago alloy steels were almost *non-existent*.

What merits have the *non*-compounds in these sentences that they should be preferred to *absence* (or *lateness*), *failure*, and *unknown*?

NO-ONE.

(See NOBODY, NO-ONE.)

NOT ONLY . . . BUT ALSO.

(See Correlative Conjunctions and Rule of Proximity.)

NOUN.

A noun is the name of a person or of anything that we can think of—*man, James, sailor, town, acting, possession.*

NOUN-CLAUSES.

A noun-clause is a part of a sentence containing a subject and predicate of its own, and having the function of a noun. A noun can be used (1) as the *subject* of a verb, (2) as the *object* of a verb, (3) *predicatively*, (4) in *apposition* to another noun. (See Subject and Predicate, Object, Predicative Words, Apposition.) Similarly, a noun-clause can be used in any of these four ways—

(1) *That he will be promoted* is unlikely.

The italicized group of words contains a subject (*he*) and a predicate (*will be promoted*), and it is used as a noun because it is the *subject* of the main verb *is*.

(2) I think *that he will be promoted.*

Here the noun-clause is the *object* of the main verb *think.*

(3) The probability is *that he will be promoted.*

The noun-clause is the equivalent of a *predicative noun.*

(4) I do not believe the rumour *that he will be promoted.*

The noun-clause names the same thing as *rumour* ; either could be taken as the object of *do believe.* The noun-clause is, therefore, in *apposition* to *rumour.*

(See Clauses.)

NUMBER.

A noun or pronoun is said to be in the *singular* number when it denotes one person or thing, and in the *plural* number when it denotes more than one—

Singular: man, he; *Plural:* men, they.

A verb is in the same number as its subject.

NUMBER.

The word *number* is a Collective Noun and may be followed by either a singular or a plural verb according to the sense. (See ERRORS IN AGREEMENT, i (f).) Thus we may say correctly—A number of the boys *have* formed a club; A number of people *were* seen running down the street. (In both cases we are thinking of the separate individuals, and not of a body as an entity.) On the other hand, we say—The number of students *is* not so great this year as last.

OBJECT (DIRECT AND INDIRECT).

The object of a sentence or clause is the noun or noun-equivalent that names the person or thing on which the action is performed—

I posted the *letter* (*letter* names the thing on which the action of posting was performed).

I met *him* (*him* names the person who underwent the action of meeting).

The object may be found by asking the questions Whom? or What? after the verb—

Whom did I meet?—*him* (object).

Except when the object is a pronoun ending in *-self* (I hurt *myself*), it always names a person or thing different from the subject.

In the examples given above we have *Direct Objects.* Some sentences contain an *Indirect Object*, i.e. a noun or pronoun naming a person or thing indirectly affected by the action denoted by the verb—

I sent *him* (indirect obj.) the parcel (direct obj.).

I bought my *brother* (indirect obj.) a present (direct obj.).

Note that the indirect object in the first example is equivalent to *to him*, and in the second to *for my brother*.

OBJECTIVE CASE.

This is another name for the Accusative Case. (See CASE.)

OBLIGATORY.

Two pronunciations exist—(1) oblĭg'ătory, (2) ŏb'lĭgātory. The first is to be preferred.

Obligatory is followed by *on*—

The law makes it *obligatory on* proprietors of theatres to take precautions against fire.

OBLIVIOUS.

Followed by *of*.

Oblivious of the manager's presence, he continued his conversation at the telephone.

Oblivious to, though established in American usage, is not allowable in Standard English.

OBSCURITY.

The first essential in any piece of writing is that it shall be clear. No statement is satisfactory if it has to be read more than once before the meaning is grasped. This is so obvious that it may seem hardly worth mentioning. Yet, in fact, the paramount need for clarity is too often neglected. In the daily Press (especially in the correspondence columns) and in the reports of business proceedings, there are frequently to be found passages whose meaning is more or less obscured by careless wording or bad sentence-construction. Indeed, in order to avoid vagueness and ambiguity in expression, a writer needs to exercise not only the most watchful attention, but also considerable technical skill. A number of examples of obscure writing are collected below and grouped so as to illustrate some of the main causes of the faults.

1. **Long and Involved Sentences.** An association of British steel manufacturers recently sent a letter to the Press in which the following paragraphs occurred—

> The heavy steel industry of the United Kingdom has, almost without exception, since the termination of the Great War, been struggling against the greatest difficulties, chief among which was the continuously increasing pressure of foreign competition, aided as it was by longer working hours and lower wages of Continental workmen, subsidies to Continental makers by their Government, especially designed to aid exports, low railway rates, negligible social service costs, low rates and low taxation, and depreciating exchanges, in comparison to which the heavy steel makers of the United Kingdom were faced by a high standard of living which necessitated high wages and comparatively short hours of work for their operatives, together with greatly increased charges for transport and social services, which exceeded what was paid for these charges in 1913 by about 230 per cent . . .
>
> The signatories of the rebate scheme are offering substantial rebates at considerable sacrifices to themselves with the object of encouraging British consumers to confine their purchases to British materials manufactured by British workmen, in the certain expectation that the result will be both beneficial to the heavy steel industry and to the consumers of

> heavy steel products, by reason of reduced steel costs consequent upon increased production and the operation of the steel mills nearer to their full capacity and generally to improving trade conditions in the United Kingdom as a result of once again having the British heavy steel industry busy and prosperous.

What the writers of this letter set out to do was presumably to explain as clearly as possible the disabilities from which the steel industry had been suffering, and the desirability of introducing the rebate scheme. What they actually did was to produce a long rigmarole which is unintelligible until it has been read two or three times. Obviously the passages quoted above should have been split up into shorter sentences, each containing one definite idea.

The following involved passage is taken from the report of a company meeting—

> He trusted that his survey of the balance-sheet and of certain of the corporation's holdings had served to show that the present strength and position of the corporation had not been built up on haphazard lines, and that those avenues in which the board had chosen to invest somewhat big sums had been in directions to which they had given the closest study and had employed all the resources at their disposal for making as certain as humanly possible that the employment of funds on the principles indicated would be profitable and provide to the corporation increasingly valuable assets.

Again two or three sentences should have been written instead of one.

2. **Faulty Sentence-construction.** The following examples show how the meaning may be obscured if the sentence is badly constructed—

> The inevitable evolution, which has brought about

> the extinction of the old Liberal Party, is also demonstrated in the manifesto of the expiring residuum of that once great political force, and is almost identical with that issued by the Socialists, and contains the same transparently inaccurate criticisms of the work of the Municipal Reform Council.

What " is almost identical " ? At first sight it seems to be the evolution, but a second reading shows that it must be the manifesto. The confusion results from the telescoping of several facts into the single sentence. The sentence should end with "force," and a new one should follow beginning with " This document is almost identical . . . "

> There lies close at hand a very simple remedy which the vested interests pressing for the continued preference which they have had for many years of using the roads for industrial traffic without paying anything like the cost of the damage they cause oppose, and thus seek to continue to leave as a burden on the community instead of having it placed, as it should be, on that portion of the industry which is properly chargeable.

This is from a report of a company meeting. The first part is made unnecessarily difficult to follow because *oppose* is separated so far from *vested interests*, its subject. And as for the second part of the sentence, what does it mean ? What do they seek to continue to leave as a burden ? Apparently the remedy. But this is nonsense. Is it the damage ? Possibly. But as the sentence is now constructed, nobody would take *it* as referring to *damage*.

3. Ambiguity in Expression due to Various Causes.

(*a*) BAD ARRANGEMENT OF WORDS—

> Undoubtedly girls gain much from co-education. There is a welcome drop in sentimentalism amongst them, less affectation, due to male influence.

As the phrase *due to male influence* is now placed, it seems to refer to *affectation*, but it should really go with *drop*. Write : " Owing to male influence, there is . . . "

> The Government, while admitting that the heavy steel makers' case had been conclusively proved, declined to render any assistance on the plea of political expediency.

Two meanings are possible here according to whether we take *on the plea of political expediency* with *declined* or *to render*. In order to state clearly the sense evidently intended, we must write : " declined on the plea of political expediency to render . . . "

(*b*) Omission of Necessary Words—

> The overthrow of Charles I was ultimately effected by the Independents, who had little more sympathy with the Covenanters than the Anglicans.

Does this mean that the Independents had little more sympathy with the Covenanters than the Anglicans *had*, or that the Independents had little more sympathy with the Covenanters than *with* the Anglicans ?

(*c*) Mere Carelessness in Phrasing—

> This is a book to be recommended to many people who think they can write as well as to beginners.

The use of *as well as* here is confusing. The sentence is so worded that the phrase at first seems to mean *as skilfully as*, but it turns out to signify *in addition to*.

> An old member of an exclusive club—an inveterate gourmet—classifies clubs as places where one either feeds or dines.

The writer no doubt meant to say that the person quoted divides clubs into two classes—those in which one dines, and those in which one feeds. What he has actually said is that clubs can be " classified " as places where one has the option on a given occasion of either dining or feeding. (It will be observed that *classifies* is now meaningless.)

> Yesterday saw a return to the beautiful weather of the last few days, with a good prospect of continuance.

The last phrase is clumsily tacked on to the main statement. The ideas should be given two sentences.

4. **Technical Jargon.** Writers on scientific and technical matters are sometimes seduced into obscurity by their love of the phraseology peculiar to their subject. When they are writing for the initiated, they naturally use the technical terms with which they are familiar. Not infrequently, however, they use a technical jargon quite needlessly to express what could be equally well put in ordinary English. An appearance of scientific precision is obtained at the expense of intelligibility. This habit becomes inexcusable when the writer is addressing the general reader rather than the specialist. The plain man is given a legitimate cause of complaint by a passage such as the following (taken from a popular work by a well-known economist)—

> When all has been said, however, every aspect of the problem of the efficiency of labour has not been presented. A community is only rendered most efficient, in the broadest sense of the term, when the most valuable productive potentiality of each person has been rendered actual. To bring out the highest powers of the individual and place him at work suited to his capacity, implies an educational system which is successful both in disclosing and training ability and a social system wherein an individual, whatever the grade of his birth, finds no difficulty in making his way into the economic ranks for functioning in which he is well endowed naturally and properly prepared. Given these conditions and a sufficiency of

initiative and perseverance in the individual, the vertical mobility of labour is said to be high.

The thought of the passage is really quite simple, but it is given the appearance of difficulty through being clothed in unnecessarily abstract language. The second sentence, in particular, is merely empty jargon. The plain English for it is—" A community has achieved its maximum efficiency only when each member of it is given the opportunity of making the best use of his special ability." The third sentence, too, is made difficult to follow by its clumsy construction : we seem to see the scientist labouring to bring his abstruse ideas within the comprehension of the lay mind.

OF ANY.

The use of *of any* in sentences like the following, though common, is quite illogical, and might well be avoided—

> Capt. . . . . . has flown the greatest mileage *of any pilot* in the service of Imperial Airways.

Write : " of all the pilots . . .," or, " has flown a greater mileage than any other pilot."

OMISSION OF NECESSARY WORDS.

In certain sentences we may quite properly omit words, e.g.—

> Come and see the car (that) I have just bought ; it is more powerful than my last (one was).

The words in brackets are supplied mentally, but they need not be written or spoken. Care must be taken, however, not to suppress words when the omission will do violence to sense or grammar—

> (1) We already have, in clubs, places where the private interest is practically non-existent, yet few would doubt that there is *as much, if not more*, excessive drinking in these places *as* in the public-house.

(*As much* must be followed by *as*, but *if not more* requires *than*.)

This machine is *as good, if not better than* the one which has just been installed.

(Insert *as* after *good*.)

(2) Your company always has, and will continue to do its utmost on behalf of the shareholders.

(Has *done* and will continue *to do*.)

(3) He ought to have lived at the court of Louis XIV, so marked is his preference for the fashionable world and so cosmopolitan his tastes.

(The verb could be suppressed before *his tastes* if it were the same as that before *his preference*, i.e. *is*; but *are* is required. Therefore we must write: "so cosmopolitan *are* his tastes.")

(4) I cannot help repeating that the interest of labourers and employers is one and the same.

(The writer intends to say that *two* things *are* one and the same. Alter thus: That the interest of labourers and *the interest of* employers *are* one and the same.)

ON TO.

Should the use of the compound preposition *on to* (corresponding to *into*) be allowed? In conversation *on to* is frequently used where *on* would be sufficient; e.g. He jumped *on to* the bus; It is not right to put the whole blame *on to* me. This use is generally avoided in writing. *Onto* (as one word) is occasionally met with in print, but it has not yet won official acceptance: it is better to use the two separate words.

Note that *on to* is not a compound preposition in such a sentence as: We must fight on to the end. Here, *on* is an adverb qualifying *fight*, and *to* is a preposition governing *end*.

ONE.

The genitive case of the indefinite pronoun *one* (meaning *anyone, people in general*) is *one's*. *One* must not be replaced by *he* or *they* in the same context. Incorrect—

When *one* loses *his* train *he* is annoyed (one's, one).

When *one* enters some people's houses *they have* the uncomfortable feeling that *they are* not wanted (one has, one is).

ONE OF THE MOST IMPORTANT, IF NOT THE MOST IMPORTANT.

Care must be exercised in using expressions of this type. The following exemplifies a fairly common error—

The heavy steel makers feel that their industry represents one of the most important, if not the most important, basic industry of the country.

After *one of the most important* we need *industries*, but after *if not the most important* we must have the singular *industry*. The difficulty can be avoided by writing: " feel that their industry is one of the most important basic industries in the country, if not the most important."

ONLY.

When this word is used as an adverb it must be placed next to the word or phrase to which it refers ; otherwise the sense is distorted. This rule is very frequently neglected. Examples—

The bonnet of the Scots Guards was once *only* saved in the nick of time from abolition by the personal interference of Queen Victoria.

(*Only* is intended to refer to either *in the nick of time* or *by the personal interference of Queen Victoria*. It should be placed immediately in front of the one or the other according to the sense required.)

The reason why it has been impossible to establish this night flying service sooner is that at present the route is *only* marked by beacons between London and Paris.

(Alter to—" only between London and Paris.")

(See RULE OF PROXIMITY.)

ORGY.

Pronounced: or'jĭ.

-OS, -OES.

Doubt often arises whether a particular word ending in *-o* makes its plural by adding *-s* or *-es*. The rules on the subject are rather vague and unsatisfactory, so that it does not seem worth while to quote them. It will be useful, however, to give lists of the chief words (1) with plurals in *-os*, (2) with plurals in *-oes*.

(1)	albinos	embryos	mementos
	archipelagos	fiascos	octavos
	arpeggios	folios	photos
	bravos (applause)	ghettos	pianos
	calicos	grottos (*or* -oes)	provisos
	cameos	halos	quartos
	cantos	infernos	Romeos
	crescendos	magnetos	solos
	dittos	magnificos	stylos
	dynamos	manifestos	tyros
(2)	banjoes (*or* -os)	dominoes	mottoes
	bravoes (bullies)	echoes	negroes
	buffaloes	heroes	potatoes
	cargoes	jingoes	tomatoes
	dagoes	mangoes	volcanoes

OTHER.

In the statement of a comparison, *other* must be used after a comparative adjective. It is incorrect to say, " Jones is more efficient than any man in his shop." *Any man* includes Jones, and we are in effect saying that he is more efficient than himself. *Other* must be inserted after *any*: we then separate Jones from the men with whom he is compared.

OTHERWISE.

Otherwise is an adverb meaning ***in a different way***, etc. It should not be used as a substitute for an adjective or a noun. It is correct to say—I am not sure whether he acted honestly ***or otherwise*** (***otherwise*** is an adverb qualifying ***acted***); but it is wrong to say—I am not sure whether he is honest ***or otherwise*** (here ***otherwise*** is substituted for the adjective ***dishonest***), or—I must be satisfied of his honesty ***or otherwise*** (here ***otherwise*** does duty for the noun ***dishonesty***). The second sentence should be written—I am not sure whether he is honest ***or not*** (***or not*** may be omitted), and the third should be simply—I must be satisfied of his honesty.

PARAGRAPH: HINTS ON CONSTRUCTION.

It is hardly necessary to explain that a paragraph is a group of sentences dealing with one idea, and that every piece of prose of any length must be divided into paragraphs. Everybody with the least experience of writing knows this. But not everybody masters the art of constructing good paragraphs, and this is partly because the importance of the matter is not realized. Yet if a letter or a statement of any kind giving an explanation or an argument is to be made convincing, it is essential that the facts or reasons should be organized into groups which clearly indicate the stages of thought. How can this be done? Of course, a well-built paragraph is ultimately the result of clear thinking; but when the thinking has been done, the written expression of the ideas is facilitated by a knowledge of the technical points concerning paragraph-structure. The purpose of the present article is to explain these technical points.

1. **Unity.** It is necessary first of all to insist on the fact stated in the definition of a paragraph. *All the sentences in a paragraph must relate to one idea.* To say the same thing in another way—no sentence must be included in a paragraph if it does not contribute to the expression of the main idea. This rule seems simple enough ; but it is often disregarded. A paragraph must be thought of as a *whole*—as a statement which has *unity*, i.e. singleness of idea.

2. **How to Emphasize the Central Idea.** Obviously, in order to construct an effective paragraph, it is necessary to make perfectly clear what the central idea is. This can be done in more than one way—

(*a*) *The main idea may be stated in the first sentence.* This is the simplest and commonest method. Consider the following paragraph from an article in *The Times*—

> Shareholders in British rubber companies have every reason to be grateful to the Government and the Committee of Civil Research, upon whose report their decision has been based, for terminating the restriction scheme as from the end of October next. All the disadvantages of that uneconomic scheme have fallen exclusively upon British companies operating in British territory and (to a lesser extent) upon British companies in foreign territory which voluntarily submitted themselves to a degree of restriction but milder than the compulsory variety. All the advantages of the scheme were secured by the growers in the Dutch East Indies and other non-restricting areas which, of course, suffered none of the disabilities of restriction. The great growth of their industry is a measure of the advantages they gained from it. Under the scheme the British sold less rubber than they could produce, received the same price as their competitors, but as their costs were higher by several pence per pound their margin of profit was smaller. On the other hand,

> the Dutch and other foreign growers sold largely increased amounts of rubber, their costs were consequently lower, and their margins of profit wider. After October the British estates will be able to sell as large amounts of rubber as their competitors, receive the same price and profit margin, since their costs, other things being equal, will be the same. In other words, the removal of restriction will be a benefit and not a menace to those concerned in the British rubber industry.

The theme of the paragraph, stated in the first sentence, is that the British rubber companies will benefit by the removal of restrictions. The following sentences give the reasons for this statement. The advantages of the restrictions to foreign companies and the disadvantages to British companies are explained, and the final sentence rounds off the argument with a repetition, in varied terms, of the main idea.

(*b*) In cases where several facts or reasons are put forward in order to lead up to a conclusion, ***the statement of the central idea is reserved for the final sentence.*** The following paragraph illustrates this method of construction—

> Here in the South we have again suffered from the depredations of pirates, while a series of political changes at Canton has also had a hampering effect on mercantile enterprise. In spite of this, the trade of this colony has shown a steady and healthy recovery from the low point reached in the previous year, though it is by no means equal in volume to that of three or four years ago. A distinct improvement has occurred in piece goods, though the trade is now feeling the effect of increased manufacturing costs, and there has been a noticeable activity in the export of wood oil which, blocked on the Yangtze, is finding

> an exit in the South. Taking all into account, Hong-Kong's record for the year is not unsatisfactory, and there are fair indications that the improvement is likely to continue.

Here a survey of the facts leads to the conclusion, given in the last sentence, that trade in Hong-Kong is not unsatisfactory and is improving.

(*c*) Sometimes the central idea of a paragraph is not stated at all completely in any one of the sentences. In such a case the connection of the facts or ideas must be made very definite, so that the reader may easily grasp the theme. *It should always be possible to express the theme in a single sentence.* Thus, in the following paragraph none of the sentences fully expresses the theme, but the central thought could be set out briefly in these terms—

> The Chinese military and civil authorities who now control the railways are entirely neglecting to provide money needed for maintenance and repairs, and therefore some of the lines will soon become unworkable.

The paragraph—

> It is well known that the maintenance in a state of efficiency of any railway necessitates the current expenditure of a considerable portion of the earned revenue for the upkeep of the permanent way and rolling stock and a hundred and one other essentials. But the Chinese military and civil authorities into whose hands the control of railways has passed have so far entirely ignored this fundamental principle. Intent only on extracting as much money as possible, they have starved the railways of even the most urgent requirements. In such circumstances the rate of deterioration rapidly gathers pace, and it is to be feared that, if some settlement of China's political

disputes is not shortly reached and the revenues restored to the railway administrations, some of the lines will before long become unworkable and will need the expenditure of many millions of dollars before they can again be rendered fit for regular traffic.

3. **Examples of Faulty Paragraph-Structure.** A criticism of one or two bad paragraphs will serve to illustrate the principles stated above.

(*a*) Consider the following paragraph from a report of a company meeting—

Cement manufacturers have for many years and to a considerable extent co-operated to secure reasonable trading conditions. For a period pre-war the acute conditions of over-production and undercutting of prices produced a situation which resulted in there being no adequate return on the capital invested in the industry; indeed, the earnings of some companies and firms were insufficient to provide for depreciation. No industry called more clearly for the benefit of co-operation than the cement trade, an industry in which there can never be a monopoly on account of the bounteous distribution of the raw materials and the small area that this country offers for the distribution of the manufactured product.

Let us see how this paragraph is built up. The ideas in the three sentences can be briefly expressed thus—(1) Cement manufacturers have co-operated for many years, (2) competitive conditions before the war were injurious to the industry, (3) the peculiar circumstances of the trade call for co-operation. There is a connection between these ideas, but the writer has not made it sufficiently clear: it is only implied, whereas it should be explicit. Evidently the first sentence is intended to give the topic, but the next two sentences do not reinforce the idea as they should do. If suitable connecting sentences were introduced, and the paragraph were re-cast as follows, it would be much more effective. The words providing the connections have been italicized)—

Cement manufacturers have for many years and to a considerable extent co-operated to secure reasonable trading conditions. *The desirability of this policy was brought home to them by their experiences in the years before the war.* For a period the acute conditions of over-production and undercutting of prices produced a situation in which there was no adequate return on the capital invested in the industry; indeed, the earnings of some companies and firms were insufficient to provide for depreciation. *Co-operation was adopted as a means of salvation. The co-operative method of working is, indeed, especially suited to the cement trade, for in this particular industry* there can never be a monopoly on account of the bounteous distribution of the raw materials and the small area that this country offers for the distribution of the manufactured product.

(*b*) The following are the first two paragraphs of an article in *The Times*.

A DAY WITH A PROVINCIAL PACK.

Those of us who hunted mildly before the war, and who have since been too busy with the struggles of post-war existence, have often wondered how people manage to hunt nowadays, when country houses are standing empty, farms are derelict, main roads are skating rinks, and hundreds of thousands of new small houses cover what were then green fields. Hunting in Leicestershire and with the other famous packs of course goes on, as we know from the papers, as keenly as ever. But Leicestershire was always for rich men;

> the local folk hunted as a matter of course, but there was always a fashionable crowd of visitors. There are still plenty of rich men and women, and Leicestershire in the winter is still the fashion.
>
> But the provincial packs—how do they exist? The old Mudshire, for instance, where we had so many happy days, now that the Duke's castle is turned into an hotel and half a dozen other great houses into schools or convents: with all the new factories round Muddleton (one on the site of a famous covert), with the main roads—and we did a lot of hunting on the roads—covered with motor-cars like Piccadilly?

The opening sentence seems to give the main idea of the paragraph, i.e. Some of us wonder how people manage to hunt at all under present-day conditions. But then the writer goes off to talk about hunting in Leicestershire, and we are forced to ask exactly what the connection is, and when he is coming back to his original point. He does not return to it until the sentence—"But the provincial packs—how do they exist?" But this is made to begin a new paragraph. Why? Clearly there should be no paragraph-division here. The whole of the passage quoted should form a single paragraph dealing with the theme suggested in the opening remark. Considerable re-casting is necessary, however, if the topic is to be made clear and the connection of ideas is to be shown. The re-writing might be carried out thus—

> Those of us who hunted mildly before the war, and have since been too busy with the struggles of post-war existence to indulge in the sport, have often wondered how people manage to hunt nowadays, when country houses are standing empty, farms are derelict, main roads are skating-rinks, and hundreds of thousands of new small houses cover what were then green fields. We know from the papers that

hunting goes on as keenly as ever in Leicestershire, and we can understand this, for the sport in that county is for rich men. There are still plenty of rich men and women, and so there is still, as there always was, a fashionable crowd of hunting people in Leicestershire during the winter. But the question is how the provincial packs continue to exist. How does the old Mudshire manage, for instance, now that the Duke's castle is turned into an hotel, and half the other great houses have become schools or convents; now that there are new factories round Muddleton (one on the site of a famous covert), and the main roads (we used to do a lot of hunting on the roads) are covered with motor-cars like Piccadilly?

PARAMOUNT.

Followed by *to*.

In coming to the conclusion not to adopt this scheme we considered the question of expense to be *paramount to* all others.

PARENTHESIS.

The use of Parenthesis, i.e. of a group of words enclosed within brackets, or marked off by dashes, has its disadvantages and should not be allowed to become a regular feature of one's style. There is, of course, no objection to an occasional and careful parenthesis, as in—

And would industry be revived faster by clapping a Surtax on the "idle, parasitic, good-for-nothing shareholder" (*as Mr. Shinwell calls him*) than by lowering the rates on his business?

By the mercy of providence, and by one man's vote—*a critical division resulted in a tie*—the County Council had been saved from cramping itself up in the Adelphi.

But a long parenthesis which reads like an afterthought clumsily thrust into the middle of a sentence instead of being given a proper place by itself has a distinctly unpleasant effect. The reader is jerked from one idea to another, and the rhythm of the sentence is spoilt. (See RHYTHM.) Examples—

Here, where was the happiest place in London to set up a beautiful thing, hard fate had decreed that there should be built—*in the days when art was at its very lowest and people thought of nothing but utility with cheapness*—one of the ugliest structures created by man.

Apparently His Majesty's Government—*perhaps it is the Ministry of Transport: perhaps the movement comes from even higher up*—have come out into the open and are prepared to take a hand. They realize the immense advantage to the capital of the Empire; they are—*we hear to our delight, indeed to our amazement*—prepared to find three-quarters of the cost.

PARIAH.

Pronounced: pār′iah, or păr′iah.

PARTICIPLES.

The Present Participle of a verb ends in *-ing*. It is found in tense forms such as: I am *seeing*, they were *walking*. *The Past Participle* sometimes ends in *-ed*, *-d*, or *-t*, sometimes in *-en*, *-n*, or *-ne*, and sometimes has no ending; e.g. walked, said, slept, ridden, sown, gone, rung. It is used to form the perfect tenses (e.g. I have *seen*) and the passive voice (e.g. I am *seen*) of a verb. *The Perfect Participle* contains the auxiliary *having*, e.g. having seen, having walked.

Besides being used with the auxiliary verbs *to be* and *to have*, as explained above, participles are often used alone. They are then *verb-adjectives*—

1. They can be employed like ordinary adjectives to qualify a noun.—A *thriving* business ; a *broken* contract.

2. They may introduce an adjective-phrase qualifying a noun or pronoun—

The flood-water, *flowing* along the street, entered the basements of the houses. (The pres. part. *flowing* introduces the adj.-phrase *flowing along the street*, which qualifies *water*.)

Broken by his misfortunes, he retired from business.

Having disposed of this matter, we may proceed to the next item on the agenda.

3. They may be used with a noun or pronoun in Absolute Phrases. (See ABSOLUTE PHRASES.)

(See also UNRELATED PARTICIPLES and CONFUSION OF PARTICIPLE AND GERUND.)

PARTS OF SPEECH.

According to the function they perform in a sentence words are said to belong to one or other of the eight "parts of speech," viz., noun, pronoun, verb, adjective, adverb, preposition, conjunction, interjection. For definitions see separate articles. Note that a given word may belong to more than one part of speech according to its work in a particular sentence. Thus, *round* is an adjective in—I need a *round* piece of wood ; a verb in—The policeman saw the car *round* the corner at high speed ; a preposition in—I walked *round* the corner ; an adverb in—The postman comes *round* three times a day ; a noun in—The actor was given a *round* of applause.

PASSIVE VOICE.

(See VOICE.)

PATENT.

This is usually pronounced pā'tent. Some people say

pă'tent in *Patent Office, letters-patent*, etc., but there is no good reason for the distinction.

PATRIOT.

Pronounced: pā'triot, or pă'triot. The B.B.C. adopts: ā.

PATRON, PATRONAGE.

Pronounced: pā'tron, pă'tronage.

PERCENTAGE.

Percentage is a mathematical term with a perfectly definite technical sense. It does not mean merely *part* or *proportion*. There is no justification for using it in such sentences as—

> Only a percentage of the readers of this journal will agree with the views expressed by the Home Secretary.
>
> A larger percentage of land has this year been laid under grass by English farmers.

The large number of writers who delight in using pseudo-scientific expressions rather than plain English seem to think that 50 *per cent* and 25 *per cent* are always interchangeable with *a half* and *a quarter*, and so they are betrayed into such absurdities as this—

> I was a season-ticket holder at Epsom for years, and can say that the fastest train to or from London now takes 50 per cent longer time than before the war.

PEREMPTORY.

The best authorities favour the pronunciation: per'-emptory. The B.B.C. Announcers, however, say: per-emp'tory.

PERFECT INFINITIVE.

The perfect infinitive of a verb is formed with *to have*; e.g. to have seen, to have gone. (See INFINITIVE.)

The perfect infinitive is often used unnecessarily in place of the present infinitive after such expressions as—*I should have liked, he would have been the first,* e.g.—

I should have liked *to have gone* if the weather had been fine.

He would have been the first *to have volunteered* if his services had been needed.

In these cases *to go* and *to volunteer* are required. The notions that I did not in fact go and that he did not volunteer are sufficiently conveyed by the use of *have* in the preceding verbs.

After *hoped, intended, expected,* etc., there is a similar use of the perfect infinitive—

I hoped *to have been* able to finish the work by Christmas.

He intended *to have given* me the money when he saw me.

Again the present infinitive (*to finish, to give*) could be used, but these examples may be defended on the ground that the perfect infinitive conveys idiomatically the idea of the non-fulfilment of the hope or intention. (This idea is not expressed by the main verb.)

PERIPHRASIS.

(See CIRCUMLOCUTION.)

PERMEATE.

This word should not be followed by *through.* Correct use—The influence of irresponsible agitators *permeated* the whole of the factory.

PERSON.

Pronouns standing for the person *speaking* are said to be in the *first person,* e.g. *I, us*; those standing for the person *spoken to* are said to be in the *second person,* e.g. *you* ; and those standing for the person or thing *spoken about* are said to be in the *third person,* e.g. *he, they.* All nouns except those in the vocative case are in the third person. A verb agrees with its subject in person.

PERSONAL PRONOUNS.

Many errors in grammar arise through the misuse of the cases (see ERRORS IN CASE). Such mistakes occur chiefly in connection with the pronouns. The following list of the Personal Pronouns is therefore useful in showing the variety of case-forms—

	Singular			*Plural*		
Person	1st	2nd	3rd	1st	2nd	3rd
Nom.	I	thou (you)	he, she, it	we	you	they
Acc.	me	thee (you)	him, her, it	us	you	them
Gen.	mine	thine (yours)	his, hers, its	ours	yours	theirs
Dat.	me	thee (you)	him, her, it	us	you	them

PERSPICACIOUS—PERSPICUOUS.

These two words are often confused, even by writers who ought to know better. *Perspicacious* means *having mental penetration or discernment*—Even the least *perspicacious* of the European statesmen should have foreseen that war with Germany was inevitable. *Perspicuous* means *clear, easily understood* ; it applies to a piece of writing or a speech—This writer has given a *perspicuous* account of a difficult subject.

PHARMACEUTICAL.

Pronounced: pharmasū'tical, or pharmakū'tical. The B.B.C. prefers the *s* to the *k* sound.

PHRASE.

In grammatical terminology a phrase is a group of words having no subject and predicate and being equivalent to a single part of speech. (See ADJECTIVE-PHRASES AND ADJECTIVE-CLAUSES and ADVERB-PHRASES AND ADVERB-CLAUSES.)

PHTHISIS.

The older pronunciation was: thī'sis; but fthī'sis is now becoming usual. The B.B.C. adopts the former.

PIANOFORTE

The B.B.C. Announcers sound the final *e*. The pronunciation without this *e* is allowable, however.

PLEBISCITE.

Pronounced: plĕb'ĭssĭt.

PLEONASM.

(See REDUNDANCY OF EXPRESSION.)

PLURAL NUMBER.

(See NUMBER.)

PLURALS OF COMPOUND NOUNS.

It is sometimes difficult to know what is the correct plural of a compound noun. Generally the most important element in the compound takes the plural sign; but usage varies. Here are some examples.—*Step-sons, sons-in-law, hangers-on, maid-servants, courts-martial, governors-general* (here *general* is an adjective), *lieutenant-generals* (here *general* is a noun), *lord-chancellors, commanders-in-chief*.

Occasionally both elements are pluralized—*men-servants, lords-justices*.

The plural of *spoonful* is *spoonfuls*.

PLURALS OF FOREIGN WORDS.

Many foreign words retain their foreign plural in English. Such words were originally learned and technical. Some of them, however, have passed into the common language and English plurals have been formed. In some cases the foreign and the English plural are merely alternatives; in others they have been differentiated in meaning. A list of foreign words with their plurals is given below—

Latin and Greek. Addendum, addenda; analysis, analyses; appendix, appendices; axis, axes; basis, bases; crisis, crises; criterion, criteria; erratum, errata; formula, formulae or formulas; fungus, fungi or funguses; genius, genii (familiar spirits) geniuses; genus, genera; hypothesis, hypotheses; index, indices (in mathematics) indexes (to books); larva, larvae; memorandum, memoranda (notes to aid memory) memorandums (legal documents); nucleus, nuclei; oasis, oases; phenomenon, phenomena; radius, radii; series, series; species, species; stimulus, stimuli; stratum, strata; terminus, termini or terminuses.

French. Beau, beaux; bureau, bureaux; portmanteau, portmanteaux.

Italian. Bandit, banditti or bandits; dilettante, dilettanti; Fascist, Fascisti or Fascists; libretto, libretti; virtuoso, virtuosi.

Hebrew. Cherub, cherubim, or cherubs; seraph, seraphim.

POPULACE.

This word is not synonymous with *people, public.* It means *the common people, the rabble.*

POSSESSIVE (GENITIVE) CASE.

(See CASE.)

POSSESSIVE PROBLEMS.

(See GENITIVE PROBLEMS.)

POSTHUMOUS.

Pronounced: pŏst'ūmous.

POTENT—POTENTIAL.

Potent means *powerful, cogent*—

There are many strata of British society, comprising thousands of people, for whom the film is the most *potent* of all educational forces.

Potential means *latent, capable of coming into being or action*—

We have not yet developed or even explored all the *potential* resources of the British Empire.

Every private in the British army is a *potential* field-marshal.

PRACTICABLE—PRACTICAL.

Practicable is applied to something that is feasible, that can be done or brought into use. Nobody is likely to confuse this word with *practical* in such examples as—

A practical mechanic; a practical knowledge of the business; his efforts had no practical effect.

But in other cases there is possibility of error. If the Government reject a scheme because it is not *practicable*, they do so because circumstances make it impossible to carry it out: the scheme might be thoroughly *practical*, i.e. useful in effecting the purpose. *Practicable* and not *practical* is the right word in the following—

The British Empire contains large areas where cotton-growing is *practicable.*

Owing to the floods the road through the low-lying plain was not *practicable.*

PRACTICE—PRACTISE.

Practice is a noun.—"Practice makes perfect"; a doctor's practice.

Practise is a verb.—You must practise more regularly.

PRECEDENCE—PRECEDENT.

The normal present-day pronunciation of these words is: prĕss'ĭdence, prĕss'ĭdent. For the former, however, the B.B.C. adopts: prēssē'dence.

PRECIPITATE—PRECIPITOUS.

The adjective *precipitate* means *headlong, hasty, rash, ill-considered*—

The enemy saved themselves by *precipitate* flight.

The firm was greatly embarrassed by the *precipitate* action of the manager in breaking off negotiations without consulting his colleagues.

Precipitous means *steep, like a precipice*—

The *precipitous* descents made the road impracticable for cars.

PREDICATE.

(See SUBJECT AND PREDICATE.)

PREDICATIVE WORDS.

Some verbs, instead of taking an object (see OBJECT), are followed by a noun, a pronoun, or an adjective referring to the subject. This word completes the predicate and is therefore called a predicative word. (The older name was COMPLEMENT)—

1. **Predicative Nouns.** Jones is the *secretary*. The girl became a *typist*. He was elected *captain*.

The italicized words in these sentences name the same person as the subject: they are thus quite distinct from objects. (An object names a person or thing different from the subject, and an action is performed on this person or thing; e.g. They elected a *captain*.)

2. **Predicative Pronouns.** Pronouns may be similarly used—

It is *I*. Was it *you* who did that? No, it was *he*.

3. **Predicative Adjectives** form part of the predicate and refer to the subject—

The man seems ***honest.*** I am *glad.*

PREFER.

The construction with this verb causes difficulty. We prefer one thing *to* another, or we prefer *doing* one thing *to doing* another. *Prefer* must on no account be followed by *than* instead of *to.* Incorrect—We should prefer to leave early *than* have the discomfort of travelling in crowded trains. The difficulty arises here because *prefer* is followed by an infinitive. We could not say—We should prefer to leave early *to* to have. . . If the word *prefer* is retained in such a sentence the only way out is to say—We should prefer to leave early *rather than* have . . . It would be better, however, to use another verb—We *would rather* leave early than . . .

PREFERABLE.

Followed by *to.* The correct constructions are—

This thing is *preferable to* that ; *Doing* this is *preferable to doing* that.

(See PREFER.)

It is obviously wrong to use the expression *more preferable,* for *preferable* by itself means " *more* desirable."

PREFERENCE.

Preference may be followed by either *to* or *over* ; e.g. His preference of his own plan *to* (or *over*) all others was obvious.

You cannot expect me to give you the preference *over* everybody else.

PREJUDICIAL.

Followed by *to.*

Such unscrupulous conduct must be *prejudicial to* his reputation.

PREMIER.

Pronounced either prĕ′mier or prē′mier. The former is preferable.

PREOCCUPIED.

Followed by *with*.

He was so *preoccupied with* the thoughts of his coming speech that he could give no attention to other matters.

PREPOSITION.

A preposition begins a phrase and is said to govern the noun or pronoun in that phrase. (See PHRASE.) E.g.—

The letter is (*in* the basket).
He walked (*through* the office).
The box was (*by* the window).

The prepositions are italicized; the phrases are in brackets; the nouns governed by the prepositions are *basket, office, window*.

Some of the chief prepositions are:—about, above, across, after, against, along, around, at, before, behind, beneath, beside(s), between, by, down, during, except, for, from, in, into, of, off, on, over, round, since, through till, to, towards, under, underneath, up, upon, with.

Many of the above words may also be used as adverbs; e.g. The boy remained *behind* (adv. qualifying *remained*). But—The boy remained *behind* the door (prep. gov. *door*).

There are a few double (or "compound") prepositions, e.g. according to, out of, as to, owing to.

PREPOSITIONS AT THE END OF SENTENCES.

It is apparently still widely taught that a sentence should not end with a preposition. There can be no question that there are cases where a final preposition is very inelegant, e.g.—

He was not willing to accept the post that the committee had nominated him *for* (*for which* the committee had nominated him).

Our agents will call on the customers that the circulars were recently posted *to* (*to whom* the circulars . . .)

But there can also be no question that there are cases where the final preposition is thoroughly idiomatic and elegant. "He asked me what I was laughing *at*," and "Our experiences will give us something to talk *about*" are surely preferable to "He asked me *at what* I was laughing," and, "Our experiences will give us something *about which* to talk."

The fact is that those who try to insist on the avoidance of the final preposition have not considered English idiom sufficiently carefully. Whether a preposition is allowable or not at the end of a sentence must be settled on the merits of the particular case.

PREPOSITIONS USED IDIOMATICALLY.

Particular prepositions are used idiomatically with certain words, e.g. acquiesce *in*, militate *against*, immune *from*, compatible *with*. It is a serious error to use the wrong preposition in such cases. (See IDIOM.)

Separate articles are given on the words which are likely to give rise to mistakes.

PREPOSITIONS USED IN EXCESS.

It is very easy to fall into the habit of writing sentences containing a long string of prepositions. Such sentences may be grammatically accurate, but, at any rate in their worst forms, they are intolerable to anyone who is at all sensitive to prose-rhythm. The following passage was taken from the report of a company meeting: one wonders how the chairman could have read it aloud without shuddering—

> It was their determination *to* act *in* a spirit *of* loyalty *to* the important and essential principles *of* standardization and co-ordination *in* the supply *of* electricity *throughout* the country *on* sound economic lines *for* the recognition *of* which some *of* them had striven *during* very long periods *of* time.

(The final circumlocution *during very long periods of time* was used instead of *for a very long time* apparently in order that one more preposition might be dragged in.)

The quotation of one or two more examples of the unpleasant results produced by a plethora of prepositions should put the reader on his guard against this particular malady. These sentences should be read aloud—

> We find it difficult *to* reconcile the British conviction *with* their present unwillingness *to* recognize our right *to* build a limited number *of* the type *of* ships we would desire, or *with* their willingness *to* risk the success *of* this conference because they fear the problematical possession *by* us *during* the life *of* this treaty *of* a small number *of* 8 in. gun cruisers.

> This brings him into religious conflict with the newly-conquered Moslem states, for example, the Hejaz, whose susceptibilities he is forced to wound *in* deference *to* the abhorrence *of* his followers *for* certain features *of* old-established ritual connected *with* the traditions *of* Islam. (Write: because his followers abhor certain features of old-established ritual connected with Mohammedan traditions.)

> The directors greatly appreciate this recognition *of* the good work which the company is doing *to* develop the generation and distribution *of* electricity *in* the West Riding and *of* the importance *of* the company *in* the settlement *of* any schemes which

may be made *for* the improvement *of* the supply *in* that area.

Such sentences generally need to be completely re-expressed, fewer abstract nouns being used.

PREVENT.

We may say—I will prevent him *from* doing this, or, I will prevent *his* doing this; but not—I will prevent him doing this. (See CONFUSION OF PARTICIPLE AND GERUND.) An example of the error—

By effecting economies and by improving equipment the tramway companies are doing all they can to *prevent* their position *being* worsened. (Write: prevent their position from being worsened, or, prevent the worsening of.)

PREVENTIVE, PREVENTATIVE.

Both forms are allowed. There is no distinction in meaning. *Preventive* is to be preferred, as the extra syllable in *preventative* is unnecessary.

PREVIOUS(LY).

Idiomatic usage requires *previous*, and not *previously*, in such sentences as—

It will be necessary to hold another meeting of the directors *previous to* signing the contract.

PRINCIPAL—PRINCIPLE.

Principal is either an adjective or a noun. Used as adjective—This is his principal source of income. As noun—He invested the principal at 7 per cent. He is the principal of the college.

Principle is always a noun and means *primary element, general law, rule of conduct*, etc.—

He is ignorant of the first principles of politics.

He is a man of no principles.

The two machines work on the same principle.

PROFILE.

The dictionaries recognize the three pronunciations: prō'fīl, prō'fēl, prō'fĭl. The second is probably the most common to-day, and is adopted by the B.B.C.

PROFUSE.

This word may be followed by either *in* or *of*—

The Prince was *profuse in* his expenditure on pleasures.

To allay the fears of his opponent he was *profuse of* compliments and assurances of his goodwill.

PRONOUN.

A pronoun is a word used in place of a noun. By means of a pronoun—

1. We avoid the repetition of a noun. Thus we say—

My friend was introduced to the manager, to *whom he* quickly explained the mistake, and *they* were soon on cordial terms;

instead of—

My friend was introduced to the manager, and my *friend* soon explained the mistake to the manager, and my *friend* and the *manager* were soon on cordial terms.

2. We mention persons or things without naming them—

This is mine. *Who* called just now? *Anyone* can see that *that* is wrong. Only *three* are left. Show me the book *which* you are reading. *Much* of it is very dull. *He* likes *it*, but *few* agree with *him*.

Grammarians distinguish many different kinds of pronouns, but this classification is unimportant for those who are not concerned with the technicalities of grammar. It is desirable, however, for practical purposes to know what Personal Pronouns, Relative Pronouns, and Interrogative Pronouns are. (See separate headings.)

PRONOUNS CARELESSLY USED.

The wrong or vague use of pronouns is one of the faults most commonly committed by the inexperienced writer. It is always necessary to see that *it, they*, etc., refer to a definite noun, and that they are so placed that the reference is clear.

The most elementary mistake consists in using a plural pronoun to refer to a singular noun, or *vice versa*. E.g.—

> We are sending you particulars of our latest model in the hope that you will be interested. *They* will be obtainable from all our agents in three weeks' time.

The ambiguous use of pronouns is exemplified in the following sentences—

> The State never interferes with a man's soul except to *its* disadvantage. (Does *its* refer to *state* or to *soul* ? Good sense is obtained either way.)
>
> The porter explained that he did not think that Mr. Smith left the manager until an hour after *he* had telephoned to the hospital. (Who telephoned ?)

The following passage illustrates the vague use of *it*—

> Sir,—The letter from Sir Robert Horne in your issue of 16 April, and Mr. Hacking's in this morning's are of peculiar interest at the present juncture, as the whole question is exercising the minds of the British industry very actively, and it is a matter of great concern for many manufacturers, knowing the position, as to exactly the method by which the situation can best be met. *It* has been most adequately expressed by Sir Robert Horne, and I am in substantial agreement with him. (What does *it* stand for ?)

On the careless use of the relative pronoun *which*, see WHICH.

PROPER NAMES: CORRECT PRONUNCIATION.

(See SURNAMES: CORRECT PRONUNCIATION.)

PROPER NOUN.

A proper noun is the name of a particular person or thing, e.g. James, London, The Vatican.

PROPOSITION.

This Americanism is being over-worked in present day English. Phrases such as "A sound business proposition," "a tough proposition," "a paying proposition," might well be confined to the colloquial language. The tendency to-day is to substitute *proposition* for a number of other words of varied meanings; e.g.—

> On the whole the British car is better built, and made of more reliable material, and is certainly worth more as a second-hand *proposition* than the foreign car (article, machine).

PROTAGONIST.

The Greek noun from which this word is derived meant the actor who took the chief part in a play. The proper sense to be attached to the English word is the chief person in the plot of a play or story. Largely owing to a mistaken notion that *protagonist* is a kind of opposite to *antagonist,* the former has gained currency in the sense of a leading person in a struggle, a champion or defender; e.g. He was one of the *protagonists* in the mid-nineteenth century struggle for factory regulation. This sense is now well established and is recognized by the dictionaries. But it is worth while objecting to one or two other misuses—

1. Since *protagonist* by itself means "*chief* actor," it is manifestly absurd to talk of "the *chief* protagonists."

2. Journalists and others are apt to use *protagonist* loosely without any regard to its true meaning. E.g.—

Two or three pioneering wheatears have made a descent on the coasts of Devon, thereby corroborating the claim of these birds to be considered the *protagonists* of the myriads of migrants that ere long will arrive. (Apparently *the first*, or *the forerunners* is intended.)

The *protagonists* of the revised Prayer Book managed their case in the House of Commons with strange lack of dexterity (*advocates*).

PROTOTYPE.

Many people who like to use this word do not appear to know its true meaning A prototype is the original thing of which some later thing is a copy, an imitation, or an improved form. The Byronic hero was the prototype of many characters in European romantic literature of the nineteenth century.

PUNCTUATION : GENERAL HINTS.

When a sentence is being written, certain stops or marks of punctuation are inserted to assist the reader to grasp the meaning. These stops indicate where the pauses should come in the reading, and so divide the words into groups according to the sense. The uses of the Full Stop (.), the Comma (,), the Semicolon (;), the Colon (:), the Dash (—), and Inverted Commas (" ") are explained in separate articles. To complete the list of stops we may mention here that the Question Mark (?) is used at the end of direct questions (Are you coming now ?), and that the Exclamation Mark (!) is used after exclamations (Oh ! What a shame !).

General Hints. It will be useful here to supplement

the special articles on individual stops with some general advice on punctuation—

1. Although writers conform in the main to certain definite rules, there is no system of punctuation which is or can be rigidly adhered to by everybody. Of course, ordinary sentences dealing with matters of fact can be punctuated strictly according to rule. But the need for latitude arises when the writing is of an abstract or imaginative character. Ideas cannot, like molten metal, be poured into ready-made moulds; subtle thoughts and feelings require an individual turn of phrase for adequate expression; and it is here that the writer finds modifications of the regular punctuation valuable.

2. The remarks in the foregoing paragraph are intended merely as an explanation of a fact which you will have observed for yourself, namely, that all people do not use stops in exactly the same way; but they are not intended to be taken as implying that it does not matter much how you punctuate. If you have to write about everyday affairs or business matters it is most important that you should adopt the recognized system of punctuation and adhere strictly to it. Proper punctuation is one of the means by which clearness of expression is to be attained.

3. Explanations of the use of the various stops necessarily involve a number of grammatical points, and therefore they may seem to you technical and complicated. Unfortunately the subject cannot be freed from technicalities. You need not, however, rely entirely on studying the rules. Observe carefully the punctuation of passages in books and newspapers. Observation of actual examples is quite as valuable as the study of rules

4. If your punctuation is weak, concentrate first on the full stop and the comma. When you have mastered

the correct use of these two stops, much more than half the battle is over. The colon is very seldom needed by most people for ordinary purposes. The semicolon is wanted more frequently, but generally no very serious error is committed if it is replaced by a comma or a full stop (according to the nature of the case).

5. One infallible rule is to be observed—*Never put a stop at any place in a sentence unless a pause would be required in the reading.*

6. It is better to under-punctuate than to over-punctuate. The absence of stops will sometimes pass unnoticed, but it is very irritating to a reader to be constantly pulled up by unwanted stops.

QUANDARY.

Pronunciation: kwŏndār′y, or kwon′dăry. The B.B.C. adopts the former.

QUITE.

This word should be used much more sparingly in writing than it is in conversation. *Quite* adds little or nothing to the sense in such sentences as—

> There was quite a large crowd present.
> He received quite a substantial sum of money.
> She had quite an overwhelming reception.

The colloquial expression *quite all right* should certainly not be admitted in writing. *Quite* is here completely superfluous, for it means the same as *all*.

REAL.

Real is an adjective and should not be used for the adverb *really*. Incorrect—

> REQUIRED, first-class layout Artist for " roughs "; must be capable of executing *real* slick pencil " roughs."

REASON WHY . . . BECAUSE.

The following sentence contains a very common error due to redundancy of expression—

> The reason why he left was because he was dissatisfied with his prospects.

Because merely repeats the idea already expressed in *the reason why*. The sentence may be altered to either (1) The reason why he left was *that* he . . ., or (2) He left *because* he . . .

Similar redundancy occurs in: *The reason why* he left was *on account of* his dissatisfaction with his prospects.

RECIPIENT.

> At a dinner held to mark his retirement Mr. —— *was the recipient of* a gold watch.

What justification is there for this favourite journalistic periphrasis for *received* or *was given* ?

RECONCILE.

One is reconciled *with* a person after a quarrel, but one becomes reconciled *to* an unpleasant situation.

RECONDITE.

Pronunciation: rĕ′condīte, or rĕcon′dīte. The B.B.C. adopts the latter.

REDUNDANCY OF EXPRESSION.

Redundancy of expression (i.e. the use of superfluous words) is always a fault, but it is particularly serious in business documents, which demand, above all, conciseness and precision of statement. Redundancy is sometimes due to sheer verbosity: long roundabout phrases are substituted for the simple, straightforward term. (See CIRCUMLOCUTION.) This article, however, deals with faults arising through the use of words which are quite unnecessary, or which merely repeat an idea expressed elsewhere in the sentence. Grammarians describe these errors under the terms *Pleonasm* and *Tautology*. Some typical examples are collected below—

We are undecided *as to* whether to go. (Omit *as to*.)

I like this *equally as well as* the other. (Omit *equally*.)

He handed in his resignation, *but* he reconsidered his decision, *however*, under pressure from the directors. (Omit *however*.)

Games, *as well as* being a relief to the mind, are *also* beneficial to bodily health. (Omit *also*.)

Fish abound *in great numbers* along the coast. (Omit *in great numbers*.)

There can be no shadow of doubt *but* that the credit of making the first aeroplane which could be flown belongs to Langley. (Omit *but*.)

A *unique* feature *in which Gorton Foundry stands alone* among the locomotive works of Great Britain lies in the possession of its Steel Foundry. (Omit *unique*.)

I feel certain that Hong-Kong, acting in *mutual co-operation* with her great neighbour, will show an increasingly fine record in years to come. (Omit *mutual*: it would be impossible for co-operation not to be mutual.)

Why the results were so poor was *because* there was difficulty in obtaining supplies of raw materials. (The results were so poor because . . .)

The effect of this deterioration was that it had brought about the necessity for sinking the shaft at this pit to the lower 4 ft. seam some few years earlier than had been anticipated. (This deterioration had made it necessary to sink . . ., or, The effect of this deterioration was that it was necessary to sink . . .)

REGARD AS.

(See CONSIDER.)

RELATIVE PRONOUN.

The Relative Pronouns are: *who, which, that, what* (and sometimes *as* and *but*). *Who* has the form *whom* for the accusative case, and *whose* for the genitive. A relative pronoun acts both as a conjunction introducing a clause, and as a pronoun which is the subject or the object of its clause or is governed by a preposition. It is called "relative" because it relates to another noun or pronoun known as its antecedent. Examples—

The traveller *who* called this morning will return this afternoon. (*Who* introduces the clause *who called this morning*, and acts as the subject of the verb *called.*)

The person *whom* he wanted was out. (The relative pronoun is here the object of *wanted.*)

The secretary is the man *to whom* you must apply. (Governed by the preposition *to.*)

Are those the books *which* (or *that*) you require?

The antecedents in the above sentences are: *traveller, person, secretary, books.*

The relative *what* is equal to *that which,* and thus contains its antecedent in itself—*What* he says must be true.

REMONSTRATE.

Pronounced: rĕmŏn′strāte.

Note the correct use of prepositions with this word. We remonstrate *with* a person *on* his conduct. This is the construction commonly employed in modern English. Occasionally the expression to remonstrate *against* something (cp. protest against) is met with.

REPLACE.

(See SUBSTITUTE.)

REPLICA.

Pronounced: rĕ′plĭca (rhyming with *Africa*).

REPORTED (OR INDIRECT) SPEECH: RULES FOR CONVERTING DIRECT INTO REPORTED SPEECH.

In writing reports of speeches and minutes of meetings it is frequently necessary to present the account in Reported or Indirect Speech; that is to say, the exact words of a speaker (i.e. Direct Speech) are not given, but what he said is reported as by another person who was present, and who writes in the past tense and the third person. The following are illustrations—

DIRECT SPEECH

"These remarks lead me to the matter of the claims made upon our advertisement columns. The demand from advertisers for more and more space continues, and your paper would have been hampered in its progress considerably had we not decided some three years ago to enlarge our printing works. As advertisers increase and their requirements for space extend, so more and more pages will be needed. Newspaper advertising in England is still in its infancy. Many manufacturers are only just beginning to realize its value."

REPORTED (INDIRECT) SPEECH

(The chairman said that) those remarks led him to the matter of the claims made upon their advertisement columns. The demand from advertisers for more and more space continued, and the company's paper would have been hampered in its progress considerably had they not decided some three years before to enlarge their printing works. As advertisers increased and their requirements for space extended, so more and more pages would be needed. Newspaper advertising in England was still in its infancy. Many manufacturers were only just beginning to realize its value.

Note.—Whereas inverted commas are used to mark Direct Speech, they are not used when the passage is turned into Reported form.

Rules for Converting Direct into Reported Speech

1. It is necessary to supply at the beginning of the passage a leading verb in the past tense—*He said that, The chairman remarked that, Mr.—— held the opinion that,* etc.

2. As a rule, verbs in the report must be in past tenses; thus—

speak	is changed to	*spoke*
is speaking	,,	*was speaking*
has spoken	,,	*had spoken*

Similarly—

shall	,,	*should*
will	,,	*would*
may	,,	*might*

3. Pronouns, adjectives, and adverbs that denote nearness in time or position must be changed to words denoting remoteness—

Direct—" *Here* we can see the position to which *these* measures have *now* brought us."

Reported—He said that *there* they could see the position to which *those* measures had *then* brought them.

This is changed to *that, these* to *those, now* to *then, here* to *there, hence* to *thence, last year* to *the year before,* etc.

4. Questions and commands need special treatment in the reported form. Examples—

Direct—(*a*) " Have the preparations been made ? "

(*b*) " Who was responsible for this scheme in the first place ? Who prepared the plans ? Have detailed estimates of the cost been submitted to the committee ? Are you satisfied that your resources will be adequate to the purpose ? "

Reported—(*a*) He asked whether the preparations had been made.

(*b*) He asked who was responsible for that scheme in the first place, and who prepared the plans. Had detailed estimates of the cost been submitted to the committee ? Were they satisfied that their resources would be adequate to the purpose ?

Direct—" Do not deceive yourselves in this matter."

Reported—He begged that they should not deceive themselves in that matter,

or—He urged them not to deceive themselves . . .

or—Let them not deceive themselves . . .

5. Names of people addressed are omitted—

Direct—" It is time, *gentlemen*, that we turned to the balance sheet."

Reported—(He said that) it was time they turned to the balance sheet.

6. When a number of pronouns like *I*, *he*, *you*, *they* are all changed to *he* or *they* in the report, ambiguity often arises. It is then necessary to substitute names for one or more of the pronouns.

Note.—For illustrations of the method of changing Direct into Indirect Speech the reader should refer to the Parliamentary Reports in *The Times*.

REPUTABLE

The accent is on the first syllable.

REREDOS.

Pronounced: rēr'dŏs (two syllables).

RESIDUARY.

Pronounced: rezĭd'uary.

RESIGN.

There is a growing practice of inserting an unnecessary *from* after ***resign***; e.g. Mr.—— has intimated his intention of resigning ***from*** his position on the board of directors. The correct idiom is "to resign a position," not "to resign *from* a position."

RESPECTIVE(LY).

Respective and ***respectively*** provide pitfalls for the unwary. The mistakes made in using them are generally quite gratuitous, for these words are often needlessly inserted. Consider some examples—

1. In connection with the London Borough Council elections it would be interesting to have the *respective* numbers of the men and women voting.

Respective is correctly used here: its purpose is to make it clear that two separate totals are referred to—one for men and one for women.

2. Our principal agents are Messrs. Harper & Co. and Messrs. Yates Bros., who have their premises *respectively* in Oxford Street and Long Acre.

What is the use of ***respectively*** here? Is anybody likely to think that the two firms jointly occupy premises in Oxford Street and also in Long Acre?

3. Six chief selling-agents will be appointed, and each will have his ***respective*** district assigned to him.

After *each* it is superfluous to add *respective*.

RESPITE.

Pronounced: rĕ′spĭt.

RETAIL—RETAILER.

When *retail* is a verb (he retails leather) the accent is on the second syllable. In other cases (a retail dealer, to sell by retail, etc.) the first syllable is stressed.

Retailer is accented on the second syllable.

RHYTHM.

One of the chief marks of good prose is its *rhythmical* quality. Rhythm is, of course, most commonly thought of in connection with verse, in which it appears in its most obvious forms; but prose also has its harmonies as can be seen from a page or two of any of the great authors. Read aloud, for instance, the following well-known passage in which Dr. Johnson described his feelings on seeing the ruins of the monastery at Iona. Notice the balance and the easy flow of individual sentences, and the harmony pervading the whole—

> We were now treading that illustrious Island, which was once the luminary of the Caledonian regions, whence savage clans and roving barbarians derived the benefits of knowledge, and the blessings of religion. To abstract the mind from all local emotion would be impossible, if it were endeavoured, and would be foolish if it were possible. Whatever withdraws us from the power of our senses, whatever makes the past, the distant, or the future, predominate over the present, advances us in the dignity of thinking beings. Far from me, and from my friends, be such frigid philosophy as may conduct us indifferent and unmoved over any ground which has been dignified by wisdom, bravery, or virtue. That man is little to be envied, whose patriotism would not gain force

upon the plain of Marathon, or whose piety would not grow warmer among the ruins of Iona.

After reading such passages it becomes clear that good writing demands something more than grammatical accuracy and clearness of expression, important as these two qualities are. Words, phrases, and clauses should be arranged in such a way that the sentence is pleasant to the ear when read aloud. It should not be imagined that good rhythm is a quality to be aimed at only by writers of great literature: everyday writing is enormously improved when it exhibits not only correctness but grace of expression. An example or two will show how irritating a sentence can be when its rhythm has been destroyed by bad phrasing—

> An outdoor life undoubtedly appeals to boys, and a speedy voyage to Canada, followed by training on a Government prairie farm, with a prospect of subsequently saving £100 by the time they reach 25 to enable them to purchase, under the special terms offered, farms of their own, can hardly fail, when brought to their notice by someone whom they respect, to appeal to healthy, high-spirited boys who have begun to think about their careers.
>
> During all this period, as may be imagined, the people of these Dominions have been trained up, and have become accustomed to, the American vehicle, as, whether they wished to or not—and apart altogether from the merits or otherwise of the vehicles being offered—they practically could not get any products from this country.

These sentences are spoiled by being chopped up into a number of short phrases and clauses and awkward parentheses.

ROMANCE.

The second syllable should be stressed.

RULE OF PROXIMITY.

The Rule of Proximity states that a word or group of words should be placed near to the word that it refers to. This is only a matter of common sense. When we are reading a sentence we naturally connect in our minds those words which are in proximity: if the wrong words are placed next to each other, we make the wrong mental connections. Breach of the rule thus causes either obscurity or absurdity. Everybody knows the sort of advertisement (real or faked) which runs—" Piano for sale by a lady with an overstrung frame." This is merely an extreme example of what happens when a phrase referring to one word is placed next to another. Notice how the position of *only* has to be varied in the following sentences—

1. He acted *only* in this play during the season.
2. He *only* acted in this play although he had been asked to produce it as well.

In (1) *only* refers to *in this play,* and in (2) it refers to *acted.*

Some examples of errors due to violation of the Rule of Proximity are given below—

No car could be produced at the present time having twelve minute cylinders in two separate crank-cases and having two crankshafts *at a reasonable cost.* (The last phrase refers to *could be produced.*)

There are no ordinary cheap ticket facilities for those who want to stay one night or two at their destination *except at week-ends.* (Put this phrase at the beginning.)

Dr. Raymond Pearl, professor of Biochemistry and Vital Statistics, Johns Hopkins University, Baltimore, in a paper printed in *Nature* in January last, gives the results of inquiries conducted by himself and Miss A. L. Bacon at the Johns Hopkins Hospital, Baltimore, covering a period of 34 years, *which may be of interest.* (The italicized clause refers to *results.* The sentence should be divided into two, with the necessary re-arrangement.)

There is no doubt that the strictest measures are *absolutely* still essential, as any sign of weakness would encourage the instigators, to locate all of whom has not yet been possible, *to further efforts.* (*Absolutely* should come before *essential,* and the last phrase should not be separated as it is from *would encourage the instigators.*)

Mistakes of this kind are particularly liable to occur in connection with the Correlative Conjunctions. (See CORRELATIVE CONJUNCTIONS.) Each member of a pair of Correlatives must be placed immediately before the word or group of words to which it relates. Examples of errors—

The result will be *both* beneficial to the heavy steel industry *and* to the consumers of heavy steel products, (Place *both* before *to.* It would be correct to say : both beneficial to the heavy steel industry *and advantageous* to the consumers.)

As an actor he was *not only* good in serious plays *but* in farce. (Place *not only* before *in.*)

The committee came to the conclusion that the project must be *either* abandoned *or* that further financial assistance must be sought. (Write : the conclusion that either the project . . . or further. . .)

He was *not* angry because of my remarks, *but* because his arrangements were upset. (Put *not* before *because.*)

RULES OF AGREEMENT.

There are certain rules governing the agreement of one word with another word in the sentence. They are very important because breaches of them lead to many of the commonest errors in composition—

1. **Agreement of a Verb with its Subject.**

(*a*) The simple rule is that a verb agrees with its subject in number and person. Thus, in the case of the verb *to be*, a subject *I* (first person, singular number) is followed by *am*, whereas *they* (third person, plural number) is followed by *are*. When the subject is a collective noun (see COLLECTIVE NOUN) the verb may be either singular or plural according to whether we are thinking of the collection as a whole or of the individual members.—

The crew *was* not large enough for the ship.
but—The crew *were* quarrelling among themselves.

Special applications of the rule are now to be noted—

(*b*) When the subject contains two or more nouns or pronouns connected by *and* the verb is plural—

Jones and Robinson *were* there.
He and I *are* partners

(*c*) When the subject consists of two or more *singular* words connected by *either* . . *or, neither* . . *nor,* the verb is singular—

Neither he (sing.) nor his partner (sing.) *was present.*

But—

Neither he (sing.) nor his friends (plur.) *were* present.

(*d*) When the subject consists of two or more words of different person, connected by *either* . . . *or, neither* . . *nor,* the verb agrees in person with the nearer—

Neither you (2nd per.) nor I (1st per.) *am* satisfied.

2. **Agreement of Nouns and Pronouns in Case.** A predicative noun or pronoun agrees in case with the

word to which it refers. (See CASE and PREDICATIVE WORDS.)—

He (nominative) is the *secretary* (nominative).

It (nominative) is *he* (nominative).

3. Agreement of Relative Pronoun. A relative pronoun agrees with its antecedent in number and person, but not in case. (See RELATIVE PRONOUN.)—

Those are the people *who* cause the trouble. (*Who* agrees with *people* (plur.); hence the plural verb *cause*).

You should not ask me *who* am ignorant of these matters. (*Me* is first person; therefore *who* and *am* are also first person. Note that while *me* is accusative case, *who* is nominative.)

(See ERRORS IN AGREEMENT.)

SALUBRIOUS—SALUTARY.

Salubrious means *healthy*, and is nearly always applied to a climate or a place (never to a person). A seaside resort may be described as salubrious.

Salutary (pronounced: săl'ūtary) means *beneficial*, or *producing good effects*. The accident taught the motorist a *salutary* lesson. Those who inspired the Factory Acts of the last century were responsible for some of the most *salutary* reforms of that period.

SAME.

The use of *same* or *the same* as a substitute for another pronoun (*it*, *them*, etc.), used to be a regular feature of "Business English"—e.g. We thank you for your order of yesterday, and will give *same* our best attention. This pointless variation from normal English has been condemned by every modern textbook on English composition, but it is still to be met with not only in letters but in business reports; e.g.—

The necessity for the modernization of stocks to

keep abreast of new developments in engineering and the requirements for the housing of *same* have led to the erection of large and well-equipped stock and show rooms in London and Glasgow.

SATIRE—SATYR.

A *satire* (pronounced: să'tīre) is a composition in prose or verse which holds up vice or folly to ridicule, or attacks an individual, a class, or a system.

A *satyr* (pronounced: să'ter) is one of a class of Greek woodland deities in half-human, half-animal form.

SCARCELY . . . THAN.

(See CONFUSION OF EXPRESSION.)

SCOTCH, SCOTTISH, SCOTS.

Which of these words (either as adjectives or nouns) should be used in reference to Scotland or its inhabitants? *Scotch* is a form of the word current in England. North Britons themselves prefer either *Scottish* (which is also in general use among the English) or *Scots* (which is rarer in England).

SEMICOLON.

The semicolon marks a longer pause than is indicated by a comma. The following are its uses—

1. It separates the two parts of a double sentence when the conjunction is omitted. (See DOUBLE SENTENCE, MULTIPLE SENTENCE.)—

> In public life he showed all the sternness and determination in his character; in his family life he was all kindness and consideration.

Compare Section (5) of the article on COMMA.

2 Even when the conjunction is inserted, a semicolon may be used in a double sentence if a longer pause

is required than would be indicated by a comma. This use of the semicolon is found frequently in longer sentences—

> There is no direct connection between unemployment and the size of the population ; but there is a fundamental connection between the numbers of the people and the standard of life which they can maintain in any given economic environment.
>
> Only a few weeks ago an alteration in the Australian Tariff Law was announced, which increases very materially the preference given to British-made pianos entering the Commonwealth ; and, from inquiries received, it is evident that this alteration should prove of substantial benefit to us in the development of our trade in that important market.

3. Sometimes several complete statements closely related in thought are grouped together in one sentence. Semicolons are used to separate them—

> The Prince began to find the study of politics less uninteresting than he had supposed ; he read Blackstone, and took lessons in English Law ; he was occasionally present when the Queen interviewed her Ministers ; and at Lord Melbourne's suggestion he was shown all the dispatches relating to foreign affairs.
>
> He had conducted an important negotiation with skill and tact ; he had been brought into close and friendly relations with the new Prime Minister ; it was obvious that a great political future lay before him.

(See PUNCTUATION : GENERAL HINTS.)

SENTENCE.

A sentence is a group of words that makes sense.

Sentences belong to three grammatical types—(1)

Simple, (2) Complex, (3) Double or Multiple. See under each heading.

It is essential that a sentence shall have *unity*. It may consist of various parts, but all these parts must relate to a central idea. The following sentence from a daily newspaper lacks unity. The writer of the news item has brought together two incongruous facts in one sentence—

> A substantial structure on a hill near the village, the barracks were provided with wireless apparatus, and the garrison, up to last February, consisted of eight men.

SERAGLIO.

Pronounced: sĕrah'lyo.

SHALL—WILL, SHOULD—WOULD.

The simple future tense of, e.g. *to go* is: 1st Person—I, we shall go. 2nd Person—You will go; 3rd Person—He, she, it, they will go. *Shall* is used in the 1st Person, and *will* in the 2nd and 3rd. Sometimes, however, we use *will* in the 1st Person and *shall* in the 2nd or 3rd. It is important to note that in such cases *something more than mere futurity is expressed*: we convey the idea of determination, of a promise or a threat. The following pairs of sentences make clear the difference—

1st Person—

> I *shall* go to-morrow if it is fine. (Mere futurity.)
>
> I have determined that I *will* go to-morrow whether it is fine or not. (Determination.)

2nd Person—

> He tells me that you *will* go to-morrow. (Mere futurity.)
>
> You *shall* go abroad with me if your work is satisfactory. (Promise.)

3rd Person—

He *will* go if he has permission. (Mere futurity.)

If his work does not improve, he *shall* not go abroad. (Threat.)

A similar distinction exists in the case of *should* and *would*. To express futurity (with respect to a point of time in the past) we must use *should* in the 1st Person, and *would* in the 2nd or 3rd.—I said that I *should* go the next day; You said that you *would* go the next day; He said that he *would* go the next day. But note the difference in meaning when *would* replaces *should* and *vice versa*—

I said that I *would* go the next day whatever happened. (Determination.)

I said that he *should* go with me if he really desired it. (Promise.)

This matter has been explained at some length because of the numerous mistakes which are made through disregard of the rule. The trouble arises partly because Scottish, Irish, and some provincial speakers tend naturally to confuse *shall* and *will*; but this does not explain the apparently wanton errors that so frequently occur. Examples—

If you will let us know your requirements we *will* be glad to send you specimens of our products (*shall*).

I am having inquiries made, and *will* have much pleasure in informing you of the result (*shall*).

When I addressed you a year ago I expressed the feeling that for the year 1927 I *would* be able to report that our business had been well maintained (*should*).

We have now secured premises at an annual cost considerably less than the rental which we *would* have had to face on a renewal of our lease (*should*).

One other point remains. If *shall* (or *will*) is used in a main clause, it should not be followed by *should* (or *would*) in the subordinate clause. Incorrect—We *shall* be very pleased if you *would* let us have a reply by return. (We shall . . if you will, or, We should . . . if you would.)

SHEIK.

Also spelt *sheikh*. Pronunciation: shēk, or shāk. The B.B.C. adopts the latter.

SIMPLE SENTENCE.

A Simple Sentence is one that contains only one subject and predicate. (See COMPLEX SENTENCE; DOUBLE SENTENCE, MULTIPLE SENTENCE; SUBJECT AND PREDICATE.)

SINECURE.

Pronounced: sī'nēcure.

SINGULAR NUMBER.

(See NUMBER.)

SLOGAN.

This word has recently been seized by journalists and advertising agents and popularized in the sense of *motto*, *maxim*, *watchword*. It is too late now to raise any objection, but it may be of interest to note that the true meaning of the word is *a Highland war-cry*.

SNOBBERY.

There is a snobbery in words as well as in manners, and the one is as objectionable as the other. Modern commercial advertising is responsible for the introduction of a large number of terms which attempt to remove the suggestion of social inferiority attaching to the ordinary word for the thing mentioned. A boarding-house becomes a "guest-house," and a boarder or lodger a "paying-guest." In the more genteel districts property is not sold: it is "disposed of." People who would hate to be caught buying a cheap article allow themselves to be attracted by something "inexpensive." Again, in times more squeamish than our own, certain people thought it desirable to replace unpleasant, downright words like "spit," "sweat," by "expectorate," "perspire." The trouble is, however, that all these polite synonyms in time acquire the same associations as the original words, so that we might as well be content to call a spade a spade.

SOVIET.

Pronounced: sō′vīĕt.

SPEED UP.

The verb *to speed up* has become so popular that many people are apt to forget that we have an older established and more elegant word, viz., *to accelerate.*

SPELLING: CHIEF RULES; WORDS FREQUENTLY MISSPELT.

This article is designed to do what is possible for weak spellers. If you are one of those unfortunate people, you will no doubt obtain some assistance from the rules given below. But you will still have considerable difficulty, because many words do not come under these rules, and many others are exceptions to the rules that seem to apply. There is really nothing for it but to make for yourself a list of the words that you find you misspell, and then set yourself somehow to learn the correct spelling. (As a protest against this drudgery you can, of course, join the Simplified Spelling Society, which will easily convince you that English spelling adds insult to injury by being thoroughly irrational as well as most difficult to learn.) For most people the best way is to write out the difficult word a number of times until they form a clear mental picture of the word which can be reproduced automatically. A few people have an aural memory: for them it is useful to spell the word aloud until they know it. A list of words commonly misspelt is given on pages 171-173; you should add any others that give you trouble.

Spelling Rules.

1. Words of one syllable ending in a single consonant preceded by a single vowel-letter double the consonant before a suffix—

dim, dimmer; jar, jarred; mad, madden.

2. A similar doubling takes place in words of more than one syllable if they end in a single consonant preceded by a single vowel-letter, *and if the accent is on the final syllable*—

acquit, acquitted; compel, compelling; defer, deferred.

3. This doubling does not take place (*a*) when the final consonant is preceded by two vowel-letters, and (*b*) when the accent is not on the last syllable. (But see Rule (4))—

(*a*) appeal, appealing; exceed, exceeded; contain, container.

(*b*) bigot, bigoted; combat, combatant; limit, limiting.

4. Whatever the position of the accent, final *l* is doubled, and in the case of final *s* usage varies—

cancel, cancelled; jewel, jeweller; label, labelled; marvel, marvellous; control, controlled.

bias, biased or biassed; focus, focusing or focussing.

5. Adverbs formed by adding *-ly* to adjectives ending in *-l* or *-ll* always contain a double *l*—

beautiful, beautifully ; dull, dully ; frugal, frugally.

6. A double *n* occurs in nouns formed by adding *-ness* to adjectives ending in *-n*—

common, commonness ; stern, sternness ; stubborn, stubbornness.

A double *n* also occurs in words formed by adding the prefixes *un-*, *en-*, *in-* to roots beginning with *n-* —

necessary, unnecessary ; noble, ennoble ; numerable, innumerable.

Those words in which the prefix *in-* is modified to *il-*, *ir-*, or *im-* have a double consonant—

legal, illegal ; regular, irregular ; mediate, immediate.

A double *s* occurs in those words formed by adding the prefix *dis-* to a root beginning with *s-* —

satisfied, dissatisfied ; similar, dissimilar.

But note the single *s* in—disappear, disappoint.

7. Words ending in silent *-e* drop the *e* before a suffix beginning with a vowel, but not before one beginning with a consonant—

move, movable, but—movement ; blame, blamable, but—blameless ; excite, exciting, but—excitement.

Exceptions.—Words in which the silent *-e* is preceded by *c* or *g* retain the *e* before a vowel in order that the *c* and the *g* may not lose their soft sound—

advantage, advantageous ; notice, noticeable.

8. Words ending in *-y* preceded by a consonant change *y* into *i* before a suffix—

lady, ladies ; cry, cried ; penny, penniless ; vary, variable

(But note—chimney, chimneys; journey, journeys. The *y* is preceded by a vowel-letter.)

Exceptions.—If the suffix begins with *i* the *y* remains—

try, trying; copy, copyist.

9. In words containing *ei* or *ie* with the sound ē (as in receive, believe) *i* comes before *e* except after *c*—

believe, chief, achieve, piece, relieve, retrieve, etc.,

but—receive, perceive, receipt, ceiling, etc.

Exceptions—

seize, weir, weird, counterfeit, inveigle;

and also proper names, e.g. Madeira, Leith.

10. On the question of *-ize* and *-ise* see -IZE OR -ISE.

11. On the proper use of the apostrophe, see GENITIVE PROBLEMS.

12. On the plural of words ending in *-o*, see -OS, -OES.

13. The American practice of using *-or* instead of *-our* in certain words (e.g. labor, favor) should not be followed.

List of Words Frequently Misspelt

Note.—1. The words which give most trouble are marked with an asterisk.

2. Words belonging to the following groups should be noted and compared—(*a*) those ending in *-able, -ible*; (*b*) those ending in *-ant, -ent, -ance, -ence*; (*c*) those ending in *-ence, -ense*; (*d*) those ending in *-al, -le*; (*e*) those beginning with *acq-, aq-*; (*f*) those containing *-ceed, -cede*; (*g*) those containing *-eem, -eme*; (*h*) those words which are pronounced alike but which are spelt differently according to their meaning or to the part of speech to which they belong.

abridgement, or— abridgment
abscess
accede
accelerate
accessible
accessory
***accommodate**
***accumulate**

WORDS FREQUENTLY MISSPELT—(*contd.*)

*achieve
acknowledgement, or—acknowledgment
*acquaintance
*acquiesce
acquitted
adjustable
admissible
adolescent
*advantageous
advice (noun)
advise (verb)
advisability
aerial
*aeroplane
*agreeable
argument
all right (not—alright)
allotted
already
annihilate
anonymous
antecedent
appalling
*arctic
ascendancy, or—ascendency
ascendant, or—ascendent
assassinate
assessable
autumn
auxiliary
battalion
*beginning
*believe
*beneficial
*benefited
besiege
biassed, or—biased
bigot
*bigoted
Britain (country)
Briton (person)
*Britannia
*Brittany
*business
calendar
canvas (noun)
canvass (verb)
cellar
changeable
chaos
chargeable
circuit
commemorate
*committee
*comparatively
compatible
complement (that which completes)
compliment (expression of praise or regard)
concession
concurrence
confidant (noun)
confident (adj.)
connoisseur
conscientious
*conscious
consistency
*correspondence
correspondent
corroborate
council (a body of people)
counsel (advice, legal adviser)
decease (death)
*deceive
*deferred
deficiency
dense
dependant (noun)
dependent (adj.)
descendant
*develop
*development
device (noun)
devise (verb)
diphthong
*disappear
*disappoint
discernible
discreet
disease
dispense
*dissatisfied
dissimilar
eccentric
efficacious
eligible
*embarrass
emigrant
enrolment
esteem
*exaggerate
excrescence
exigency
existence
*exorbitant
expense
experience
*extravagant
fascinate
favourite
forestall
*fulfil
fulfilled
*fulfilment
*gauge
*government
grievance
guarantee
*harass
hideous
honorary
humorist
humorous
identical
illegible
immigrant
imminent
immovable
incoherent
incorrigible
indefensible
indictment
*ineligible
*inexhaustible

WORDS FREQUENTLY MISSPELT—(*contd.*)

inflammable
innocuous
*inoculate
insistence
install
instalment
intense
irreducible
irrelevant
irresistible
itinerary
judgement, or—
judgment
*keenness
leisure
*livelihood
manageable
manoeuvre
Mediterranean
meteorological
millennium
*miniature
miscellaneous
*mischievous
misdemeanour
monastery
movable
murmur
naphtha
*necessary
negligible
neighbouring
noticeable
nuisance
*occasionally
*occurred
*occurrence
palate (roof of
mouth)
palette (colour
plate)
paraffin
*parallel
*paralleled
Parliament
*pavilion
peaceable
perforate

permissible
Philip
piece
plebeian
pneumatic
poignant
*possession
*practice (noun)
*practise (verb)
*precede
*preferred
prejudice
primitive
*principal (chief,—
adj. and noun)
*principle (law,—
noun)
*privilege
proceed
*procedure
*profession
proffered
prophecy (noun)
prophesy (verb)
promissory
psychological
purchase
pursue
*quarrelled
queue
*recede
*receipt
receive
recommend
recompense
reconnoitre
reference
*referred
*regrettable
relevant
relieve
reminiscent
remodelled
reprieve
resistance
resistible
reticent
retrieve

reversible
rhyme
rhythm
sagacious
*saleable
*scene
scheme
secede
sedentary
*seize
seizure
sense
*separate
sergeant
serviceable
*siege
simultaneous
*sincerely
*skilful
*soliloquy
stationary
(motionless)
stationery (writing
material)
stereotype
subterranean
succeed
successful
superintendent
*supersede
survivor
technical
*traceable
tranquillity
*transferred
tyrannical
*undoubtedly
*unnecessary
*unparalleled
*until
vaccinate
vacillate
vertical
vicissitude
*weird
wield
*woollen
worshipped

SPLIT INFINITIVE.

(See INFINITIVE.)

The so-called split infinitive occurs when an adverb or a phrase is inserted between the *to* and the verb. The following are examples—

> I want now *to* especially *direct* your attention to the item " depreciation, including renewals, upkeep, and repairs."
>
> The board have now decided *to* practically *reconstruct* the factory.

Some people make a great deal of fuss about this little point and are ready to condemn as illiterate anybody who splits an infinitive. Of course, there are extreme cases where the practice is unpardonable, e.g. I want you *to* as fully as possible *appreciate* the point at issue : this is obviously very clumsy. But no serious offence against elegance seems to be committed in the examples given above. Sometimes the avoidance of the splitting produces a more clumsy construction than the splitting would have done. E.g.—

> In December last I again returned *further to examine* the cause, and was astonished to find that a green haze of sprouting weeds carpeted the embankment.

Here it would be much less awkward to say *to further examine.* In the present state of opinion, however, in spite of the weakness of the case against the split infinitive, the novice in writing may be counselled to avoid this construction, lest it be thought that he knows no better.

It is to be observed that the passive infinitive is made up of the infinitive *to be* and a past participle, and it is not split if an adverb comes between *be* and the participle. *To be carefully considered* is not a split infinitive, but *to carefully be considered* is.

STABILIZE.

Pronunciation: stă'bilize, or stā'bilize. The B.B.C. adopts the latter.

STATIONARY—STATIONERY.

Stationary is the adjective meaning *motionless*, and *stationery* is the noun meaning *writing material*.

STATUS.

Pronounced: stā'tus.

STOPS.

(See PUNCTUATION, and separate articles under the headings of the various stops.)

STUPEFY.

This word is constantly misspelt. Even in print one frequently sees it with an *i* in the second syllable.

SUAVE.

Pronounced: swāv.

SUBJECT AND PREDICATE.

A sentence states a complete thought about a person or thing. Every sentence can therefore be logically divided into two main parts—(1) the words which name the person or thing about which something is said, i.e. the Subject; (2) the words which say something about the person or thing, i.e. the Predicate. Thus the short sentence " Prices are rising " has *prices* as the subject (it names what we are talking about) and *are rising* as the predicate (these words say something about prices).

Longer sentences may be similarly divided—

Subject	*Predicate*
Many of his clients	have now left the district.
A new manager	will be appointed very shortly.
The main cause of the dissatisfaction	was the high-handed action of the secretary.

For grammatical purposes the subject and the predicate of such sentences can be sub-divided into other parts, but for the present it is sufficient to note that the subject always contains a noun or noun-equivalent (*many, manager, cause*), which may be called the subject-word, and that the predicate always contains a verb (*have left, will be appointed, was*). The predicate often contains an Object or Predicative Words: these are explained in separate articles.

The sentences so far considered have been Simple; i.e. they contain only one subject and predicate. Many sentences, however, contain within themselves groups of words each of which has its own subject and predicate. E.g.—

Subject	*Predicate*
Many of his clients *who supported him for many years*	have now left the district *because the train service is so bad.*

The group of words *who . . . years* has a subject *who* and predicate *supported him for many years*; the group *because . . . bad* contains a subject *the train service*, and a predicate *is so bad*. (See CLAUSES; COMPLEX SENTENCE; DOUBLE SENTENCE, MULTIPLE SENTENCE.)

SUBJUNCTIVE MOOD: MODERN USAGE. (See MOOD.)

The subjunctive mood was employed very widely in older English, but for several centuries it has been gradually dropping out of use in the ordinary language, though it has been retained to a large extent in the language of poetry. Except in a few special cases the subjunctive in twentieth century English prose seems either archaic or affected. We are familiar with such old uses as "Except the Lord *build* the house, their labour is but lost that build it," and "If the salt *have* lost his savour, wherewithal shall it be salted?" But to-day we should use the indicative in both cases—"Unless the Lord *builds* . . ." "If the salt *has* lost. . ."

Modern Uses of the Subjunctive—

1. *In Simple Sentences and Main Clauses—*

In modern English main verbs are found in the subjunctive only in a few stereotyped expressions which have survived in their old form; e.g.—Long *live* the king; God *save* the king; *Come* what may; *Be* that as it may.

2. *In Subordinate Clauses—*

(*a*) After a verb of wishing—

I wish he *were* here; I wish it *were* all over.

(In vulgar language the indicative *was* is found in these sentences.)

(*b*) In stating a supposition that is not likely to be fulfilled—

If only he *were* here we should soon overcome our difficulties.

(But the implication is that he cannot be here.)

Notice the difference between the meanings of the following—

If that *were* true I should be sorry (Subj.).

If that *is* true I am sorry (Indic.).

In the first case we imply that the supposition is false; in the second we leave it an open question whether the supposition is true or not.

(*c*) Sometimes after *though*—

We do not think it likely that prices will fall even though the number of imported cars *be* reduced by the imposition of a duty.

The second clause means: even on the supposition that . . ., and the implication is that no reduction has yet occurred. If we substituted the indicative *is reduced* the meaning would be: even in spite of the fact that . . ., and we should imply that a reduction has actually taken place.

(*d*) Sometimes after *lest*—

He will meet them lest it *be* thought that he is unwilling to compromise.

(*e*) Sometimes after an impersonal verb, i.e. a verb having the indefinite *it* as subject—

It is requested that the full name and address of the applicant *be* written in block capitals.

Wrong or Unnecessary Uses. Many people seem to think that they can give what they would no doubt call "a literary touch" to their writing by introducing subjunctives where, in their less inspired moments, they would use the indicative. The result is mere affectation, if not actual incorrectness. Examples—

I question if there *be* amongst birds of prey of the commoner order a greater miscreant than the sparrow-hawk (is).

Whether the film *be* judged to be inspiring or degrading is immaterial to the argument (is).

It is common knowledge that watches are apt to go (or stop) according to the personality of the wearers, whether they *be* worn in the old-fashioned pocket or on the new-fangled wrist (are).

Government must be admired if it *persuade* man to some degree of orderliness, if it *induce* among nations behaviour slightly better than that of tigers or wolves. (The subjunctives here are wrong as well as being affected. The conditions are not stated as being unlikely or impossible to be fulfilled.)

There is no reason why the subjunctive should be used any more frequently in written prose to-day than it is in good conversation.

SUBSIDENCE.

The Oxford English Dictionary recognizes two pronunciations—subsī'dence, and sub'sĭdence, of which it prefers the first. The present day tendency, however, is strongly in favour of the second, and this is adopted by the B.B.C.

SUBSTITUTE.

The idiomatic uses of the verbs *to substitute* and *to replace* are often confused. We may say either: The firm will *substitute* new typewriters *for* the old ones, or—The firm will *replace* the old typewriters *by* new ones. It is wrong to say: The firm will *substitute* the old typewriters *by* new ones.

SUCH.

There is a use of *such* in place of *that, it, them,* etc., which must be condemned as most inelegant. Examples—

In these circumstances I think I have a claim against the railway, but the company refuses to recognize *such* (it).

Though we may lament the butchery which is the sparrow-hawk's means of life, *such* is hardly a reason for blind and illogical vituperation of the economy which regulates and is bound up with its destiny (that).

Sir Arthur says, in effect, that, unable to find evidence of the existence of the soul as distinct from the body, he and his friends are reluctantly forced to the conclusion that *such* does not exist, and that death is the end of all things. (*Such* is here not only inelegant but ambiguous.)

SUCH-LIKE.

The use of *such-like* is vulgar, and should be avoided. Examples—

The hall was filled with shop-keepers, artisans, and *such-like* (and the like, or—and such people).

It was the claim of the ferry service that they were in a position to offer facilities to the British manufacturer and exporter of pottery and *such-like* goods (similar).

SUMMON, SUMMONS.

A magistrate issues a *summons*. An offender is *summoned* to attend the court.

It is a common but bad error to say that a person is *summonsed* to attend the court.

SUPERIOR.

Superior must be followed by *to* and not *than*. Incorrect—

The facilities provided by the larger stores are far superior in all respects *than* those offered by the small shops (to).

SUPERLATIVE DEGREE.

(See DEGREES OF COMPARISON.)

SURNAMES: CORRECT PRONUNCIATION.

The following is a list of selected surnames with their correct pronunciation—

Arbuthnott: arbuth'not
Ayers: ārs
Ayscough: ăsk'ew
Bagehot: băj'ot
Beatty: bē'ty
Beauchamp: bē'cham
Beaulieu: bū'ly
Berkeley: bark'ly
Besant: bess'ant or bĕzant'
Bethune: bē'ton
Bigelow: big'elow
Blount: blunt
Bolitho: bolī'tho
Bompas: bum'pas
Bosanquet: bō'sanket or boo'sanket
Boscawen: boscō'en or boscaw'en

SURNAMES—(*contd.*)

Boughton: bow'ton or baw'ton
Bourchier: bow'cher
Brough: bruff
Brougham: broo'am *or* brō'am
Buccleuch: buckloo'
Buchan: buck'an
Buchanan: bucăn'an
Cadogan: cadug'an
Capell: cā'pel
Carew: cār'y *or* căroo'
Carmichael: carmī'cle
Carnegie: carnĕg'y *or* carnēg'y
Carruthers: caruth'ers
Cavan: căv'an
Cavanagh: căv'ana
Chalmers: chah'mers
Charteris: char'ters *or* char'teris
Chetwode: chet'wood
Chisholm: chiz'om
Cholmeley: chum'ly
Cholmondeley: chum'ly
Clough: cluff
Cochrane: cock'ran
Cockburn: cō'burn
Colnaghy: colnah'gy
Colquhoun: cohoon'
Compton: cump'ton
Constable: cun'stable
Conyngham: cun'ingham
Couch: cooch
Coutts: coots
Coventry: cuv'entry
Creagh: crā
Creighton: crī'ton
Crichton: crī'ton
Dalhousie: dalhow'zy
Dalmeny: dalmĕn'y
Dalrymple: dalrim'ple
Dalzell: dē-ĕl'
Dalziel: dē-ĕl'
Decies: dē'shēz
Doughty: dow'ty
Dunsany: dunsā'ny
Falconer: fawk'ner
Farquhar: fark'wer *or* fark'er
Farquharson: fark'werson *or* fark'erson
Fenwick: fĕn'ick
Fildes: fīlds
Findlater: fĭnd'later
Findlay: fĭn'ly
Foljambe: fool'jam
Fremantle: frēman'tle *or* frē'mantle
Froude: frood
Gairdner: gard'ner *or* gārd'ner
Galbraith: galbrāth'
Gallagher: gal'aher
Geddes: gĕd'iz
Geikie: gē'ky
Gerard: jĕr'ard
Giffard: gif'ard *or* jif'ard
Gillespie: gillĕs'py
Gilmour: gil'mor
Gough: gŏff
Gower: gōr *or* gower
Greig: grĕg
Grier: grēr
Haldane: hawl'dane
Halsbury: hawl'sbry
Harcourt: har'curt
Heneage: hĕn'ij
Hennessey: hĕn'essy
Hepburn: hĕ'burn
Hervey: har'vy
Hobart: hub'art
Hoey: hoy
Holmes: hōmes
Home: hūm
Houghton: haw'ton *or* how'ton
Inge: ing
Ingelow: in'jelow
Innes: in'is
Iveagh: I'ver *or* I'vy
Jerome: jerōm'
Jervis: jar'vis
Keightley: kēt'ly
Kekewich: keck'wich
Kennard: kennard'
Keogh: kyō
Kernahan: kern'ahan
Kesteven: kest'even
Keynes: kāns
Knollys: nōls
Kynaston: kĭn'aston

SURNAMES—(*contd.*)

Laffan: laffan′
Lascelles: lass′els
Lathom: lā′thom
Lefevre: lefē′ver
Lehmann: lā′man
Le Queux: le kew
Leven: lē′ven
Leverhulme: lē′verhūm
Lowther: lō′ther *or* low′ther
Lysaght: lī′saht
Macara: macah′ra
Maccullagh: macul′la
McEvoy: mack′evoy
McKay: mackī′
Mackie: mack′ĭ
Maclean: maclān′
Macleod: macloud′
Macmahon: macmahn′
Macnamara: macnamah′ra
Madan: măd′an
Mahan: mahn
Mahon: mahoon′ *or* mahn
Mahony: mah′ny
Mainwaring: măn′ering
Martineau: mar′tĭnō
Maughan: mawn
Meiklejohn: mĭck′lejohn
Melhuish: mĕl′ish
Menzies: meng′iz *or* ming′iz
Meux: mĕūz
Meyer: mī′er
Meynell: mĕn′el
Meyrick: mĕr′ick
Moncrieff: moncrēf′
Monro(e): munrō′
Montefiore: montĭfiōr′y
Montgomery: muntgum′ery
Montmorency: montmoren′cy
Morant: morant′
Moray: murry
Mordaunt: mōr′dunt
Morrell: morel′ *or* murr′el
Moulton: mōl′ton
Mowat: mō′at
O'Hagan: ohā′gan
O'Shaughnessy: oshaw′nessy
Outram: oo′tram
Pakenham: păck′enum
Palgrave: pawl′grave
Pegram: pē′gram
Petrie: pē′try
Pinero: pĭnēr′o
Ponsonby: pun′sunby
Powell: pō′el
Powys: pō′is
Prothero: prŏth′ero
Rea(y): rā
Renwick: rĕn′ick
Rhys: rēs
Rolleston: rol′ston
Routh: rowth
Rowton: rō′ton
St. Clair: sin′clair
St. John: sin′jun
Sandys: sands
Saunders: sahn′ders
Saunderson: sahn′derson
Scrymgeour: scrĭm′jer
Souttar: soo′tar
Speight: spāt
Strachey: strā′chy (*ch* as in church)
Stra(c)han: strawn
Sudeley: sūd′ly
Symons: sĭm′ons
Synge: sing
Thesiger: thĕss′ijer
Thorold: thur′old
Tighe: tī
Tollemache: tol′mash
Trefusis: trefū′sis
Treloar: trelōr′
Tyrwhitt: tĭr′it
Urquhart: er′kert
Vanbrugh: van′brer
Walmesley: wawm′sly
Waugh: waw
Wemyss: wēms
Whitefield: whĭt′field
Willard: willard′
Winstanley: win′stanly
Wodehouse: wood′house
Worsley: wer′sly
Wyl(l)ie: wī′ly
Yonge: yung

SYCOPHANT.

Pronounced : sĭck′ophant.

SYNCOPE.

Pronounced : sĭn′copē.

SYNONYMS.

Synonyms are words which have very nearly the same meaning. It is extremely difficult, if not impossible, to find any two English words which are exactly synonymous. Words which at first sight seem to be identical in signification are seen on further examination to be distinguished by some shade of meaning or some point of usage. A consideration of the three synonyms, *brief, concise, laconic,* will illustrate the differences to be looked for in the members of such a group. The following sentences exemplify the uses of the three words—

1. His interview with the manager was very *brief.*
2. Although his speech was *brief* he did not succeed in giving a *concise* account of the proposed scheme.
3. In reply to my long and earnest appeal that he would give us his assistance he gave me the *laconic* answer, " No, I won't."

Clearly both *concise* and *laconic* suggest more than *brief. Concise* applies to writing or speaking, and suggests condensation and neatness of expression. *Laconic* includes the further notion of curtness and abruptness; it would not be suitable in sentence (2) for it applies only to single remarks. Sentence (2) shows that a speech may be brief without being concise, although brevity is the usual accompaniment of conciseness. Neither *concise* nor *laconic*, of course, could replace *brief* in sentence (1).

The above words are not difficult to differentiate. Other synonyms, however, are so nearly alike that very careful analysis is needed to make clear the distinctions. We often feel the special shade of meaning attached to a particular word and consequently prefer this word to its synonym, even when we should be puzzled to give a reason for our preference. How many people without special consideration and reference to dictionaries could explain the differences between *effective, effectual, efficacious, efficient?* These words are the subject of a special article.

So far we have insisted on the differences between synonyms. The fact that in many cases synonyms are interchangeable is sufficiently obvious. We can speak of a man's business as being either *profitable* or *lucrative*: the sense is the same with either word. (But we can describe, e.g. a conversation as *profitable,* although the adjective *lucrative* would be quite unsuitable.)

One of the chief requirements of those who would write well is the ability to distinguish between words that resemble each other in meaning. Precision of expression is impossible without a nice appreciation of shades of meaning and a feeling for idiom. These qualities are to be acquired only by wide reading of good literature. The study of the dictionary and of books of synonyms is, of course, valuable; but it should be only subsidiary to reading.

TAUTOLOGY.

(See REDUNDANCY OF EXPRESSION.)

TECHNICAL JARGON.

(See OBSCURITY.)

TENSE.

A Tense is a form of a verb which indicates three things—

1. *Time.* An action may be described as taking place in the Past, the Present, or the Future—

I walked; I walk; I shall walk.

These forms are the Simple Past, the Simple Present, and the Simple Future Tenses.

2. *Continuance.* We may speak of an action as being in progress for some time in the Past, the Present, or the Future—

I was walking; I am walking; I shall be walking.

These forms are called the Past Continuous (or Imperfect), the Present Continuous (or Imperfect), and the Future Continuous (or Imperfect) Tenses.

3. *Completion.* An action may be described as completed at some point of time in the Past, the Present, or the Future—

I had walked; I have walked; I shall have walked.

These forms are called the Past Perfect, the Present Perfect, and the Future Perfect Tenses. ("Perfect" means "finished, completed.")

Sometimes a verb denotes an action that is about to take place after some point of time in the past—

I expected that I ***should walk*** ten miles in the afternoon.

This tense is called the Future in the Past. It may have a Continuous form (***should be walking***) and a Perfect form (***should have walked***).

TERM.

The verb *term* should not be followed by *as*. The following illustrates the correct use: Great Britain may be termed a crowned republic. (But we may correctly say: Great Britain may be *regarded as* a crowned republic.)

THAN.

Mistakes are often made through the use of the wrong form of a pronoun after *than*; e.g. He seems to be much older than *me*. *Than* is not a preposition and should not therefore be followed by an accusative case. (See CASE.) It introduces a clause of comparison of which the verb is suppressed (as it is usually in such clauses). But if this verb is supplied (than I *am*) it is at once seen that the pronoun should be *I* (nominative case, subject to *am*). *Me* would be correct in the sentence—He likes you better than (he likes) *me*. The pronoun is here the object of the understood verb.

THE.

(See ARTICLES.)

THESE (*THOSE*) *KIND OF THINGS*

The expression "I do not like *these kind* of things" contains a curious error. *Kind* is obviously a singular word, yet it is qualified by a plural adjective *these*. We ought to say *this kind of thing*, or *things of this kind*. But the expressions *these kind*, *those sort*, are so commonly used even by educated people that perhaps they should be accepted as established idioms.

THUS AND A PRESENT PARTICIPLE.

> The electric light failed, *thus causing* great inconvenience.

On the slovenly use of the present participle in such sentences as this see UNRELATED PARTICIPLES

TITLES: SPECIAL FORMS OF ADDRESS AND SALUTATION.

In the case of letters written to persons of title or rank special forms of address and salutation are required for the letter-heading. A selected list of these forms is given below—

MEMBER OF THE ROYAL FAMILY. *Address :* His Royal Highness the Prince of Wales, or—His Royal Highness the Duke of Gloucester. *Salutation :* Your Royal Highness.

DUKE. *Address :* His Grace the Duke of ——. *Salutation :* My Lord, or—Your Grace.

DUCHESS. *Address :* Her Grace the Duchess of ——. *Salutation :* My Lady, or—Madam.

MARQUIS. *Address :* The Most Honourable the Marquis of——. *Salutation :* My Lord Marquis.

MARCHIONESS. *Address :* The Most Honourable the Marchioness of ——. *Salutation :* My Lady.

EARL OR COUNTESS. *Address :* The Right Honourable the Earl (Countess) of ——. *Salutation :* My Lord (My Lady).

VISCOUNT. *Address :* The Right Honourable the Viscount——. *Salutation :* My Lord.

BARON. *Address :* The Right Honourable Lord ——. *Salutation :* My Lord.

BARONET. *Address :* Sir Harley Staples, Bt. *Salutation :* Sir.

KNIGHT. *Address :* Sir Walter Raleigh. *Salutation :* Sir.

LORD CHANCELLOR. *Address :* The Right Honourable the Lord Chancellor. *Salutation :* My Lord.

LORD CHIEF JUSTICE. *Address :* The Right Honourable the Lord Chief Justice. *Salutation :* My Lord.

JUDGE. *Address :* The Honourable Mr. Justice ——, or (if a knight)—The Honourable Sir Harcourt Riley. *Salutation :* Sir. (A County Court Judge is addressed as His Honour Judge ——)

PRIVY COUNCILLOR. The Right Honourable David Farmer, P.C. *Salutation :* Sir.

LORD MAYOR OF LONDON OR YORK. *Address :* The Right Honourable the Lord Mayor of ——. *Address :* My Lord, or—My Lord Mayor. (Of the English Lord Mayors only those of London and York are entitled to the prefix " Right Honourable.")

MAYOR. *Address :* The Worshipful the Mayor of ——. *Salutation :* Sir.

LORD PROVOST AND PROVOST. The forms of address for these Scottish officials correspond to those for Lord Mayor and Mayor.

ALDERMAN. *Address :* Mr. Alderman Jones.

COUNCILLOR. *Address :* Mr. Councillor Jones.

ARCHBISHOP. *Address :* The Most Rev. the Lord Archbishop of ——. *Salutation :* My Lord Archbishop, or—Your Grace.

CARDINAL. *Address :* His Eminence Cardinal ——, or (if an archbishop)—His Eminence the Cardinal Archbishop of ——. *Salutation :* Your Eminence.

BISHOP. *Address :* The Right Rev. the Lord Bishop of ——. *Salutation :* My Lord.

DEAN. *Address :* The Very Rev. the Dean of ——. *Salutation :* Sir.

ARCHDEACON. *Address :* The Ven. Archdeacon of ——. *Salutation :* Sir.

CLERGYMAN. *Address :* Rev. T. G. Parsons, or (if the Christian name or initials are not known)—Rev. Mr. Parsons. (Never: Rev. Parsons.) *Salutation :* Rev. Sir, or—Sir.

TRAIT.

This word is pronounced without the final *t*, as in French (trā).

TRANSITIVE VERB.

A Transitive Verb is one that is followed by an object; e.g. The firm *pays* the wages. (See OBJECT, DIRECT AND INDIRECT.) An Intransitive Verb denotes an action that is not performed on an object; e.g. The engine *runs* well.

Some verbs can be either transitive or intransitive according to the sentence in which they are used; e.g.—

His duties *begin* to-morrow (intrans.);
He *begins* work to-morrow (trans.).

TRANSPIRE.

It is a common error to use *transpire* as though it meant *happen*; e.g.—

The manager of the club was instructed to lay before the members of the board a full statement of what had *transpired* and invite them to deal with the case.

The true meanings of the word are *breathe through*, *become known*. It is correctly used in the following—

After some hours it *transpired* that the king had secretly left the palace in a closed car.

TRYST.

Pronunciation: trīst, or trĭst. The B.B.C. adopts the former.

UNDER THE CIRCUMSTANCES.

There are people who object to the expression *under the circumstances* on the ground that it is foolish to talk of being beneath (under) something which is round (circum-) you. The correct phrase is, they say, *in the circumstances.* The objectors lose sight of the fact that *under* does not always mean *beneath*: its other sense is seen in the phrases: under sentence of death; to be under a delusion; to be under an obligation, under examination, under repair, etc. In all these cases the notion of pressure is present. In the same way we may legitimately think of circumstances as exerting a pressure which influences actions in a certain direction. *Under these circumstances* is therefore just as good an idiom as *under these conditions.*

UNIQUE.

A thing is unique when it is the *only one of its kind.* If, therefore, we use this adjective in its true sense it will only seldom be applicable. Further, we ought not to speak of something as *very* unique, or *rather* unique. A thing is either unique or it is not, just as it may be either first or not first: there can be no degrees of "uniqueness" or "firstness."

UNLESS AND UNTIL.

> There can be no hope of a revival of trade *unless and until* the crushing burden of taxation is lightened.

This popular use of *unless and until* is open to the same objection as applies to *if and when.* (See under that heading.)

UNTOWARD.

Pronounced: untō′erd.

UNRELATED PARTICIPLES.

The error of the unrelated participle is a very common one—largely because it involves a point of grammar that is not obvious to those who lack a grammatical training. It is necessary first of all to understand the nature of participles. (See PARTICIPLES.)

Consider the following sentences—

1. *Turning* the corner by the church, it is only two minutes' walk to the station.

2. *Bronzed* by the heat of the Italian sun, ours was indeed a life of health and pleasure.

In (1) *turning* is a present participle introducing an adjective-phrase which should relate to a noun or pronoun. What was turning? Not *it,* nor *station.* Clearly it is a person who turns. But no person is mentioned. The sentence would be right if we said: Turning the corner by the church, *we* (or *you*) have only a short walk. . .

In (2) there is a past participle *bronzed* introducing a phrase. What was bronzed?—We were. Therefore the second part of the sentence should read: *we* were indeed living a life of health and pleasure.

Some other examples of the error—

Having worked for nine years in an industrial area, my experience is that not one patient in a thousand fails to consult the panel doctor in case of illness.

(The *experience* has not worked. Write: *I* have found that . . .)

Before the building of this foundry all steel castings had to be obtained from outside firms, often *resulting* in very serious delays.

(To what previous noun does *resulting* relate? Eliminate the participle, and write: so that serious delays were often caused.)

The slipshod use of participles is particularly common with *thus* and *thereby*; e.g.—

> All typescript is carefully checked with your original MS., *thus ensuring* absolute accuracy.

(*Ensuring* is not related to a previous noun. Write: *We* carefully check all typescript with your original MS., thus ensuring . . ., or eliminate the participle and recast.)

> Our staff has been reduced to a minimum, *thereby securing* the utmost economy in working.

(Write: By reducing our staff to the minimum we have secured . . .)

VAGARY.

Pronounced: văgār'y.

VAGRANT.

Pronounced: vā'grant.

VALET.

The *t* should be sounded.

VERB.

A verb is a word by means of which something is said about a person or thing. It is the essential part of the predicate of every sentence. (See SUBJECT AND PREDICATE.)

A verb denotes either—(1) an Action, e.g. Rain *falls*; The boat *is sailing* to-morrow; The clerk *has posted* the letter;

or (2) a State, e.g. He *is* the captain; They *seem* very friendly; He *did* not *appear* happy.

From the above examples it will be observed that a verb-form often includes more than one word. (See AUXILIARY VERB and PARTICIPLES.)

VERBOSITY.

(See REDUNDANCY OF EXPRESSION.)

VERY AND PAST PARTICIPLES.

The following sentences are wrong—

He was *very* surprised by the news.
They were all *very* annoyed by what occurred.
I shall be *very* concerned to hear the result.

Much or *very much* should be used in each case. It is not easy to give a simple rule to explain when *very* is permissible with a past participle. Everybody will recognize, however, that whereas *very* is unidiomatic in the above sentences, it could be quite correctly used in—

His face wore a very surprised, or very annoyed, or very concerned expression.

Here the participles *surprised, annoyed, concerned,* are used as pure adjectives qualifying the noun *expression*: in the original sentences they were used with the auxiliary verbs *was, were, shall be,* in a compound verb-form. The distinction thus depends on the double nature of participles. (See PARTICIPLES.) When a participle is used like an ordinary adjective it may be preceded by *very* alone; when it is used in a compound verb-form *much* or *very much* is required.

VICE VERSA.

The first word is pronounced: vī′sē.

VIKING.

Pronounced: vī′king.

VIOLA.

The name of the musical instrument is pronounced: vĭō'la. The name of the flower is pronounced: vī'ŏla.

VISA.

Pronounced: vē'za.

VITAMIN.

Pronunciation: vītamin, or vĭ'tamin. The B.B.C. adopts the former.

VOICE.

A verb is said to be in the Active Voice when the person or thing named by the subject performs the action; e.g.—

The journalist *interviewed* the principal actors.

A verb is said to be in the Passive Voice when the person or thing named by the subject undergoes or suffers the action, e.g.—

The principal actors *were interviewed* by the journalist.

VOLUNTARY, VOLUNTARILY.

It is a common mistake to use the adjective *voluntary* instead of the adverb *voluntarily*. We say that a hospital is supported by *voluntary* contributions, or that a person gives *voluntary* help. But we must say that someone undertakes the work *voluntarily*, or that a criminal *voluntarily* gave himself up to justice.

WAIVE—WAVE.

To waive means *to forbear to insist on*; *to make a tacit surrender of a right, claim,* etc.—

In consideration of the compensation now offered the company is prepared to *waive* its claim for the use of this site.

It now appears that he is prepared to *waive* the condition which he originally made regarding his acceptance of a directorship.

The verb *wave* is required in the following—

Public opinion is becoming loud on this matter, and the Government cannot *wave aside* the demand as of no consequence.

The older writers often spelt both verbs *wave*, but the distinction between the two should be carefully observed in modern English.

WHICH.

When used as a relative pronoun, *which* should always have a definite antecedent. (See RELATIVE PRONOUN.) The following sentence is faulty—

The electric light failed, *which* caused great inconvenience.

What previous noun does *which* stand for ? Not *light.* It was the *failure* which caused the inconvenience ; but this noun is not used. The pronoun *which* is, in fact, made to refer to the whole of the preceding clause. Sentences of this type will pass in conversation, but they should not be admitted in writing

WHO, WHOM.

For examples of *who* wrongly used for *whom* and *vice versa* see ERRORS IN CASE

WILL.

(See SHALL—WILL, SHOULD—WOULD.)

WITH A VIEW TO—WITH THE VIEW OF.

Note that the first of these two idioms contains *to* (not *of*), and it should be followed by a verb-form ending in *-ing*, e.g. with a view to *carrying* out several improvements. Avoid—

1. With a view *of* carrying out several improvements.
2. With a view to *carry* out several improvements.

There is another idiom—*with the view of*. (Note that this contains *the*, not *a*)—

He went to London with the view of consulting his solicitors. (See IDIOM.)

WITHOUT.

There are two colloquial uses of *without* which should not appear in writing—

1. *Without* used for *unless* to introduce a clause of condition—

We cannot reduce our prices *without* we make certain of obtaining a constant supply of raw materials at lower rates.

2. *Without hardly*—

A new company has taken over the business *without hardly* making any changes in the personnel. (Write: and has made hardly any changes. . .)

WOULD.

(See SHALL—WILL, SHOULD—WOULD.)

WRATH.

Pronounced with the vowel heard in *broad*.

WRITE YOU.

It is normal English to say: I will write you a letter, but it is unidiomatic to say: I will write you about the matter to-morrow. *To you* is required in the second case.

The use of *write you* instead of *write to you* is very

common in business correspondence, but there seems no reason for tolerating this departure from common usage; it might well go the way of the other old-fashioned business phrases which are generally being eliminated by the more progressive firms to-day. (See "BUSINESS ENGLISH.")

YOU AND I.

Many people whose grammatical sense is weak, and who appear to think that there is a peculiar refinement attaching to *you and I*, use this expression on all occasions, even when *you and me* would be correct. Which of the two phrases is right depends on the question of case. (See CASE.)

You and I should be *you and me* in the following—

> He will blame you and I for what has happened.

(*I* is an object of the verb *will blame*; the accusative case *me* is therefore required.)

> The communications were sent to you and I at the same time.

(*I* is governed by the preposition *to*; again the accusative *me* is needed.)